PROBLEMS IN

THE ORIGINS AND DEVELOPMENT

OF THE ENGLISH LANGUAGE

PROBLEMS IN
THE ORIGINS AND DEVELOPMENT
OF THE ENGLISH LANGUAGE

John Algeo
UNIVERSITY OF FLORIDA

Thomas Pyles
NORTHWESTERN UNIVERSITY

HARCOURT, BRACE & WORLD, INC.
New York · Chicago · Burlingame

Preface

This manual is intended as a supplement for courses in the development of the English language. Though it has been specifically designed to accompany Thomas Pyles's *The Origins and Development of the English Language* (Harcourt, Brace & World, 1964), much of the manual could be used with other texts to illustrate how English has evolved from its prehistoric beginnings. A good knowledge of any language in its historical development can best be gained by working with samples of the language in its various historical stages and various branches: phonology, morphology, syntax, lexicon, semantics, and graphemics.

The problems included are of a variety of types. Some ask the student to demonstrate knowledge of specific facts to be derived from the textbook or a similar source. Others provide supplementary data for the student to analyze and draw conclusions from. Still others are open-ended problems, notably the illustrative passages at the end of several chapters, which can be used in a variety of ways to demonstrate the structure of English at various periods in its history. Some of the exercises are intended for class discussion; others are designed to be worked out independently, with the answers to be written in a form to permit easy checking.

The manual contains a wealth of material, and selectivity in its use may well be a necessity. Some of the problems, such as 1.14, on the history and plan of the *OED*, might be assigned to individual students for oral reports. Others, such as 1.17, on the process of dictionary-making, can be the basis for an extensive research assignment. Still other exercises, such as 1.16, on using the *OED*, are large enough for the questions in the exercise to be divided among the students in a class so that no undue strain need be placed on limited library facilities.

Experience suggests that the chapters can profitably be taken up in more than one order. The most obvious order, that of passing from first to last, can be varied by following the three introductory chapters with chapters 10, 11, and 12 on the lexicon, and then returning to the central chapters 4 through 9; the advantage of this arrangement is that drill on the sounds of modern English can be continued during the study of the lexicon to lay a firmer basis for the consideration of historical sound changes which begins with chapter 4.

The materials presented here have been derived from many sources. Specific acknowledgments have been made wherever possible, and reference is provided to the fuller original treatments. Standard historical grammars such as those by Jespersen, the Wrights, Abbott, Campbell, Mossé, Prokosch, and Wyld have been cheerfully pillaged for examples, but no list of authors could encompass the debts which are owed.

Adele S. Algeo assisted in every stage of the book's preparation; indeed her continual aid and encouragement made possible its completion.

JOHN ALGEO
THOMAS PYLES

Contents

PROBLEMS IN

THE ORIGINS AND DEVELOPMENT

OF THE ENGLISH LANGUAGE

Facts, Assumptions, and Misconceptions About Language

1.1 *QUESTIONS FOR REVIEW AND DISCUSSION*

1. Here is a list of terms used in Chapter I of *Origins and Development*. Some of them are explicitly defined in the text; others are defined by the context in which they are used. You should be familiar with all of them. Consult a recent dictionary for any whose meaning is not clear to you.

language	juncture	colloquial(ism)
writing	stress	usage
orthography	morphology	prescriptivism
phonology	inflection	structural linguistics
phonetic	syntax	transformational-generative grammar
pitch	function word	Indo-European

   Two terms that do not occur in Chapter I, but that you may find useful, are *synchronic linguistics* and *diachronic* or *historical linguistics*.

2. How old is language? What evidence can be advanced to suggest an answer to this question?

3. What theories have been suggested to explain how language first began? What are the weaknesses of these theories?

4. Why is the language of a primitive people not necessarily a primitive language?

5. The history of the English language is customarily divided into three periods: Old English, Middle English, and Modern English. What dates are assigned to these periods? Look up the terms in several dictionaries. Can you explain the discrepancies you are likely to find?

6. How old is writing?

7. What are some differences between language (that is, speech) and writing?

8. What is the difference between *translation* and *transliteration*?

9. What means other than language or writing do human beings use in communicating with one another?

10. What is meant by the statement that language is *systematized*?

11. What varieties of system does language possess?

12. What devices does language use to indicate grammatical relationships?

13. How does animal communication differ from human language?

14. The following is a fragment of an actual conversation. About what characteristic of language is the second speaker ill-informed?

   "When the Spanish talk about bread, they call it *pan*."
   "That's silly. Why don't they use its real name?"

15. The following statement argues the need for spelling reform; what misconception underlies it?

   It may well be that a reconstructed and well-arranged American language is the best answer [to the need for an international language]. We would not want, of course, to force our language on the rest of the world, especially when it is imperfect, but we can institute a program of reform to make it worthy of the acceptance it is beginning to receive.[1]

16. The distinguished philologist Otto Jespersen invented an artificial language called Novial. Of Jespersen's project, G. B. Shaw said, "Everybody can learn Novial, there is very little grammar in it; but one must be English to understand how one can get along splendidly without grammar." What did Shaw probably mean by the word *grammar*?

17. How would you rate these terms as adequate descriptions of "good English": *pure, aesthetically pleasing, cultivated, familiar, correct, effective*?

18. How would you define "good English"?

19. What is the function of a dictionary?

20. Much of Chapter I is devoted to misconceptions about language; make a summary list of the popular errors that are discussed in that chapter.

21. Pyles defines language as "systematized combinations of sounds which have meaning for all persons in a given cultural community" (*Origins and Development*, p. 3). What characteristics of language are mentioned in this definition? What other characteristics are illustrated in Chapter I?

1.2 WRITING AND SPEECH

1. Speech has certain resources for conveying meaning that writing can represent imperfectly at best. Say this sentence aloud in a way that will convey the meanings indicated in parentheses.

He's a very enthusiastic person.	(I am simply giving you the fact.)
He's a very enthusiastic person.	(I like him; his enthusiasm is to his credit.)
He's a very enthusiastic person.	(I dislike him; enthusiasm is depressing.)
He's a very enthusiastic person.	(I am hesitant or reluctant to describe him.)
He's a very enthusiastic person.	(Enthusiasm is the only good thing about him, and it isn't much; I could say more, but I won't.)
He's a very enthusiastic person.	(I mean him, not her.)
He's a very enthusiastic person.	(I am asking you, not telling you.)
He's a very enthusiastic person.	(Is that what you said? I can hardly believe it.)
He's a very enthusiastic person.	(I think the degree of his enthusiasm is quite extraordinary.)

---

[1] William Russell, *Better American Spelling for a Post-War World* (no publication data), p. 2.

Describe as precisely as you can how the various meanings are signaled. Can any of these meanings be shown in writing by punctuation or typographical devices?

2. Are these pairs distinguished in speech? If so, how?

blue blood (aristocrat)	blue blood (cyanotic condition)
red eye (cheap whiskey)	red eye (bloodshot eye)
hot line (direct telephone line to Moscow)	hot line (heated cord)
New Year (January 1)	new year (fresh year)
long shot (bet with bad prospects but good odds)	long shot (shot-putting at a far distance)
short order (pertaining to food that is quickly cooked)	short order (brief command)
big head (conceit)	big head (large skull)
a man's store (store selling men's clothing)	a man's store (store owned by a man)
an English major (student of English)	an English major (officer of British army)
a fishing pole (rod for fishing)	a fishing Pole (Polish fisherman)
a bull's-eye (center of a target)	a bull's eye (eye of a bull)
Is his brother-in-law? (Is his wife's brother?)	Is his brother in law? (Is his brother a lawyer?)

3. Are these pairs distinguished in speech? If so, how does the distinction differ from that of the preceding pairs?

New Jersey (the state)	new jersey (blouse purchased recently)
old maid (spinster)	old maid (serving-woman of advanced years)
vice chairman (deputy chairman)	vice chairman (chairman in charge of vice)
little woman (wife)	little woman (small female)

4. Each of these sentences is ambiguous in writing. Say each sentence in two different ways to make the potential meanings clear. Describe the means you use to make the spoken sentences unambiguous.

Old men and women should be the first to abandon ship.
The doorman asked her quietly to telephone the police.
They are advertising fresh strawberry pie.
She gave him an order to leave.
They went by the old highway.
He painted the picture in the hall.

5. Are these sentences usually distinguished in speech? Can they be distinguished?

He came to.
He came too.

He found a pear.
He found a pair.

The straight way is best.
The strait way is best.

The mathematics department is teaching plane geometry.
The mathematics department is teaching plain geometry.

The directions read, "Leave address with Miss Jones."
The directions read, "Leave a dress with Miss Jones."

1.3 WRITING IS NOT LANGUAGE

All four of the following passages, as well as this paragraph, are representations of the same language, although they may look somewhat dissimilar. They are merely alternate ways of recording English which are useful for different purposes. You should be able to read them in spite of the unfamiliar symbols and combinations.

ſhis is printed in an augmented rœman alfabet, ſhe purpos ov which is not, as miet bee suppœsd, tœ reform our spelliŋ, but tœ imprœv ſhe lerniŋ ov reediŋ. it is intended ſhat when ſhe beginner has acheevd ſhe iniſhal suksess ov flœensy in ſhis speſhally eesy form, his fuetuer progress ſhœd bee konfiend tœ reediŋ in ſhe present alfabets and spelliŋs ov ſhem œnly.[2]

ðis iz printəd in ə fənetik ælfəbet, ðə pərpəs əv wič iz nat, æz mayt biy səpowzd, tə rəfərm awr speliŋ ər tuw impruwv ðə lərniŋ əv riydiŋ, bət tə rikord ðə prənənsiyeyšən əv iŋgliš æz ækyərətliy æz pasəbəl. ðis ælfəbet iz yuwzd bay meniy liŋgwists in ðə yuwnaytəd steyts fər raytiŋ ðə sawndz əv madərn iŋgliš.

ðɪs ɪz prɪntəd ɪn ə fənɛtik ælfəbɛt, ðə pərpəs əv wɪč ɪz nɑt, æz maɪt bi səpozd, tə rəfərm aʊr spɛlɪŋ ər tu ɪmpruv ðə lərnɪŋ əv ridɪŋ, bət tə rɪkord ðə prənʌnsiešən əv ɪŋglɪš æz ækjərətli æz pɑsəbl. ðɪs ælfəbɛt ɪz juzd ɪn ðə tɛkst ən wɜrkbʊk fər dəskraɪbɪŋ ðə hɪstəri əv ɪŋglɪš saʊndz.

ᵗḥis iz printəd in ə fənetik alfəbet, ᵗḥə pûrpəs əv wich iz not, az mīt bē səpōzd, tə rəfôrm our speling ôr tōō imprōōv ᵗḥə lûrning əv rēding, bət tə rikōrd ᵗḥə prənunsēāshən əv wûrdz in dikshənârēz. ᵗḥis alfəbet, yōōzd in ᵗḥə standərd kolij dikshənârē, iz tipikəl əv such sistəmz.

1. Which of the four writing systems looks most like the conventional spelling of English, and which least? _____

2. What special difficulties are presented by each system? _____
    _____
    _____
    _____
    _____

3. In 1961, when the Augmented Roman Alphabet was first noticed by the American press, *Time* magazine said of it, "If successful, it may revolutionize English." What misconception is implied in that statement? _____
    _____
    _____

4. English can be represented by many other writing systems, some of them—such as Gregg shorthand—very different in appearance from our conventional orthography. What other such systems can you mention? Do any of them stand for normal spelling rather than for language directly? _____
    _____
    _____
    _____

[2] I. J. Pitman, "Intermedia," *The Linguistic Reporter* (Supplement Number 3), 3.

The sound-system of Modern English permits certain combinations of sounds and precludes others. Here is a list of the regular sequences of consonants that can begin a word. The sequences are given both in their most common spelling and in phonetic symbols within square brackets. The phonetic symbols will be explained in Chapter 3; they are given here so that you may refer to them later. For each sequence, write a word that begins with that combination of sounds. If you have difficulty thinking of a word, use a dictionary.

pr-	[pr]	_____	*cl-*	[kl]	_____
tr-	[tr]	_____	*bl-*	[bl]	_____
cr-	[kr]	_____	*gl-*	[gl]	_____
br-	[br]	_____	*fl-*	[fl]	_____
dr-	[dr]	_____	*sl-*	[sl]	_____
gr-	[gr]	_____	*sp-*	[sp]	_____
fr-	[fr]	_____	*st-*	[st]	_____
thr-	[θr]	_____	*sk-*	[sk]	_____
shr-	[šr] or [sr]	_____	*sph-*	[sf]	_____
tw-	[tw]	_____	*sm-*	[sm]	_____
qu-	[kw]	_____	*sn-*	[sn]	_____
dw-	[dw]	_____	*spr-*	[spr]	_____
gw- or *gu-*	[gw]	_____	*spl-*	[spl]	_____
thw-	[θw]	_____	*str-*	[str]	_____
sw-	[sw]	_____	*scr-*	[skr]	_____
wh-	[hw] or [w]	_____	*squ-*	[skw]	_____
pl-	[pl]	_____	*scl-*	[skl]	_____

The foregoing list of initial consonant sequences could have been extended with other combinations:

1. The initial sounds of words like *pew, cue, bugle, gules, few, view, mew, hew, spume, skew, smew,* and for some speakers *tune, dew, new, student, thew, suit, zeugma, lewd,* include a consonant or consonant-like sound that is not recorded in the spelling. What is this sound?

_____

2. Some combinations are rare or recent in English, such as the [pw] sound used in some pronunciations of *puissant* or the [bw] sound of *bwana*. Four quite recent consonant sequences begin with the initial sound of *ship*. Can you supply words to illustrate them?

schl-	[šl]	_____	*schm-*	[šm]	_____
schw-	[šw]	_____	*schn-*	[šn]	_____

3. Dictionaries often record sequences that are seldom heard because they violate the system of English. What dictionary pronunciations do you find for the initial consonants of *phthisis, svelte,* and *tmesis*? _____

4. There are a number of foreign names like *Mrumlinski, Pforzheim,* and *Pskov* that English speakers sometimes make an effort to pronounce "properly." Can you think of any other foreign words or names that contain initial consonant sequences not permitted by the habits of English? _____

The consonant sequences that begin English words are not merely a random selection of sounds combined in any order. They follow a precise system which we will not detail but which you should be able to describe after you have studied Chapter 3.

A quite different and more complex system obtains among the consonant sequences that end English words. In final position, English permits such combinations as [mpst] as in *glimpsed*, [mpts] as in *exempts*, [lkts] as in *mulcts*, or even [mpfst] as in the admittedly contrived "Methinks thou *humphst* too much." Good descriptions of the permitted sound sequences of English can be found in Bloomfield's *Language* and in Malone's "The Phonemes of Current English," which are listed in the bibliography of *Origins and Development*.

1.5   THE GRAMMATICAL SYSTEM: PLURAL SUFFIXES

The common plural ending of nouns, written -*s* or -*es*, is pronounced in three ways (see *Origins and Development*, pp. 3–4). Thus *duck* adds an *s*-sound; *dog*, a *z*-sound; and *horse*, a vowel plus the *z*-sound. This kind of systematic variation in the pronunciation of a meaningful form is called morphophonemic alternation.

Write each of these nouns in the appropriate column, according to the *pronunciation* of its plural ending: ace, almanac, bag, book, burlesque, church, cough, cup, curb, dish, dress, fall, graph, hat, house, hunch, judge, lad, lash, lathe, maze, moor, myth, oaf, pillow, room, tax, thing, train, wisp.

s-SOUND	*z*-SOUND	VOWEL + *z*-SOUND

1.6   THE GRAMMATICAL SYSTEM: PAST TENSE SUFFIXES

The regular past tense form of verbs is made by adding a suffix, usually spelled -*ed*, to the verbal stem. The past tense ending has three pronunciations. What is the sound of the ending in *walked*? _____ In *jogged*? _____ In *trotted*? _____ The three pronunciations of the past tense suffix are in morphophonemic alternation with one another.

Write each of these verbs in the appropriate column, according to the *pronunciation* of its past tense ending: blind, bluff, brag, club, cough, discuss, doze, fade, flood, froth, glimpse, grant, heat, include, melt, mold, neck, own, persist, poach, prove, refute, show, snore, thank, try, urge, wipe, wish, yell.

LIKE *walk*	LIKE *jog*	LIKE *trot*

1.7 *THE GRAMMATICAL SYSTEM: TWO CLASSES OF NOUNS*

Nouns are words that fit into certain definite patterns. Some of the noun patterns are illustrated by these frame-sentences:

  1. He likes _____.
  2. The _____ is good.
  3. He wants a(n) _____.
  4. _____ (e)s are good.

Consider these words:

amazement	cup	home	loathe
amiss	desk	house	news
ask	drink	illumine	noise
bank	entertainment	lamp	postage
cash	fun	light	seldom

1. Which of the words will fit into patterns 1 and 2, but not into 3 and 4? _____

_____

Such words are often called uncountable nouns or mass-nouns.

2. Which of the words will fit into patterns 2, 3, and 4, but not into 1? _____

_____

Such words are called countable nouns or count-nouns.

3. Which of the words will fit into all four of the patterns? _____

_____

Such words function as both mass- and count-nouns. You may be able to detect some change of meaning in these nouns between their use in pattern 1 and their use in pattern 3.

7

List five different examples for each of the three noun subclasses:

MASS-NOUNS	COUNT-NOUNS	MASS- AND COUNT-NOUNS

1.8 *THE GRAMMATICAL SYSTEM: TWO FUNCTION WORDS*

Although native speakers of a language manage its complex system with ease, they often have difficulty describing the system which they habitually and unconsciously use. Function words, described on page 11 of *Origins and Development*, are especially complex in their use. For example, what is the difference in use between the function words *some* and *any*? Observe the words in these sentences:

I know some examples.
He has some problem.
The class needs some liveliness.

I don't know any examples.
He doesn't have any problem.
The class doesn't need any liveliness.

Do you know some examples?
Does he have some problem?
Does the class need some liveliness?

Do you know any examples?
Does he have any problem?
Does the class need any liveliness?

Don't you know some examples?
Doesn't he have some problem?
Doesn't the class need some liveliness?

Don't you know any examples?
Doesn't he have any problem?
Doesn't the class need any liveliness?

Describe the systematic difference you observe in the use of *some* and *any*. _____

_____

_____

The use of *some* and *any* is more complex than the sentences above would suggest. Consider these sentences:

The book has some examples.
The book doesn't have some examples you want.

The book has any examples you want.
The book doesn't have any examples.

How would the description you just wrote need to be modified in the light of these sentences? Consider the pronunciation of *some* and *any*. Consider also the structure of the sentences in which they occur. _____

_____

_____

1.9 THE GRAMMATICAL SYSTEM: DEVICES TO INDICATE RELATIONSHIP

The following constructions, which are written in bad newspaper-headline style, are ambiguous. Rephrase each headline in at least two different ways to make the potential meanings clear. You may need to change the word order, change words, add function words, or alter the inflections.

Heavyweight Fights Tonight _____

_____

Bank Rates High _____

_____

Presidents Elect to Appear _____

_____

Brakes Fall from Cliff _____

_____

Whiskey Still Illegal _____

_____

State Wins over Opponent _____

_____

New Student Assembly Held _____

_____

Army Cashiers Failure _____

_____

1.10 FOR DIFFERENT LANGUAGES, DIFFERENT SYSTEMS

Language systems differ from one another in many ways. Here are four sets of equivalent expressions from different languages. The second column is Melanesian Pidgin, spoken in New Guinea,[3] the third is Latin, and the fourth is Esperanto, an artificial language invented in the nineteenth century.

ENGLISH	PIDGIN	LATIN	ESPERANTO
a good man	gudfela man	vir bonus	bona viro
a good woman	gudfela meri	femina bona	bona virino
a big house	bigfela haus	domus magnus	granda domo
a little book	smolfela buk	liber parvus	malgranda libro
a man's wife	meri bilong man	virī uxor	edzino de viro
a woman's house	haus bilong meri	feminae domus	domo de virino
a wall of a house	wol bilong haus	domus paries	muro de domo
I look.	Mi luk.	Videō.	Mi rigardas.
He looks.	Em i-luk.	Videt.	Li rigardas.
She looks.	Em i-luk.	Videt.	Ŝi rigardas.
I see a man.	Mi lukim man.	Virum videō.	Mi rigardas viron.
He sees a woman.	Em i-lukim meri.	Feminam videt.	Li rigardas virinon.

[3] The Pidgin material has been adapted from Robert A. Hall, Jr., *Hands Off Pidgin English!* (Sydney, Australia, 1955), *Melanesian Pidgin English* (Baltimore, 1943), and *Melanesian Pidgin Phrase Book and Vocabulary* (Baltimore, 1943).

ENGLISH	PIDGIN	LATIN	ESPERANTO
She reads a book.	Em i-ridim buk.	Librum legit.	Ŝi legas libron.
I see him.	Mi lukim.	Eum videō.	Mi rigardas lin.
He sees her.	Em i-lukim.	Eam videt.	Li rigardas ŝin.
She reads it.	Em i-ridim.	Eum legit.	Ŝi legas ĝin.
You look.	Yu luk.	Vidēs.	Vi rigardas.
You looked.	Yu luk.	Vīdistī.	Vi rigardis.
They (are) read(ing) a book.	Em i-ridim buk.	Librum legunt.	Ili legas libron.
They (have) read a book.	Em i-ridim buk.	Librum lēgērunt.	Ili legis libron.
This house is big.	Disfela haus i-bigfela.	Magnus hīc domus.	Tiu-ĉi domo estas granda.
This woman is good.	Disfela meri i-gudfela.	Bona haec femina.	Tiu-ĉi virino estas bona.
He is a man.	Em i-man.	Vir est.	Li estas viro.
It is a book.	Em i-buk.	Liber est.	Ĝi estas libro.
It rains.	I-ren.	Pluit.	Pluvas.

Each of the following statements describes the grammatical system of one or more of the four languages. If we were considering a larger body of material, some of the statements would need qualification, but for this exercise you should suppose that the expressions given above represent the complete corpus of the languages. For each statement, circle the names of the languages to which it applies.

1. Nouns must be modified by an article, a pronoun, or a possessive noun.   Eng.   Pid.   Lat.   Esp.

2. Nouns, as a part of speech, can always be identified by their endings.   Eng.   Pid.   Lat.   Esp.

3. Adjectives, as a part of speech, can always be identified by their endings.   Eng.   Pid.   Lat.   Esp.

4. Adjectives change their endings to agree with the nouns they modify.   Eng.   Pid.   Lat.   Esp.

5. Adjectives usually follow the nouns they modify.   Eng.   Pid.   Lat.   Esp.

6. "Possession" is shown by a function word.   Eng.   Pid.   Lat.   Esp.

7. "Possession" is shown by inflection.   Eng.   Pid.   Lat.   Esp.

8. The pronoun of the third person has different forms for different genders.   Eng.   Pid.   Lat.   Esp.

9. Nouns change their form when they are the object of a verb.   Eng.   Pid.   Lat.   Esp.

10. Pronouns change their form when they are the object of a verb.   Eng.   Pid.   Lat.   Esp.

11. Verbs have an ending that signals that the action is directed toward some goal.   Eng.   Pid.   Lat.   Esp.

12. Verbs change their form according to the subject.   Eng.   Pid.   Lat.   Esp.

13. Verbs change their form to show the time of the action. Eng. Pid. Lat. Esp.

14. Grammatical meaning is shown by vowel changes within a word as well as by endings. Eng. Pid. Lat. Esp.

15. A linking verb is required in all sentences of the type "X is Y." Eng. Pid. Lat. Esp.

16. Verb inflections can be added to nouns and adjectives. Eng. Pid. Lat. Esp.

17. Every sentence must have a subject. Eng. Pid. Lat. Esp.

18. The usual word order of sentences is subject–verb–object. Eng. Pid. Lat. Esp.

Translate these expressions into each of the other three languages:

ENGLISH	PIDGIN	LATIN	ESPERANTO
a good house	_____	_____	_____
_____	smolfela meri	_____	_____
_____	_____	paries magnus	_____
_____	_____	_____	bona libro de viro
She is a woman.	_____	_____	_____
_____	Disfela man i-smolfela.	_____	_____
_____	_____	Eum legunt.	_____
_____	_____	_____	Vi rigardis libron.

1.11 LANGUAGE SYSTEMS ARE CONVENTIONS

Even echoic words are conventional. On the left are a number of words designating various noises and on the right are the sources of those noises. Match the two columns. The correct answers are printed below, but try your ear before you look at the key.

_____ guau	1. a Spanish dog	
_____ glouglou	2. an Irish dog	
_____ kuckeliku	3. a Serbo-Croatian dog	
_____ plof	4. a Hebrew cat	
_____ bim-bam	5. an Italian sheep	
_____ amh-amh	6. a Swedish horse	
_____ bats	7. a Hungarian pig	
_____ gakgak	8. a French turkey	
_____ tsiltsul	9. a Swedish cock	
_____ bè	10. a Turkish duck	
_____ yimyum	11. an English nightingale	
_____ av-av	12. a Dutch door slamming	
_____ gnägg	13. a Russian door slamming	
_____ jug jug tereu	14. a German bell ringing	
_____ röff-röff	15. a Hebrew bell ringing	

KEY: 1, 8, 9, 12, 14, 2, 13, 10, 15, 5, 4, 3, 6, 11, 7.

11

Here are three translations of the paternoster corresponding to the three major periods in the history of our language: Old English (or Anglo-Saxon), Middle English, and early Modern English. The first was made about the year 1000, the second is from the Wyclif Bible of 1380, and the third is from the King James Bible of 1611.

OLD ENGLISH: Fæder ūre, þū þe eart on heofonum, sī þīn nama gehālgod. Tōbecume þīn

rīce. Gewurðe þīn willa on eorðan swā swā on heofonum. Ūrne gedæghwāmlican hlāf syle ūs tō

dæg. And forgyf ūs ūre gyltas, swā swā wē forgyfað ūrum gyltendum. And ne gelæd þū ūs on

costnunge, ac ālȳs ūs of yfele. Sōðlice.

MIDDLE ENGLISH: Oure fadir that art in heuenes halowid be thi name, thi kyngdom come to, be thi wille don in erthe as in heuene, yeue to us this day oure breed ouir other substaunce, & foryeue to us oure dettis, as we foryeuen to oure dettouris, & lede us not in to temptacion: but delyuer us from yuel, amen.

EARLY MODERN ENGLISH: Our father which art in heauen, hallowed be thy Name. Thy kingdome come. Thy will be done, in earth, as it is in heauen. Giue vs this day our dayly bread. And forgiue vs our debts, as we forgiue our debters. And leade vs not into temptation, but deliuer vs from euill: For thine is the kingdome, and the power, and the glory, for euer, Amen.

1. Try to make a word-for-word translation of the Old English by comparing it with the later versions. Write your translation in the blank spaces under the Old English words.

2. Some Old English words that may look completely unfamiliar have survived in Modern English in fixed expressions or with changed meanings. Finding the answers to these questions in a dictionary may help you to translate the Old English paternoster:
   What is a 'bishop*ric*'? (cf. *rīce*) _____
   What is the meaning of *worth* in 'woe *worth* the day'? (cf. *gewurðe*) _____
   What are the Old English words from which came Modern English *so* and *as*? (cf. *swā swā*)

   _____
   What is the Old English source-word for Modern English *loaf*? _____
   What is the meaning of *sooth* in *soothsayer* or *forsooth*? (cf. *sōðlice*) _____

3. What three letters of the Old English writing system have been lost from our alphabet?

   _____

4. At first sight, the letters *v* and *u* seem to be used haphazardly in the King James translation, but a more careful inspection will reveal a system in their use. What is it? _____

   _____

5. What different forms does Old English have for the word *our*? _____
   Can you suggest why Old English has more than one form for this word? _____

   _____

   _____

6. List three phrases from the Wyclif translation in which the use of prepositions differs from that in the King James version. _____

7. List three phrases from the Wyclif translation in which the word order differs from that in the Old English version. _____

_____

8. In general, does the Middle English version appear to be more similar to the Old English translation or to the King James translation? Give several reasons to support your answer.

_____

_____

_____

9. The King James version of the paternoster may be familiar, but in many ways its language is archaic. Rewrite the prayer in normal, contemporary English. Notice the kinds of change you must make to avoid an ecclesiastical flavor.

10. What reasons might an Elizabethan have for thinking the language of your version to be "corrupt"? What reasons might an Englishman of the year 1000 have for thinking the language of the King James version "corrupt"? Why would they both be wrong?

_____

_____

1.13 *THE QUESTION OF USAGE*

Which of the following expressions are considered good usage today? Which would you yourself say differently?

_____ 1. "These kind of knaves, I know." (Shakespeare, *King Lear*)

_____ 2. "I want to take this opportunity of thanking you on behalf of the Duchess of Windsor and I." (Edward, Duke of Windsor, in a radio speech, January 1965)

_____ 3. "and this she did . . . with a certain melancholy, as if life were all over for her and she was only shouting a few last messages to the fading shore." (J. B. Priestley, *The Good Companions*)

_____ 4. "I shall return." (General Douglas MacArthur on leaving Corregidor, March 1942)

_____ 5. "I only asked the question from habit." (B. Jowett, *The Dialogues of Plato*)

_____ 6. "The great point of honor on these occasions was for each man to strictly limit himself to half a pint of liquor." (Thomas Hardy, *The Mayor of Casterbridge*)

_____ 7. "No data is as yet available on how far this increase continues." (New York *Times*, August 10, 1958)

_____ 8. "Those assemblies were not wise like the English parliament was." (J. C. Morison, *Macaulay*)

_____ 9. "Here there does seem to be, if not certainties, at least a few probabilities." (H. G. Wells, *Mankind in the Making*)

_____ 10. "Whom do men say that I the Son of man am?" (Matt. xvi.13).

1.14 *THE* OXFORD ENGLISH DICTIONARY: *HISTORY AND PLAN*

One of the most useful tools for studying the history of the English language is the *Oxford English Dictionary* (*OED*), originally named *A New English Dictionary on Historical Principles* (*NED*). It is the best dictionary of its kind for any language in the world. Abridged versions of this work have been made, but the student of English should make himself familiar with the thirteen volumes of the complete *OED*. Examine the dictionary and read the prefatory material, noting especially these points:

1. The *OED* is based on a large collection of quotations. How were the quotations gathered and by whom?

2. From what kind of material and from what historical periods were the quotations taken?

3. How many quotations were gathered as the basis for the *OED*, and how many quotations actually appear as illustrative citations in the dictionary?

4. What "new principles in lexicography" were followed by the editors of the *OED*?

5. Who was responsible for the initial preparation of the dictionary materials, and in what year was the work begun?

6. Who were the chief editors of the *OED*?

7. What difficulties did the editors encounter as they prepared the material for publication?

8. In what year was the first part of the dictionary published, and in what year was the publication completed?

Write a short report on the *OED*, considering the questions above and explaining why the *OED* is uniquely valuable among dictionaries. For what purposes is it most useful? What limitations does it have? That is, for what kind of information or for what uses might you prefer another dictionary?

1.15 *THE* OXFORD ENGLISH DICTIONARY: *THE TREATMENT OF ENTRIES*

As an example of the kind of information you will find in the *OED*, examine the sample entry that follows.[4]

Enthusiasm (enþiū·zi‚ǽz'm). Also 7 enthusiasme, (entousiasme, 8 enthysiasm). [ad. late L. *enthūsiasm-us*, Gr. ἐνθουσιασμός, f. ἐνθουσιά-ζειν, f. ἐνθουσία (Zonaras *Lex.*) the fact of being ἔνθεος possessed by a god. Cf. Fr. *enthousiasme*.

The word ἐνθουσία has been explained by Leo Meyer as for *ἐνθεουσία, abstr. sb. f. *ἐνθεούντ- stem of pr. pple. of *ἐνθεεῖν to be ἔνθεος.]

†1. Possession by a god, supernatural inspiration, prophetic or poetic frenzy; an occasion or manifestation of these. *Obs.*

[**1579** E. K. *Gloss. Spenser's Sheph. Cal.* Oct. *Argt.*, A certaine ἐνθουσιασμός and celestiall inspiration. **1608** Sylvester *Du Bartas* 210, I feel the vertue of my spirit decayed, The Enthusiasmos of my Muse allaid.] **1603** Holland *Plutarch's Mor.* 1342 The Dæmons use to make their prophets and prophetesses to be ravished with an Enthusiasme or divine fury. **1620** J. Pyper tr. *Hist. Astrea* I. v. 146 The Bacchanals runne thorow the streets raging and storming, full of the Enthusiasme of their god. **1651** Baxter *Inf. Bapt.* 87 Doth he think they knew it by Enthusiasm or Revelation from Heaven? **1674** Hickman *Hist.*

Quinquart. (ed. 2) 8 Nothing made the Anabaptists so infamous as their pretended enthusiasms or revelations. **1693** Urquhart *Rabelais* III. Prol., It is my sole Entousiasm. **1807** Robinson *Archæol. Græca* III. xii. 253 The second sort of θεομάντεις..were such as pretended to enthusiasm.

† b. (cf. 3.) Poetical fervour, impassioned mood or tone. *Obs.*

1693 Dryden *Juvenal* Pref. (J.), Poetry, by a kind of enthusiasm, or extraordinary emotion of soul, makes it seem to us that we behold, etc. **1779-81** Johnson *L. P., Cowley* Wks. II. 70 He [Cowley] was the first who imparted to English numbers the enthusiasm of the greater ode, and the gaiety of the less.

2. Fancied inspiration; 'a vain confidence of divine favour or communication' (J.). In 18th c. often in vaguer sense: Ill-regulated or misdirected religious emotion, extravagance of religious speculation. *arch.*

1660 H. More *Myst. Godl.* To Rdr., If ever Christianity be exterminated, it will be by Enthusiasme. **1711** Shaftesb. *Charac.* § 7 (1737) I. 53 Inspiration is a real feeling of the Divine Presence, and Enthusiasm a false one. **1747** Dodd-

---

[4] From the *Oxford English Dictionary*. Reprinted by permission of the Clarendon Press, Oxford.

RIDGE *Life Col. Gardiner* § 137. 163 There is really such a Thing as Enthusiasm, against which it becomes the true Friends of the Revelation to be diligently on their Guard. **1766** WALPOLE *Let.* 10 Oct., Towards the end he [Wesley] exalted his voice and acted very ugly enthusiasm. **1772** PRIESTLEY *Inst. Relig.* (1782) I. 121 Enthusiasm [makes us] imagine that we are the peculiar favorites of the divine being. **1829** I. TAYLOR *Enthus.* ii. (1867) 20 The most formal and lifeless devotions..are mere enthusiasm unless, etc. **1841-4** EMERSON *Ess. Over-Soul* Wks. (Bohn) I. 118 Everywhere the history of religion betrays a tendency to enthusiasm.

3. The current sense: Rapturous intensity of feeling in favour of a person, principle, cause, etc.; passionate eagerness in any pursuit, proceeding from an intense conviction of the worthiness of the object.

1716 KENNETT in Ellis *Orig. Lett.* II. 429 IV. 306 The King of Sweden..must have much more enthusiasm in him to put it in execution. **1766-7** MRS. S. PENNINGTON *Lett.* III. 167 Different religions have introduced prejudices, Enthusiasms, and Scepticisms. **1792** *Anecd. W. Pitt* I. xviii. 282 A passion for glory which was nothing short of enthusiasm. **1808** SIR JOHN MOORE in Jas. Moore *Camp. Spain* 76 The armies you see are also without enthusiasm, or even common obstinacy. **1817** MISS MITFORD in L'Estrange *Life* II. i. 11 Enthusiasm is very catching, especially when it is very eloquent. **1863** MARY HOWITT tr. *F. Bremer's Greece* I. ii. 56 Enthusiasm for the ideals of his country and of humanity.

There are four parts to the treatment of each entry:

I. The **identification** begins with the *main form* in bold-faced type. It is the usual or typical spelling under which the rest of the information for the word is entered. Next follows the *pronunciation*, within parentheses; the symbols used in writing the sound of the word are explained in the front of each volume of the dictionary. The pronunciation will often be followed by an abbreviation designating the part of speech, for example, *a* for adjective or *v* for verb; these abbreviations are also explained in the front of each volume. If no part of speech is designated for a word, as in the case of "Enthusiasm," the word is a substantive or noun. If the word is a technical term restricted to one field of knowledge, the restriction will be indicated next by an abbreviated *specification of use*, such as Mus. (music) or Bot. (botany). Or if the word is otherwise limited in its use because it is obsolete, archaic, colloquial, dialectal, and so forth, its *status* will be indicated by an appropriate abbreviation. Neither of these restrictions applies to "Enthusiasm." Next follows a list of *earlier forms* or spellings. For "Enthusiasm," three such earlier spellings are given: the spelling "enthusiasme" was used in the seventeenth century (hence the 7 preceding the form), and less commonly the spellings "entousiasm" and "enthysiasm" were used in the seventeenth and eighteenth centuries respectively. The identification ends with a list of *inflections* if they are in any way irregular. Since "Enthusiasm" has only the regular noun plural in *-s*, no inflections are listed for it.

II. Next the **form history** of the word is given within square brackets. The *etymology* or origin of the word is traced as far back as the editors were able to track it. "Enthusiasm" is an adaptation (ad.), that is, a scholarly borrowing, from the late Latin *enthūsiasmus* or from the Greek *enthousiasmos*, which was formed from (f.) the verb *enthousiazein*, in turn formed from the noun *enthousia*, which means "the fact of being *entheos*, possessed by a god." With the English word, we might compare the French *enthousiasme*, which has a similar etymology. The "Cf." indicates that although the English and French words have a similar origin, they are not directly connected with one another. The remainder of the etymology in small type traces the earlier history of the Greek word *enthousia*. We need not be concerned with it except to point out that the asterisk which occurs before several of the words has a special significance; it means that the word it precedes is not actually preserved in written records but is a reconstructed form. The asterisk says, in effect, "The word *entheousia* does not occur in the Greek writings that have come down to us, but it is useful in discussing the history of the word to postulate the existence of some such form." We will have occasion to use the asterisk in this way in Chapter 4 (see *Origins and Development*, p. 76, n. 19).

III. The third part of the treatment is the **signification** or meaning of the word. "Enthusiasm" has had three different meanings in English, so all three of these meanings are listed and numbered in roughly chronological order. The dagger before the first definition, as well as the abbreviation *Obs.* after it, indicates that this sense is obsolete; the word is no longer used with this meaning. The earliest English meaning of the word, "possession by a god," gave rise to a subsidiary meaning, "poetical fervour," which is sublettered **b** and also marked obsolete. The comment "cf. 3" in parentheses refers the reader to the third sense of the word and implies some connection between the two senses. It is likely that the current meaning of the word developed out of sense 1b. For the second major sense of the word, "fancied inspiration," the editors of the *OED* have quoted a definition from Samuel Johnson's dictionary (J.): "a vain confidence of divine favour or communication." They have also added some information about the use of the word in the eighteenth century. The abbreviation *arch.* stands for *archaic*, which indicates that this meaning of the word survives in current English only in highly specialized use, in this case chiefly in discussions of eighteenth-century religious practices. The third meaning is the "current sense," that is, the sense current at the time the *OED* was compiled.

IV. The last part of the treatment is the **illustrative quotations** which follow each meaning and show the word being used in that sense. Thus the first quotation under the first meaning of "Enthusiasm" is from Spenser's *Shepheardes Calender*, the October Eclogue. More precisely, the quotation is from the Argument to that eclogue, which is part of the Gloss written by the otherwise anonymous E. K. The work was published in 1579. In Volume XIII of the *OED* there is a bibliography of the works from which the quotations were most often taken. It is usually possible to find there the full title of a source abbreviated in the quotations. Occasionally, however, the reader must simply use his own ingenuity.

The first quotation given for every meaning is the earliest use in that sense which the editors of the *OED* were able to find. It would, of course, be unwarranted to assume that the word had not been used earlier, but it is likely in most cases that the earliest date given is close to the initial appearance of the word in English. The quotations for each meaning are given in roughly chronological order. For practical purposes, we can use the quotations given in the *OED* as reliable indications of the appearance, frequency, and desuetude of the word. Further, the quotations supply more information about the history of the word than might be apparent from a casual glance. Some of this information will be pointed out in the questions below.

After you have examined the entry for "Enthusiasm" and have made yourself familiar with the treatment accorded the word, answer these questions:

1. Why might you be cautious about using the pronunciation given for *enthusiasm*? (Consult the preface of the *OED* to find when the dictionary was compiled and where.)

   _____

2. In the form history, *enthusiasm* is said to have been adapted (ad.) as a scholarly loan-word. Other words, such as *entice*, are said to have been adopted (a.) as popular loan-words. What evidence do the quotations supply that *enthusiasm* in fact entered English as a scholarly word rather than as a common word used freely by the people? _____

   _____

   _____

3. The quotation from 1608 is out of chronological order. Why are it and the quotation from 1579 put in square brackets? (Notice the form of the word in these two quotations.)

   _____

4. Several recent dictionaries trace the etymology of *enthusiasm* directly to the Greek *enthousiasmos* without mentioning the Latin *enthūsiasmus* at all. Judging from the quotations, which of the two possible etymologies would you think more likely to be correct?

   _____

5. How do the quotations from 1579, 1603, 1651, 1674, and 1693 (Dryden) especially help to define the word? _____

   _____

6. Do those five quotations suggest that the word would have been a familiar or unfamiliar one to readers in the late sixteenth and the seventeenth centuries? Why? _____

_____

_____

7. The last quotation for the meaning "possession by a god" is from 1807. What indication is there that this meaning may in fact have been archaic by the early nineteenth century?

_____

_____

8. The meaning "poetical fervour" has been included as a subdivision of the earliest sense of the word. How do the quotations from 1579 and 1608 justify its inclusion there?

_____

_____

9. Why did the editors of the *OED* quote Johnson's definition as part of the second meaning of the word? _____

_____

_____

10. The second definition is "fancied inspiration," but inspiration can be poetical, political, religious, scholarly, and so forth. What kind of inspiration is meant by *enthusiasm* in the quotations for the second definition? _____

_____

11. Which quotations from the sense "possession by a god" most clearly foreshadow the typical eighteenth-century meaning "fancied inspiration"? _____

_____

12. Which quotation from the third or current sense suggests most clearly how that sense developed out of the second meaning? _____

13. Does the contemporary use of *enthusiasm* differ in any respect from the definition given by the *OED* for the "current sense" of the word? If so, how? In answering this question, decide which of these two phrases seems more natural:

    an enthusiasm which was nothing short of passion
    a passion which was nothing short of enthusiasm

and compare it with the quotation from 1792. _____

_____

_____

14. Quite apart from its denotation or literal meaning, a word may change its connotation or emotional value. Of the twenty-three quotations cited to illustrate the denotations of *enthusiasm*, some use the word with an unfavorable connotation, some with a favorable connotation, and some with a neutral or indeterminate connotation. Which connotation has predominated during the entire history of the word in English? _____
Of what subject matter has *enthusiasm* been used most often with an unfavorable connotation? _____
With a favorable connotation? _____
What connotation does the word most often have in current use? _____

_____

15. When you consult the *OED* for the history of a word, in what part of the treatment will you find the most information? _____

_____

The questions about each of these words can be answered from the information in the *Oxford English Dictionary*.

1. **algebra**   From what language is this word ultimately derived? _____
   What nonmathematical meaning has the word had? _____
   According to Burton in his *Anatomy of Melancholy*, who invented algebra? _____
   Was he right? _____

2. **anatomy**   What was the earliest spelling of this word in English? _____
   What misunderstanding created the word *atomy*? _____
   _____
   In what century did the word come into common use, as opposed to the century of first occurrence? _____

3. **anesthetic**   Under what "main form" is this word entered in the *OED*? _____
   In what century was the word first used? _____
   Who is credited with proposing the term? _____

4. **ask** *v.*   In what centuries was the spelling *axe* used? _____
   From what dialect did the spelling *ask* enter Standard English? _____
   What prepositions other than *of* have been used in the expression "ask (something) *of* a person"? _____

5. **belfry**   In what century did the *l* first appear in the spelling of *belfry*? _____
   In what century did the word acquire the meaning "bell-tower"? _____
   Name another word in which an *r* has been replaced by an *l*. _____

6. **cheap**   The adjective *cheap* results from the shortening of what phrase? _____
   _____
   What was the meaning of *cheap* in that phrase? _____
   Are cognates (related forms) of this word common in other Germanic languages? _____

7. **child** *sb.*   Are cognates (related forms) of this word common in other Germanic languages?
   _____
   The word has had five varieties of plural. Identify them by citing one spelling for each.
   _____
   What does the word mean in Byron's poem *Childe Harold*? _____

8. **collate**   What other English verb is derived from the same Latin source as *collate*? _____
   What is the oldest English meaning of this word? _____
   What technical meaning does the word have in bookbinding? _____
   _____

9. **crocodile**   What is the oldest spelling of this word in English? _____
   In what century was the modern spelling introduced and what was the motive for its introduction? _____
   Who was the first English author to refer to a crocodile's weeping? _____
   _____

10. **dip**   Are *dip* and *deep* cognate (historically related) forms? _____
    Was *dip* first a noun or a verb? _____
    What does the noun mean in thieves' slang? _____

11. **diploma**   What two plural forms has the word had in English? _____
    _____

What is the literal sense of the Greek word from which *diploma* ultimately derives?

_____

What meaning of *diploma* connects it with *diplomat*? _____

_____

12. **error**   In what century was the spelling *errour* generally replaced by the current form?

_____

What sense does the word have in Tennyson's "The damsel's headlong error thro' the wood"? _____

How did the word acquire that sense? _____

13. **ether**   What was the earliest sense of this word in English? _____

When was the word first used to name the anesthetic substance? _____

Which English spelling is earlier: *aether* or *ether*? _____

14. **father**   In what century did the spelling with *th* become common? _____

What medial consonant did the word have in earlier times? _____

In what other words has a similar change taken place? _____

_____

15. **fiber**   What is the main entry form of this word in the *OED*? _____

What is the earliest English meaning of the word? _____

How do the quotations of 1598 and 1601 suggest that the earliest meaning is modeled on Latin usage? _____

16. **glamour**   *Glamour* is an altered form of what common English word? _____

What is the oldest sense of *glamour*? _____

Who is responsible for popularizing the word in standard literary English?

_____

17. **gossip**   This word was originally a compound of what two words? _____

_____

What was the earliest meaning of the word? _____

In what century was the word first used in the meaning "idle talk"? _____

18. **humour** *sb.*   Which pronunciation is older: the one with or the one without the *h*-sound?

_____

What did Shakespeare mean by the word in this phrase from *Julius Caesar*: "the humours Of the danke Morning"? _____

In what century did the meaning "amusement, jocularity" become common?

_____

19. **inn** *sb.*   Is the word related to the modern preposition-adverb *in*? _____

James Howell wrote, "Queen Mary gave this House to Nicholas Heth, Archbishop of York, and his successors for ever, to be their Inne." Are we to suppose that the archbishop ran a public house? If not, what? _____

What are the Inns of Court? _____

20. **jail** *sb.*   Briefly explain why this word has two spellings in contemporary use.

_____

Give the date of a quotation which suggests that the word formerly had two pronunciations. _____

Examine the quotations cited for the first definition. Which spelling is more common in official records? _____

21. **knave** *sb.*   With what contemporary German word is *knave* cognate? _____

What is the earliest recorded meaning of *knave*? _____

As a name for a playing-card, which word is older, *knave* or *jack*? _____

22. **leech** *sb.*[1]   What semantic connection is there between this word and the homophonous *leech, sb.*[2]? _____

Can you offer any explanation for the lack of figurative uses of the word after the sixteenth century? _____

_____

Why was the *leech-finger* so called? _____

23. **legend**   What is the etymological sense of the word, that is, the meaning it had in the language from which it is ultimately derived? _____

What is its earliest recorded meaning in English? _____

In what century does the sense "unauthentic or non-historical story" appear?

_____

24. **Mrs.**   What is the origin of the title? _____

In what century did the abbreviation become common? _____

Mrs. Bracegirdle was a popular actress on the Restoration stage. Why would it be wrong to assume that a Mr. Bracegirdle was her husband? _____

_____

25. **nostril**   This word was originally a compound of what two words? _____

_____

In what century was the *r* first metathesized (reversed in order) with the vowel?

_____

Judging from all the quotations, which spelling has been more usual: that with *th* (*þ*) or that with *t*? _____

26. **off**   What is the origin of this word? _____

In what century did *off* become the only standard spelling of the word? _____

_____

Explain how *off* has come to function sometimes as a verb. _____

_____

27. **pandemonium**   What is the earliest meaning of the word? _____

Who coined the word? _____

In what year is the sense "uproar," as opposed to "place of uproar," first recorded?

_____

28. **plow**   What is the main entry form of this word in the *OED*? _____

What is the difference between the two spellings in current English use? _____

_____

What is the earliest recorded meaning of the word in English? _____

29. **prestige**   What is the earliest meaning of the word in English? _____

Although there are quotations from 1870 and 1881 illustrating the word in its earliest meaning, how do they suggest that the meaning was already obsolete? _____

_____

What evidence is there in the quotations that the meaning "influence or reputation" was derived from French? _____

_____

30. **protocol**   What is the etymological sense of *protocol* (its meaning in the ultimate source-language from which the word is derived)? _____

What is the earliest sense of the word in English? _____

If the editors of the *OED* were rewriting the fifth definition today, what changes might they make? Specifically, which two qualifications might they omit? _____
_____

31. **quiz**   In what century did the word first appear in English? _____
What was its earliest meaning? _____
When and where did the meaning "short test" develop? _____
_____

32. **rooster**   What is the source of the word? _____
How is its use limited geographically? _____
In what century was it first used? _____

33. **salmagundi**   From what language was the word derived? _____
Which two occasional spellings of the word show the influence of folk etymology (see *Origins and Development*, p. 289)? _____
Cite a quotation which clearly shows the connotations of the word when it is used figuratively. _____
_____

34. **shift** *sb.*   What is the origin of the noun? _____
How did the word acquire the meaning "garment"? _____
_____
What meanings not listed in the *OED* has the word acquired in contemporary English?
_____

35. **snob**   What is known about the origin of the word? _____
_____
What was its earliest meaning? _____
Who do the quotations suggest popularized the word in its current sense?
_____

36. **sphinx**   What plurals does the word have? _____
In what century was the spelling *spynx* used? _____
Was the English word first applied to the Greek or the Egyptian creature?
_____

37. **story** *sb.*[2]   What is the apparent origin of this word? _____
_____
According to the *OED*, what distinction is usually made in England between the first story and the first floor? _____
_____
Which meaning of *story* is reflected in *clerestory*? _____

38. **swing** *v.*[1]   Which past tense form is older: I *swung* or I *swang*? _____
During what centuries was the past participle *swinged* used? _____
A fifteenth-century recipe says, "Recipe (take) brede gratyd, & eggis; & swyng them togydere." What is the cook supposed to do? _____

39. **thimble**   Describe the origin of this word. _____
_____
Name another word which has developed an excrescent *b*. _____

Give the earliest quotation you can find that implies that thimbles were made of metal.

_____

40. **tomato** What is the oldest English form of the word? _____

How is the spelling *tomato* explained? _____

What earlier English name did the tomato have? _____

41. **uncouth** What is the earliest English sense of the word? _____

In what century is the modern sense "uncomely, awkward" first recorded?

_____

Explain the meaning and origin of *unco* in Burns's poem "Address to the Unco Guid."

_____

_____

42. **victual** *sb.*   In what century does the *c* first appear in Standard English, as contrasted with Scottish, spellings of the word? _____

What is the origin of the *c*? _____

Examine all the quotations dated after 1800. Describe any change you detect in the use of the word during the nineteenth century. _____

_____

43. **wretch** *sb.*   What is the meaning of the Modern German cognate of this word?

_____

What is the earliest meaning of the word in English? _____

Judging from the spellings of this word, by what century had final *a* sounds changed in pronunciation? _____

44. **yankee** What origin of this word do the editors of the *OED* think most plausible?

_____

Why do they prefer it to the other possibilities they list? _____

_____

The word apparently originated as a derisive term. How early does it seem to have acquired a neutral connotation in some uses? _____

45. **zest** If a recipe calls for a teaspoon of grated zest, what ought the cook to use?

_____

Does the seventeenth-century quotation suggest that the word was in common English use at that time? Explain your answer. _____

_____

How early was the word used metaphorically? _____

1.17 *THE PROCESS OF DICTIONARY-MAKING, OR EVERY MAN HIS OWN LEXICOGRAPHER*

Because the publication of the *Oxford English Dictionary* extended over some forty-five years and even the supplement was completed a generation ago, this greatest of all dictionaries is less than satisfactory as a record of present-day English. For the historical study of our language, the *OED* is unsurpassed, but for contemporary usage, it is inadequate.

Take any one of the following words, or some similar term that has come into use since the publication of the *OED*, and investigate its meaning by using a technique similar to that of the *OED*.

1. Consult books and magazines or newspaper stories dealing with the subject area of the word to find examples of its use. The library catalogue, the *Readers' Guide to Periodical Literature*, the *New York Times Index*, or similar indexes will help you locate relevant material. Look especially for quotations in which the context helps to define the word or in which there is an indication that the word has recently come into existence.

2. For each use of the word that you find, prepare a 4×6 slip of paper giving the information described in the "Historical Introduction" to the *OED*.

3. When you have collected enough useful quotations, frame a definition for the word and illustrate it with the quotations. Your definition should be based on all of the quotations that you have collected. If the quotations justify it, you may need to recognize more than one sense for the word. List the "main form" of the word and write the definition and quotations in the style of the *OED*, but you need not write further identification or form history.

SOME RECENT WORDS

astronaut	dust bowl	newscast	seat belt
atom bomb	existentialism	nylon	sit-in
benzedrine	extrasensory	pastrami	socialite
bucket seat	fellow traveler	phoneme	video
cold war	hairdo	ponytail	winterize
collage	hydroponics	prefabricate	zip code
cyclotron	iron curtain	quasar	
discotheque	microfilm	sanforize	

Letters and Sounds:

A Brief History of Writing

2.1 QUESTIONS FOR REVIEW AND DISCUSSION

1. Define the following terms:

ideographic writing	dieresis	ligature
phonogram	acute accent mark	runes (runic alphabet)
rebus	grave accent mark	futhorc
syllabary (syllabic writing)	circumflex accent mark	Insular hand
alphabetic writing	wedge	thorn
boustrophedon	tilde	eth
majuscule	cedilla	wynn
minuscule	bar	æsc (ash)
Cyrillic alphabet	circle	yogh
diacritical markings	digraph	spelling pronunciation

2. How do the drawings of preliterate societies, such as those of the cave men or of the American Indians, differ from true writing?

3. In modern times, stylized drawings are still used for some purposes, for example, road signs. Cite some specific examples.

4. Arabic numerals and symbols like & or % are basically ideograms. Can you cite other examples of ideograms in current use?

5. What evidence is there that the Greeks acquired their writing system from the Semites?

6. In the Semitic script there was no way of writing vowel sounds. Explain the origins of the Greek vowel letters.

7. What is the origin of these Greek letter names: beta, epsilon, omicron, omega, upsilon, digamma?

8. What accounts for the difference between the angular (Γ, Δ, Σ) and the rounded (C, D, S) forms of what are historically the same letters?

9. Explain the Latin use of *C.* as an abbreviation for the name *Gaius*.

10. What letters and ligatures, formerly used in the English writing system, have passed out of common use?

11. Chaucer's Wife of Bath used to berate her husbands by asking such questions as "What rowne ye with oure mayde?" and in *A Winter's Tale* Leontes says, "They're here with me

already, whispering, rounding, 'Sicilia is a so-forth.'" What is the etymological connection between the obsolete verb *rown* or *round* and *runic* writing?

12. In what ways has the Roman alphabet been adapted for writing the un-Latin sounds of such a language as Polish, German, or English?

13. What is the origin of the dot over the letter *i*?

14. Why do the vowel letters in Modern English spelling represent sounds that differ greatly from the sounds represented by the same letters in other languages?

15. Name four spelling devices used in Middle English to indicate whether a vowel was long or short in duration.

16. Old English spelling was a reasonably good representation of the sounds of the language. Modern English spelling is notoriously bad in this respect. What causes for the widened gap between English sound and spelling can you suggest?

17. Pyles writes on page 45 of *Origins and Development*, "in a period of widespread (if perhaps only thinly spread) literacy, misunderstanding of the true relationship of writing to speech can bring about changes in language." Explain what he means by the statement, and cite examples of the kind of change he is referring to.

18. Describe the logical development, which is not necessarily the actual historical development, of writing systems. Use an outline like the following one to classify the kinds of writing systems.

> Pictures (American Indian)
> Ideographs (Egyptian ideographs, Sumerian ideographs)
> Phonograms
>   Rebuses
>   Syllabaries
>   Full syllabaries (Cherokee, Japanese)
>   Consonantal syllabaries (Egyptian phonograms, Semitic)
>   Alphabets (Greek, Roman, Cyrillic, runic)

2.2 A PICTOGRAPH

The Indian "letter" mentioned by Pyles on page 21 of *Origins and Development* is adapted here from Henry R. Schoolcraft, *Information Respecting the History, Condition, and Prospects of the Indian Tribes of the United States*.[1] An interpretation of the pictograph is also given. Compare the interpretation with the drawing to discover the conventions the "writer" used. How is each of the following concepts expressed in the pictograph?

an agreement of opinion ⸻⸻⸻⸻⸻⸻
an offering of friendship ⸻⸻⸻⸻⸻⸻
the rank of chief (vs. mere warrior) ⸻⸻⸻⸻⸻
the rank of a more important chief ⸻⸻⸻⸻⸻
a settled or civilized way of life ⸻⸻⸻⸻⸻
the location of the writer's home ⸻⸻⸻⸻⸻
the totem-group to which the Indians belong ⸻⸻⸻⸻
⸻⸻⸻⸻⸻⸻⸻⸻⸻⸻

[1] (Philadelphia, 1853), Vol. I, pp. 418–19.

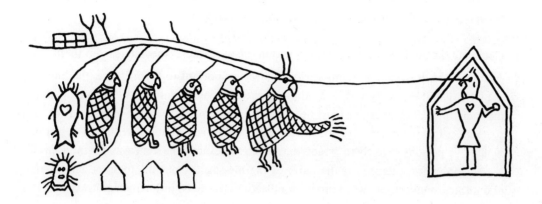

INTERPRETATION: A chief of the eagle totem who lives on the bank of a river, four of his warrior-kinsmen, a fifth warrior (of the catfish totem), and another chief, who is more powerful than the first leader, are all agreed in their views. They extend friendship to the president of the United States in the White House. Three of the eagle totem warriors have agreed to abandon their way of life and to settle in houses, thus adopting the white man's culture. It is hoped the president will understand the offer of friendship and return it.

2.3 *ANOTHER PICTOGRAPH*

The following "letter" was sent by an Ojibwa girl to a young man, inviting him to her lodge. The lover is given directions for finding his way and other information appropriate to such an invitation. Only the R.S.V.P. is lacking. (The letters have been added to the original for purposes of identification.)

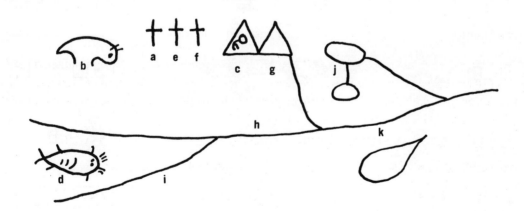

INTERPRETATION: The writer of the letter is a girl of the bear totem (   ). She and two companions, all three of whom are Christians (   ) (   ) (   ), live in two lodges (   ) (   ) near a lake (   ). A trail leads from the lodges to a main road (   ), which runs between two other lakes (   ) not far from the lodges. The letter is being sent to a man of the mud puppy totem (   ), who is reminded of a trail (   ) which leads from his lodge to the main road. A hand extending through the door of one of the dwellings (   ) both invites the young man (the purpose of the letter) and tells him which lodge he should visit.[2]

1. Complete the interpretation by writing within the parentheses the letters from the drawing.

2. Although the drawing represents various objects important to the message, the import of the letter is not explicitly stated. Nothing in the drawing actually says, "Come up and see me sometime." That message must be inferred because picture writing has no way of being so specific. In what other ways does pictography differ from genuine writing? For example, would two persons be likely to "read" the message in exactly the same way? Is there any one correct order for interpreting the parts of the message? Does the message tell anything about the pronunciation, word order, or inflections of the Ojibwa language?

_____

_____

_____

_____

_____

2.4   IDEOGRAPHS: SUMERIAN CUNEIFORM

The Sumerians, who lived in southern Mesopotamia, were enthusiastic bookkeepers. The phrases in this exercise are adapted from a collection of records, invoices, and receipts which were written between 2400 and 2300 B.C.[3] Although the cuneiform style was also used for phonograms, the Sumerian in this sample is written in ideographs.

two bulls

two lambs

four sheep

one suckling lamb

ten fattened bulls

five pastured cows

seventeen pastured bulls

twenty suckling bull calves

(an) offering (for the) king

offerings (for the) goddess Nina

_____

_____

_____

_____

_____

[2] Adapted from Garrick Mallery, *Picture Writing of the American Indians* (Tenth Annual Report of the Bureau of Ethnology, 1888–89 [Washington, D.C., 1893]), pp. 362–63.

[3] William M. Nesbit, *Sumerian Records from Drehem*, "Columbia University Oriental Series," Vol. VIII (New York, 1914).

28

1. Consult a dictionary for the literal meaning of the word *cuneiform*. _____
   _____

2. How did the writing materials that were used for cuneiform influence the shape of the symbols? _____
   _____

3. Cuneiform symbols were originally pictures of the objects they represent. Find at least one that still has some pictorial value. Suggestion: Rotate the page 90 degrees clockwise.
   _____

4. The symbol for "offering" is a combination of which two other symbols? _____
   _____

5. Translate the last five phrases in the blanks on the preceding page.

6. How is the plural of nouns indicated when there is no accompanying numeral?
   _____

7. How is the plural of nouns indicated after a numeral? _____
   _____

8. What is the position of modifiers with relation to the noun they modify? Is there more than one kind of modifier? _____
   _____

9. List two or three ways in which these ideographs differ from the pictograph of the preceding exercise. _____
   _____
   _____
   _____

10. How might the notion "ten fattened bulls" be expressed in a pictograph?

_____

2.5 *EGYPTIAN HIEROGLYPHICS*

Egyptian writing is a mixture of phonograms, which represent sounds, and ideographs, which represent ideas or general concepts. The phonograms stand for consonants only; vowels were not represented in Egyptian writing. Consequently the exact pronunciation of Egyptian is unknown. Here are some typical hieroglyphs:

PHONOGRAMS AND TRANSLITERATION		IDEOGRAMS AND MEANING
y	m	sun
' (a glottal sound)	n	light, shine
w	r	heaven
b	h	moon
p	t	

From these hieroglyphs, the following sentences can be made:[4]

HIEROGLYPHS	TRANSLITERATION	TRANSLATION
	wbn rꜥ m pt	The sun rises in the sky.
	yw rꜥ m pt	The sun is in the sky.
	wbn yꜥḥ	The moon rises.
	_____	_____
	_____	_____

1. Transliterate and translate the last two sentences in the blanks above.

2. What is the Egyptian word order for subject, verb, and adverbial phrase? _____
   _____

3. The hieroglyphs above are written from left to right, but other orders of writing are possible.
   For example: ⊙ 𓏲 𓅓 𓇯
   What is the translation of this sentence? _____

4. How can you tell from looking at hieroglyphic writing whether it is to be read from right to left or from left to right? _____

5. The ideograms used in these sentences are called determinatives. What useful functions do they serve? _____
   _____

6. In what way are these hieroglyphs a more adequate representation of language than the cuneiforms of the preceding exercise? _____
   _____

2.6 HEBREW WRITING

1. The Semitic writing systems are in many ways like Egyptian phonograms, which were, indeed, probably the model for the first Semitic writing. Hebrew script, one variety of Semitic, is written from right to left. At its simplest it is like Egyptian phonograms in making no provision whatever for representing the vowels; however, since Hebrew is still a spoken language, the vowels can be supplied in a transcription.

אבא	'abbā'	papa	חדש	chādāsh	new
בת	bath	daughter	ילד	yeled	child
בית	bayith	house	כל	kol	all
בקר	bōqer	morning	נער	na'ar	boy
גז	gēz	mowing	פסח	pesach	Passover
הר	har	hill	עט	'ēt	pen
וו	wāw	hook	צמח	tsemach	plant
חדש	chodesh	month	שמש	shemesh	sun

[4] Adapted from Sir Alan Henderson Gardiner, *Egyptian Grammar* (London, 1950).

30

Here are the twenty-two letters of the Hebrew script. Supply a transliteration for each of them.

א _____   ו _____   כ _____   ס _____   ק _____

ב _____   ז _____   ל _____   ע _____   ר _____

ג _____   ח _____   מ _____   פ _____   ש _____

ד _____   ט _____   נ _____   צ _____   ת _____

ה _____   י _____

Does Hebrew spelling distinguish between double and single consonants? _____

2. Sometimes letters which normally stand for consonants are used to represent vowels. When so used, they are called *matres lectionis*, 'mothers of reading.'

מי	mī	who	סום	sūs	horse
איש	'īsh	man	כום	kōs	goblet
מיתר	mēthār	string	אור	'ōr	light
בית	bēth	the house of	מה	mā	what
ספור	sippūr	story	בחורה	bachūrā	girl

These three Hebrew letters are sometimes used as *matres lectionis*; what vowels can each represent?

י _____   ו _____   ה _____

3. In the sixth century A.D., a group of scholars called the Massoretes, from *massōrā* 'tradition,' invented a system of diacritics for a more precise writing of the Hebrew vowels. These scholars were motivated by a desire to preserve the exact pronunciation of the Scriptures and were probably influenced by the alphabetic system which the Greeks had evolved much earlier. The diacritic marks they invented are called massoretic points.

DIACRITICS ADDED TO SIMPLE SPELLINGS			DIACRITICS ADDED TO *matres lectionis*		
בת	bath	daughter	מה	mā	what
וו	wāw	hook	בית	bēth	the house of
שמש	shemesh	sun	מי	mī	who
גז	gēz	mowing	אור	'ōr	light
בית	bayith	house	סום	sūs	horse
כל	kol	all			
בקר	bōqer	morning			
נפח	nuppach	blown up			

The points, except for those that represent long *o* and *u*, are written beneath the consonant that they follow. Notice that the same diacritic is used for long *a* and short *o*; in some dialects of Hebrew these two sounds are pronounced alike. Even when distinct from long *a*, short *o* is relatively rare.

Transliterate these Hebrew words:

חִידָה	______________	riddle	עֵז	______________	she-goat
שֹׁמֵר	______________	watchman	נוּס	______________	flee
שַׁחַר	______________	dawn	חַיִל	______________	power
קוֹל	______________	voice	אֶחָד	______________	one

4. The Hebrew writing system is sometimes referred to as an alphabet, but is perhaps better called a syllabary. How does it represent a transitional stage between syllabaries and alphabets? ____
____
____

2.7 *THE CHEROKEE SYLLABARY*

In 1821 Sequoya, who has been called the Cherokee Cadmus, invented a script for writing his native language. Sequoya's invention made Cherokee the only Indian tongue to have an indigenous, fully developed writing system. Although he seems to have known no English, many of Sequoya's symbols are clearly derived from the Latin alphabet. The Cherokee writing system is, however, not an alphabet, but a syllabary, as the chart on the facing page will make clear.[5]

Transliterate the following Cherokee words by consulting the chart.

CHEROKEE	TRANSLITERATION	TRANSLATION
ᏣᎳᎩ	______________	Cherokee
ᏏᏉᏯ	______________	Sequoya
ᏚᏂᏃᏗ	______________	October, harvest month
ᎤᏏᎮᏒᏩ	______________	instantly
ᎠᏞᎦ	______________	war club

[5] Grant Foreman, *Sequoyah* (Norman, Okla., 1959); and John K. White, "On the Revival of Printing in the Cherokee Language," *Current Anthropology*, III (1962), 511–14. Cherokee syllabary type courtesy of the Carnegie Corporation Cross-Cultural Education Project of the University of Chicago, Tahlequah, Oklahoma.

Cherokee Syllabary

	a	e	i	o	u	ʌ
	a	e	i	o	u	ʌ
ka	ga	ge	gi	go	gu	gʌ
	ha	he	hi	ho	hu	hʌ
	la	le	li	lo	lu	lʌ
	ma	me	mi	mo	mu	
hna nah	na	ne	ni	no	nu	nʌ
	kwa	kwe	kwi	kwo	kwu	kwʌ
s	sa	se	si	so	su	sʌ
	da	de	di	do	du	dʌ
	ta	te	ti			
dla	tla	tle	tli	tlo	tlu	tlʌ
	tsa	tse	tsi	tso	tsu	tsʌ
	wa	we	wi	wo	wu	wʌ
	ya	ye	yi	yo	yu	yʌ

Japanese can be written with ideographic, syllabic, or alphabetic scripts. Katakana is only one of its writing systems.

KATAKANA	TRANSLITERATION	TRANSLATION
ワタシ	watashi	I
アナタ	anata	you
イチ	ichi	one
ヨル	yoru	night
ハイ	hai	yes
シロ	shiro	white
カモク	kamoku	thing
ヨイ	_____	good
ハナ	_____	flower
シカル	_____	blame

1. Transliterate the last three words in the blanks above.

2. What kind of writing system is Katakana?_____

3. How does Katakana differ from the Semitic writing system? _____

    _____

    _____

    _____

4. Languages differ from one another not only in the sounds they use, but also in the order in which their sounds may be arranged. The possible arrangements of sounds (technically, *phonotactics*) has some bearing on the kind of writing system most appropriate for a language. In Japanese each syllable tends to be composed of a single consonant (C) followed by a single vowel (V). Thus we can describe the canonical, or regular, form of the Japanese syllable as CV. The words *yo-ru* and *wa-ta-shi* are made entirely of syllables of this sort. Notice that the spellings *sh* and *ch* in the transliterations stand for single consonants each. There are, of course, other possibilities; for example, any of the five vowels of Japanese may form a syllable by itself with no preceding consonant. The word *i-chi* begins with such a syllable, and the word *ha-i* ends in one. Moreover certain consonants such as the *n*-sound can form a syllable without a vowel. The Japanese word *hon* 'book' consists of two syllables: *ho-n*. Such a syllable division seems strange to English-speakers, but English sound patterns must seem even stranger to speakers of Japanese. The point to notice is that Japanese has no syllables of the form VC or CVC and no syllables beginning with consonant combinations like *st*, *tr*, *sw*, or *spl*. The canonical form of Japanese syllables is quite different from that of English syllables. Consequently, when the Japanese language

borrows words from a language like English, it must adapt the arrangement of sounds to its own patterns. Thus *beer* appears in Japanese as *bīru*, and *butter* as *bata*. In recent years such borrowing has increased so much that a large portion of Don C. Bailey's *Glossary of Japanese Neologisms* (Tucson: University of Arizona Press, 1962) is devoted to recording them. According to Mr. Bailey, Western culture has introduced Japanese politicians to the *firibasutā* 'filibuster,' businessmen to the *wōru-sutorīto-jānaru* '*Wall Street Journal*,' and suburbanites to the lawn *supurinkurā* 'sprinkler' and the *disukaunto-hausu* 'discount house.' My fair Japanese lady has the benefit of *kosuchūmu-jueru* 'costume jewelry,' the *negurije* 'negligee,' or a *fēsu-rifuto* 'face lift.' The *jitabagu* 'jitterbug' has doubtless been replaced by *puroguresshibu-jazu* 'progressive jazz' as the *kūru* 'cool' form of music preferred by those who put a *sutereo-rekōdo* 'stereo record' on the *rekōdo-pureyā* 'record player' and adjust the *tsuītā* 'tweeter' and the *ūfā* 'woofer.' It is hardly surprising if some Japanese swallows a *torankiraizā* 'tranquilizer' and shouts *Yankī-go-hōmu*!

Explain why the phonotactics of Japanese makes the katakana an appropriate kind of writing system for the language. _____

_____

_____

5. Compare the phonotactics of Japanese with that of Cherokee. Are they generally similar or dissimilar?_____

How appropriate is Sequoya's writing system for Cherokee? _____

_____

6. Compare the phonotactics of Japanese with that of Hebrew. What are the canonical forms (consonant and vowel patterns) for Hebrew words of one syllable? _____

How does Hebrew differ most noticeably from Japanese in its phonotactic patterns?

_____

Which language probably has the larger number of different syllables—Hebrew or Japanese? _____

7. Compare the phonotactics of Japanese with that of English. What are the canonical forms for the following monosyllabic English words?

a _____ at _____ pant _____ spit _____ prompts _____
no _____ pan _____ pants _____ split _____ splints _____

Would a syllabary be an appropriate writing system for English? Explain your answer.

_____

_____

_____

2.9 THE DEVELOPMENT OF THE ALPHABET

The invention of the alphabet is one of those rare events in human history that seem to have occurred only once. When the Greeks adapted the Semitic syllabary to their own language, they used some of the extra consonant letters to write vowels. All subsequent alphabets spring from this bit of Greek cleverness. The chart on the next page traces, in a greatly simplified fashion, the development of the alphabet from Semitic to Greek to Latin to English. By referring to pages 22–26 of *Origins and Development* and to the table that can be found under the entry *Alphabet* in most desk dictionaries, you can complete the chart.

SEMITIC			GREEK		ROMAN	
Hebrew letters	*Hebrew letter names*	*Phoenician letters*	*letters*	*letter names*	*Classic Latin letters*	*Modern English letters*
א	aleph	∢	A	alpha	A	A
ב		∆				
ג		ꓤ				
ד		◿				
ה		Ⴈ				
ו		Υ	F	digamma		
ז		Ⲓ				
ח		Ⴌ				
ט		⊕				
י		Ꙅ				
כ		⅄				
ל		∟				
מ		ꓦ				
נ		⅄				
ס		ⲫ				
ע		○				
פ		ꓛ				
צ		⊬				
ק		Ϙ	Q	qoppa		
ר		ꓘ				
ש		W				
ת		X				

The Cyrillic alphabet, used in Russian and some other Slavic languages, is a development of the Greek alphabet. A comparison of the Cyrillic letter-shapes with those of Greek will reveal many similarities. The alphabet given here is the form of Cyrillic used in writing Russian; there are slight differences for other languages.

LETTER	TRANSLITERATION	LETTER	TRANSLITERATION	LETTER	TRANSLITERATION
А а	a	Л л	l	Ц ц	ts
Б б	b	М м	m	Ч ч	ch
В в	v	Н н	n	Ш ш	sh
Г г	g	О о	o	Щ щ	shch
Д д	d	П п	p	Ъ ъ	none
Е е	e	Р р	r	Ы ы	y
Ж ж	zh	С с	s	Ь ь	' (palatalization)
З з	z	Т т	t	Э э	e
И и	i	У у	u	Ю ю	yu
Й й	i (in diphthongs)	Ф ф	f	Я я	ya
К к	k	Х х	kh		

Transliterate these Russian words:

Чехов	_____	Пушкин	_____
Хрущев	_____	самовар	_____
Толстой	_____	спутник	_____
дрожки	_____	рубль	_____
степь	_____	бабушка	_____
интеллигенция	_____	тройка	_____

2.11 *THE RUNIC INSCRIPTION OF THE RUTHWELL CROSS*

The Ruthwell (sometimes riming with *civil*) Cross is a Scottish stone monument that has engraved upon it part of an Old English poem, "The Dream of the Rood." The inscription, which is in runic symbols, has been badly damaged by the ravages of the weather and of the Scottish Covenanters who objected to "idolatrous monuments." In the 1640's the cross was broken into pieces and cast into the churchyard; consequently the inscription is now fragmentary. Most of what survives is reproduced here, with some of the missing letters supplied; the text has also been divided into words, although in the original the runes follow one another without spaces. The speaker in the poem is the True Cross, which relates the events of the Crucifixion as the Old English poet conceived them. The poem dates from the early eighth century and is in the Northumberland dialect.[6]

[6] Bruce Dickins and Alan S. C. Ross, *The Dream of the Rood* (London, 1954); and Ralph W. V. Elliott, *Runes* (New York, 1959).

NE FRAGMENT

ᚠᚪᚷᛖᚱᛗᛖᚪ ᚻᛁᚾᚪ ᚷᛖᚻ ᚠᛏᛗᛖᛋᛏᛏᛁᚷ ᚦᚪ

ᚻᛖ ᚠᚪᛚᚻᛖ ᚠᚪ ᚷᚪᛚᚷᚢ ᚷᛁᛋᛏᛁᚷᚪ ᛗᚪᚻᛁᚷ

TRANSLITERATION AND GLOSS

ongeredæ hinæ   ḡod almeȝttig þa he walde on   ḡalḡu   gistiḡa modig
Unclothed himself god almighty. For he would onto the cross ascend courageous.

SE FRAGMENT

ᚠᚻᚪᚠ ᛁᚻ ᚱᛁᛁᚻᛏᚪ ᚄᛗᚾᛁᚷᚻ ᚻᛖᚠᚢᚾᚪᛋ

ᚻᛚᚪᚠᚪᚱᚻ   ᚻᚪᛚᚻᚪ ᛁᚻ ᚾᛁ ᚻᚪᚱᛋᛏᚪ

ᛒᛁᛋᛗᚪᚱᚪᚻᚢ ᛏᛚᚷᛗᛏ ᛗᛖᚾ ᛒᚪ ᚪᛏᚷᚪᚻᚱᚪ

ᛁᚻ ᚠᚪᛋ ᛗᛁᚦ ᛒᛚᚪᚻᚪ ᛒᛁᛋᛏᛖᛗᛁᚻ

TRANSLITERATION AND GLOSS

ahof   ic riicnæ k͡yniŋc he͡afunæs hlafard hælda ic ni   dorstæ bismærædu uŋ͡ket men
Lifted up I a great king, heaven's Lord. Bow I did not dare. Mocked   us two men

ba   ætḡadræ ic wæs miþ blodæ bistemid
both together.[7] I was with blood bedewed.

SW FRAGMENT

ᚴᚱᛁᛋᛏ ᚠᚪᛋ ᚪᚾ ᚱᚪᚻᛁ   ᚻᚹᛖᚦᚱᚪ ᚦᛖᚱ

ᚠᚢᛋᚪ ᚠᛏᚱᚱᚪᛋ ᚴᚹᚪᛗᚢ ᚪᚦᚦᛁᛚᚪ ᛏᛁᛚ ᚪᚾᚢᛗ

ᛁᚻ ᚦᚪᛏ ᚪᛚ ᛒᛁᚻᚪᛚᚻ   ᛋᚪᚱᚪ ᛁᚻ

ᚠᚪᛋ ᛗᛁᚦ ᛋᚪᚱᚷᚢᛗ ᚷᛁᚻᚱᚪᚾᚠᛁᚻ

TRANSLITERATION AND GLOSS

krist wæs on rodi   hweþræ þer fusæ   féàrran kwomu æþþilæ   til
Christ was on the cross. And   there hastening from afar came   noblemen[8] towards (me)

anum ic þæt al bihéàld saræ   ic wæs miþ sorḡum gidroefid
alone. I that all beheld. Sorely I was with sorrows troubled.

NW FRAGMENT

ᛗᛁᚦ ᛋᛏᚱᛖᛚᚢᛗ ᚷᛁᚠᚢᚾᚻᚪᚷ   ᚠᛚᛖᚷᚻᚢᛏ

ᚻᛁᚠ ᚻᛁᚾᚪ ᛚᛖᛗᚠᚱᛁᚷᚾᚪᛋ   ᚷᛁᛋᛏᚪᚻᚻᚢᛏ

ᚻᛁᛗ ᚪᛏ ᚻᛁᛋ ᛚᛁᚻᚪᛋ ᚻᛏᚠᚪᛚᚢᛗ   ᛒᛁᚾᛏᛗᚢᛏ

ᚻᛁᚠ ᚦᛖᚱ ᚻᛏᚠᚪᚾᚪᛋ ᚻᚱᛗᚻᛏᛖᛋ

<hr>

[7] That is, "Men mocked both us two together."

[8] Joseph of Arimathea and Nicodemus.

____	________	_________	__________	____	____	______________	
(I was)	*with*	*arrows*	*wounded.*	*Laid down*	*they*	*him*	*weary in limb.*

___________	_______	__	___	_______	_____
They stood	*by him*	*at*	*his*	*body's*	*head.*

__________	_____	______	_________	______
Beheld	*they*	*there*	*heaven's*	*Lord.*

1. Complete the chart below by giving the transliteration for each rune.
2. Transliterate the runic letters of the fourth fragment.
3. What does the style in which the letters are made—angular with few curves—suggest about the original material and method for writing runes?

THE FUTHORC

RUNE	TRANS.	RUNE	TRANS.	RUNE	TRANS.	RUNE	TRANS.
ᚠ	____	ᚻ	____	ᛏ	____	ᚪ	____
ᚢ	____	ᚾ	____	ᛒ	____	ᚫ	____
ᚦ	____	ᛁ	____	ᛖ	____	ᚣ	____
ᚩ	____	ᛡ	îo	ᛗ	____	ᛠ	____
ᚱ	____	ᛇ	____	ᛚ	____	ᛣ	____
ᚳ	____	ᛈ	p	ᛝ	____	ᛤ	____
ᚷ	____	ᛉ	x	ᛟ	____	ᚸ	____
ᚹ	____	ᛋ	____	ᛞ	____		

The accompanying illustration is a page from an Old English manuscript written in the Insular hand, probably in the early eleventh century.[9]

9 British Museum Manuscript Cotton Julius E vii, folio 59.

In the middle of the page, at the large capital letter, there begins a homily with the abbreviated Latin title "VII ID. MR. NATL. SCOR. QUADRAGINTA MILITUM," that is, "The Seventh Day Before the Ides of March: Feast of the Holy Forty Soldiers." You will find this passage transliterated and translated on pages 133–36 of *Origins and Development*. Notice that word division does not always conform to modern practice. Notice also the letter shapes that differ significantly from modern forms, especially *g*, *r*, the three forms of *s*, the letter called *eth*, and the runes *thorn* and *wynn*.

At the top of the page is the end of another homily which includes the story of the virgin St. Felicula, who was a companion of St. Peter's daughter, Petronilla. Felicula had received unwanted amorous attention from an important and powerful pagan named Flaccus. The fragment of the story on this page tells how she spurned Flaccus and how he took revenge. The passage is translated and partly transliterated here; complete the transliteration.

(Ne beo)   ic næfre þin wif · forðan þe ic sylfwylles   eom criste   gehalgod · ne ic
(Not shall be) I never thine wife because   I of my own will am to Christ hallowed, nor I

þam hæþenum godum lac   ne geoffrige · forðan þe ic on crist gelyfe · Þa het
to the heathen   gods   sacrifice not will offer because   I in Christ believe. Then commanded

se arleasa flaccus · þa femnan gebringan   on þysterfullu[m] cwearterne · & cw[æþ] ·
the merciless Flaccus the virgin to be brought into a dark   prison   and said

þ[æt] man ne sceolde ænigne bigleofan hire don binnon seofon nihton ·
that one not should any   food   her give for   seven nights.

_____ _____ _____ _____ _____ _____ _____ _____ _____ _____

She dwelt then so seven nights meatless, and afterwards was

_____ _____ _____ _____ _____ _____ _____ _____ _____ _____ _____

tortured for the true faith and for her maidhood until she

_____ _____ _____ _____ _____ _____ _____ _____ _____ _____ _____

was martyred, and her ghost fared free to heaven. Then came

_____ _____ _____ _____ _____ _____ _____ _____ _____

Nicomedis the foresaid mass-priest, and buried her body to

_____ _____ _____ _____ _____ _____ _____ _____ _____

praise of the Almighty. Then seized Flaccus the faithful

_____ _____ _____ _____ _____ _____ _____ _____ _____

priest, and because he would not to the foul gods offer,

_____ _____ _____ _____ _____ _____ _____ _____ _____

commanded him to be scourged until he died. He departed then

_____ _____ _____ _____ _____ _____ _____ _____ _____ _____

to heaven to the Savior Christ, to whom is glory and honor

_____ _____ _____ _____ _____

in all worlds' worlds.[10] Amen.

[10] That is, 'world without end.'

2.13 MODERN SPELLINGS: CONSONANTS

1. The spelling conventions of Modern English provide more than one spelling for most of our consonant sounds. The following list of words illustrates some of the variant spellings.

bobbin	fission	liquor	pass	teeth
breeze	fizz	logger	pleasure	teethe
bridge	fustian	machine	purr	thyme
cent	garage	match	quiz	tissue
cheese	ghetto	metal	reddish	union
choir	gin	mutt	rhythm	vice
claque	gradual	myrrh	roll	vision
cliff	guitar	nation	rough	were
copper	humming	nature	scent	what
curve	is	of	singe	who
dinner	judgment	once	sink	wreck
facial	lapse	onion	sugar	xylophone

Find in the list above as many alternate spellings as you can for each of the sounds described below. The first sound has been done as an example. Complete the rest of the blanks.

THE SOUND SPELLED   ALTERNATE SPELLINGS

p- (as in *pin*)   -pp (copper) _____

b- (as in *bin*) _____

t- (as in *tin*) _____

d- (as in *din*) _____

ch- (as in *chin*) _____

j- (as in *Jim*) _____

k- (as in *kin*) _____

g- (as in *gun*) _____

f- (as in *fin*) _____

v- (as in *vim*) _____

th- (as in *thin*) _____

th- (as in *then*) _____

s- (as in *sin*) _____

z- (as in *Zen*) _____

sh- (as in *shin*) _____

-z- (as in *azure*) _____

m- (as in *men*) _____

n- (as in *net*) _____

-ng (as in *sing*) _____

l- (as in *limb*) _____

r- (as in *run*) _____

w- (as in *win*) _____

y- (as in *yen*) _____

h- (as in *hit*) _____

2. The letter *x* can represent several different sounds or sound-combinations. Sort the following words into groups according to the various sounds which are spelled *x*. You may have four to six groups, depending on how you pronounce several of the words.

anxiety	axis	executor	luxurious	ox
anxious	execute	exist	luxury	xenon

2.14   *MODERN SPELLINGS: VOWELS*

Vowels have even greater variation in their spelling than do consonants. The following list of words illustrates some of the ways vowel sounds may be spelled in monosyllabic words.

aisle	cow	glyph	pique	suit
awe	crepe	go	plaid	suite
aye	crew	grow	prey	swap
bald	cry	head	put	talk
beau	day	height	reign	theme
been	do	herb	rude	through
blood	does	high	said	tie
bough	dog	isle	says	toe
break	dough	join	scourge	touch
broad	draught	key	search	two
brooch	dye	laid	seize	type
build	eye	load	sew	veil
buy	find	ma	shah	we
calm	fir	mauve	shoe	weigh
caught	flea	mould	sieve	what
chief	folk	myrrh	sign	wolf
clue	fraud	ohm	sleuth	won
cough	friend	ought	soup	word
could	gauge	owe	stein	yacht

Find in the list above as many alternate spellings as you can for each of the sounds described below.

THE SOUND SPELLED   ALTERNATE SPELLINGS

-ee- (as in *beet*)   _____

                            _____

-i- (as in *bit*)   _____

                            _____

THE SOUND SPELLED	ALTERNATE SPELLINGS
-a- . . . *-e* (as in *mate*)	_____
	_____
	_____
-e- (as in *met*)	_____
	_____
-a- (as in *mat*)	_____
-oo- (as in *boot*)	_____
	_____
	_____
-oo- (as in *foot*)	_____
-o- . . . *-e* (as in *mote*)	_____
	_____
	_____
-aw (as in *law*)	_____
	_____
-o- (as in *pot*)	_____
	_____
-u- (as in *but*)	_____
	_____
-u(r)- (as in *curt*)	_____
	_____
-ou- (as in *bout*)	_____
-i- . . . *-e* (as in *bite*)	_____
	_____
	_____
-oy (as in *boy*)	_____

2.15 *CHANGES IN THE ENGLISH WRITING SYSTEM*

Many influences have contributed to the shaping of Modern English orthography. The origins of our spellings are discussed on pages 30–46 of *Origins and Development*. Summarize what is said there about the source of each of the following spellings.

w _____

th in *thin* _____

y in *Ye Olde Antique Shoppe* _____

z in *Kenzie* _____

gh in *knight* _____

g in *gun* _____

j in *judge* _____

v	in *driven*	_____
h	in *honor*	_____
th	in *throne*	_____
th	in *author*	_____
th	in *Gotham*	_____
ph	in *philosophy*	_____
ph	in *Ralph*	_____
ch	in *child*	_____
ch	in *chorus*	_____
ch	in *schedule*	_____
gh	in *ghost*	_____
gh	in *ghoul*	_____
sh	in *shall*	_____
sc	in *scene*	_____
sc	in *scissors*	_____
wh	in *what*	_____
wh	in *whole*	_____
c	in *city*	_____
k	in *kin*	_____
que	in *critique*	_____
z	in *freeze*	_____
qu	in *queen*	_____
gu	in *guest*	_____
ee	in *feet*	_____
oo	in *rood*	_____
ai	in *raid*	_____
oa	in *road*	_____
o	in *son*	_____
ou	in *house*	_____
ow	in *dower*	_____
y	in *marry*	_____
b	in *debt*	_____
mp	in *comptroller*	_____
l	in *fault*	_____

2.16 *LEARNED AND PSEUDOLEARNED RESPELLINGS*

The spellings of some words have been changed by men with more sense of historical continuity than of contemporary reality. Thus a learned *b* was inserted in Middle English *det* to show that it is ultimately derived from Latin *debitum*. Sometimes these learned respellings, such as the *h* added to earlier *trone*, have resulted in new pronunciations. Occasionally, those who like to tinker with orthography have possessed more enthusiasm than knowledge. As a result some words have been respelled to show a wrong etymology; the pseudolearned *comptroller* for *controller* is a case in point.

1. The following Modern English words have remodeled spellings. Compare their current spellings with earlier written forms of the words, which you will find in the etymological entry of a desk dictionary or in the *Oxford English Dictionary*. In the blanks, write the

consonants that have been added to the spellings. Be prepared to discuss whether the re-spelling has influenced the pronunciation of the word and whether the respelling is a learned one such as *debt* and *throne* or a pseudolearned one such as *comptroller*.

_____	adventure	_____	island	_____	schedule
_____	aisle	_____	limb 'arm or leg'	_____	schism
_____	anthem	_____	mortgage	_____	school
_____	asthma	_____	myrrh	_____	scythe
_____	bankrupt	_____	nephew	_____	soldier
_____	could	_____	palm	_____	sovereign
_____	delight	_____	perfect	_____	subtle
_____	falcon	_____	receipt	_____	vault
_____	foreign	_____	rhyme	_____	verdict
_____	indict	_____	salmon	_____	victual

2. Consult the *OED* to find the centuries in which the foregoing words were first respelled to include the new consonants. Indicate here the number of words respelled in each century:

before 1200 _____   1400–1500 _____   1700–1800 _____
1200–1300 _____   1500–1600 _____   1800–1900 _____
1300–1400 _____   1600–1700 _____   after 1900 _____

2.17 SPELLING PRONUNCIATIONS

1. Pyles, in *Origins and Development*, mentions, as examples of words that have acquired spelling pronunciations, *often, forehead, clapboard, grindstone*, and the proper names *Daventry, Shrewsbury, Cirencester, Magdalen(e)*, and *Theobald*. Below are some additional examples. For some of these words, a spelling pronunciation is uncommon in educated speech; for others, it is almost universal and completely respectable. By comparing your normal pronunciation of these words with their spelling and with the pronunciations listed in a dictionary, try to determine the traditional pronunciation and the spelling pronunciation.

balk	draught	holm	thither
bass 'drum'	falcon	human	thyme
blackguard	forecastle	isthmus	tortoise
boatswain	gooseberry	kiln	toward
bourbon 'whiskey'	grovel	lichen	wainscot
breeches	guerdon	lightwood	waistcoat
brooch	gunwale	oboe	Wednesday
Christmas	halfpenny	pestle	wont
coxswain	handkerchief	steelyard	worsted
dour	hiccough	sumac	yolk
Birmingham	Edinburgh	Milne	Pembroke
Concord	Greenwich	Norfolk	St. John
Cowper	Home	Norwich	Southwark

2. Suggest some additional examples of spelling pronunciation from your own experience.

_____

_____

The Sounds and Spelling of Current English

1. Define the following terms:

phonetic transcription	velar	semivowel
distinctive sounds	manner of articulation	off-glide
contrastive pair	stop (explosive)	diphthong
phoneme	fricative (spirant)	schwa
allophone	affricate	front vowels
aspiration (aspirate)	liquid	back vowels
complementary distribution	lateral	central vowels
place of articulation	nasal	higher vowels
labial	voice (vibrancy)	lower vowels
labiodental	linking [r]	rounded vowels
dental	intrusive [r]	vowel quantity (length)
alveolar	intrusion (svarabhakti,	stress
palatal	epenthesis, anaptyxis)	

2. The discussion of the phoneme in *Origins and Development* includes seven characteristics which might be summarized as in the following list. Look up the word *phoneme* in several recent dictionaries. How many of these characteristics are included in the dictionary definitions?

(1) A phoneme is a group, class, or set of sounds used in speech.

(2) The sounds of which a phoneme consists are phonetically similar to one another.

(3) The sounds of which a phoneme consists alternate with one another in different phonetic environments (that is, they occur in complementary distribution).

(4) The difference between two phonemes is contrastive (that is, phonemes serve to distinguish utterances from one another).

(5) The difference between two sounds belonging to the same phoneme is not contrastive (that is, allophones do not serve to distinguish utterances).

(6) The speakers of a language commonly regard the sounds that make up a single phoneme as the "same sound."

(7) Two sounds that belong to the same phoneme in one language may belong to different phonemes in another language.

3. The difference between vowels in the English words *sit* and *seat* is not phonemic in Spanish. On the other hand, the difference between [t] sounds in English *tone* and *stone* is phonemic in Chinese, Classical Greek, and Sanskrit.

   If you are sufficiently familiar with some foreign tongue, cite some similar variations between the phonemic systems of that language and of English.

4. Describe the place and manner of articulation of the English consonants.

5. A Korean general who wanted Westerners to pronounce his name not [pæk] but rather [pɑk] changed its Romanized spelling from *Pak* to *Park*. What dialect of English had he probably learned? How would most Americans pronounce the new spelling? For most Americans what spelling would most adequately represent the pronunciation General Park wanted?

6. Describe the articulatory positions of the English vowels.

7. What is the meaning of each of these symbols as used in transcribing sounds?

$$[\ ] \qquad /\ / \qquad : \qquad \mathsf{I} \qquad \prime \qquad \grave{} \qquad \mathsf{I}$$

3.2 WRITING PHONETIC SYMBOLS

Phonetic symbols should always be in printed, never in cursive, form. Do not try to join them together like the letters of the longhand alphabet. Write [bot], not [*bot*].

Phonetic notation does not use upper case and lower case letters like those of our conventional spelling. All phonetic symbols are lower case. *Jones* is transcribed phonetically as [jonz].

Always enclose phonetic symbols within square brackets. The brackets indicate that the symbol stands for a sound. When you refer to a symbol as a written letter of the alphabet or as part of a normal spelling, it should be underlined or italicized. Thus, *boat* represents a spelling; [bot] represents a pronunciation.

Notice the wedge over [š ž č ǰ]. Always write it as part of these symbols. Distinguish it from the circumflex mark which may be used over vowels, as in *rôle*.

Distinguish clearly between these pairs of letters:

[n] and [ŋ]   [d] and [ð]   [i] and [ɪ]   [u] and [ʊ]
[e] and [ɛ]   [ɛ] and [ɜ]   [ɑ] and [a]   [a] and [ə]

Write [æ] with one continuous stroke of the pen:

Here is a list of most of the phonetic symbols we will have occasion to use. Each symbol is given in both printed and handwritten form. Practice writing the symbols distinctly and legibly.

b	b		n	n		z	z	
d	d		p	p		g	g	
f	f		r	r		j	j	
h	h		s	s		ŋ	ŋ	
k	k		t	t		š	š	
l	l		v	v		ž	ž	
m	m		w	w		č	č	

ǰ	ǰ	_____	ɛ	ɛ	_____	ʊ	ʊ	_____
θ	θ	_____	ɜ	ɜ	_____	ʌ	ʌ	_____
ð	đ	_____	i	i	_____	ə	ə	_____
ɑ	ɑ	_____	ɪ	ɪ	_____	aɪ	aɪ	_____
a	a	_____	o	o	_____	au	au	_____
æ	æ	_____	ɔ	ɔ	_____	ɔɪ	ɔɪ	_____
e	e	_____	u	u	_____	ju	ju	_____
						ɪu	ɪu	_____

3.3 TRANSCRIPTION FOR READING PRACTICE

Since the pronunciation of English varies somewhat from one dialect to another, no transcription can represent the speech of all readers. The pronunciation indicated by this transcription will differ in certain details from that recorded by Pyles in *Origins and Development*, and may differ from your pronunciation in various ways.

Read these words aloud. Write each word in conventional spelling. Some of the pronunciations correspond to more than one spelling.

[pæt	_____	[rɪč	_____	[træpt	_____
pat	_____	rɪǰ	_____	θwɔrt	_____
pɛt	_____	bæg	_____	kjur	_____
pet	_____	tɔɪd	_____	šaur	_____
pɪt	_____	hjuǰ	_____	straɪk	_____
pit	_____	ðɪs	_____	bɑks	_____
pʊt	_____	ðiz	_____	blɑks	_____
pʌt	_____	θim	_____	krɔld	_____
pɜrt	_____	sʌŋ	_____	glænst	_____
paut	_____	lʌv	_____	skrʌbd	_____
rɑt	_____	ɛr	_____	sɛnts	_____
rɔt	_____	hɛr	_____	sɛndz	_____
rot	_____	ɪr	_____	šɜrts	_____
rut	_____	wɜr	_____	čɜrč	_____
raɪt]	_____	wɛr]	_____	ǰʌŋk]	_____

3.4 MORE READING PRACTICE

Here are some sentences in phonetic notation. To assist you, the punctuation and word division of conventional writing have been used. In a strictly phonetic transcription, they would be replaced by symbols for pitches and junctures, which would more accurately indicate what is said. Word stress, but not sentence stress, has been indicated.

Read these sentences aloud using the pronunciation represented by the symbols. Notice any instances in which your own pronunciation differs from the one transcribed here. Unstressed vowels may very likely differ. Also notice that the pronunciation a word has in isolation may change considerably when the word is spoken normally in a sentence.

[ˈæfəˌrɪzəmz
frʌm eč ɛl mɛŋkɪn[1]

wɛn ə mæn læfs æt ɪz ˈtrʌblz, hi ˈluzəz ə gud ˈmɛni frɛnz. ðe ˈnɛvər fərˈgɪv ðə lɔs əv ðɛr prɪˈrɔgətɪv.

ˈfrɛnˌšɪp ɪz ə ˈkɑmən bɪˈlif ɪn ðə semˈfæləsɪz, ˈmauntəˌbæŋks ænd ˈhɑbˌgɑblɪnz.

ˈkɑnčənts ɪz ði ˈɪnər vɔɪs wɪč wɔrnz ʌs ðæt ˈsʌmˌwʌn me bi ˈlukɪŋ.

ˈivl ɪz ðæt wɪč wʌn bɪˈlivz əv ʌˈðərz. ɪt ɪz ə sɪn tə bɪˈliv ˈivl əv ʌˈðərz, bʌt ɪt ɪz ˈsɛldəm ə məˈstek.

æn aɪˈdiələst ɪz wʌn hu, ɑn ˈnotəsɪŋ ðæt ə roz smɛlz ˈbetər ðæn ə ˈkæbɪǰ, kənˈkludz ðæt ɪt wɪl ˈɔlso mek ˈbetər sup.

ˈsuəˌsaɪd ɪz ə bɪˈletəd ˌækwiˈɛsənts ɪn ði əˈpɪnjən əv wʌnz waɪfs ˈrɛlətɪvz.

temˈtešən ɪz ən ˌɪrəˈzɪstəbl fors æt wɜrk ɑn ə ˈmuvəbl ˈbɑdi.

bɪˈfor ə mæn spiks, ɪt ɪz ˈɔlwɪz sef tu əˈsum ðæt hɪz ə ful. ˈæftər i spiks, ɪt ɪz ˈsɛldəm ˈnɛsəˌsɛri tu əˈsum ɪt.

wɛn ˈwɪmɪn kɪs, ɪt ˈɔlwɪz rɪˈmaɪnz wʌn əv ˈpraɪzˌfaɪtərz ˈšekɪŋ hænz.

ɪf ˈwɪmɪn bɪˈlivd ɪn ðɛr ˈhʌzbənz, ðe wud bi ə gud dil ˈhæpiər. ænd ˈɔlso ə gud dil mor ˈfulɪš.

ə ˈbæčlər ɪz wʌn hu wɔnts ə waɪf, bʌt ɪz glæd hi ˈhæznt gɑt ər.

dɪˈmɑkrəsi ɪz ðə ˈθɪri ðæt ðə ˈkɑmən ˈpipl no wʌt ðe wɔnt, æn dɪˈzɜrv tə gɛt ɪt gud n hɑrd.

ˈpjurətəˌnɪzəm ɪz ðə ˈhɑntɪŋ fɪr ðæt ˈsʌmˌwʌn, ˈsʌmˌwɛr, me bi ˈhæpi.

ə ˈpæstər ɪz wʌn ɪmˈplɔɪd baɪ ðə ˈwɪkəd tə pruv tə ðem baɪ hɪz ɪgˈzæmpl ðæt ˈvɜrču ˈdʌznt pe.

ə ˈkætəˌkɪzəm. ˈkwɛsčən—ɪf ju faɪnd so mʌč ðæt ɪz ˌʌnˈwɜrði əv ˈrɛvrənts ɪn ðə juˈnaɪtəd stets, ðen waɪ du ju lɪv hɪr? ˈænsər—waɪ du mɛn go tə zuz?

ˈɛpəˌtæf. ɪf, ˈæftər aɪ dɪˈpɑrt ðɪs vel, ju ˈɛvər rɪˈmembər mi ænd hæv θɑt tə pliz maɪ gost, fərˈgɪv sʌm ˈsɪnər ænd wɪŋk jər aɪ æt sʌm ˈhomli gɜrl.]

3.5 CONTRASTIVE SETS

A contrastive set is a group of words which differ from one another by a single sound. Thus *hat–bat–rat* are a contrastive set which differ only in their initial consonants; *hat–had–ham* are another set which differ in their final consonants; and *hat–hot–hit* are a set which differ in their vowels. A contrastive set like *causing–caulking–coughing–calling* differ only in their medial consonants. Notice that it is a difference in sound, not in spelling, that we are concerned with. Furthermore, notice that *shawl–tall* are a contrastive pair because they differ only in their initial sound, [š]–[t], but that *shawl–stall* are not a contrastive pair because they have more than a minimum difference, [š]–[st].

On the next three pages are a number of contrastive sets which show variation in (1) the initial consonant, (2) the final consonant, and (3) the vowel. Make each set as complete as you can by adding appropriate words, that is, words which show a minimum contrast in sound. For example, on the page devoted to initial consonants, the next word in the third column might be *dough* or *doe*.

---

[1] From H. L. Mencken, *A Mencken Chrestomathy* (New York, 1953), pp. 616–27 *passim*. Reprinted by permission of the publisher, Alfred A. Knopf, Inc.

	pie	pooh	Poe	pay	peas	pore	pain	pill	pail	peer	pair
[p]	pie	pooh	Poe	pay	peas	pore	pain	pill	pail	peer	pair
[b]	by	boo	beau	bay	___	___	___	___	___	___	___
[t]	tie	two	toe	___	___	___	___	___	___	___	___
[d]	die	do	___	___	___	___	___	___	___	___	___
[k]	Chi	coo	___	___	___	___	___	___	___	___	___
[g]	guy	goo	___	___	___	___	___	___	___	___	___
[č]	___	chew	___	___	___	___	___	___	___	___	___
[j]	___	Jew	___	___	___	___	___	___	___	___	___
[f]	fie	___	___	___	___	___	___	___	___	___	___
[v]	vie	___	___	___	___	___	___	___	___	___	___
[θ]	thigh	___	___	___	___	___	___	___	___	___	___
[ð]	thy	___	___	___	___	___	___	___	___	___	___
[s]	sigh	sue	___	___	___	___	___	___	___	___	___
[z]	Xi	zoo	___	___	___	___	___	___	___	___	___
[š]	shy	shoe	___	___	___	___	___	___	___	___	___
[m]	my	moo	___	___	___	___	___	___	___	___	___
[n]	nigh	new	___	___	___	___	___	___	___	___	___
[l]	lie	lieu	___	___	___	___	___	___	___	___	___
[r]	rye	rue	___	___	___	___	___	___	___	___	___
[w]	wye	woo	___	___	___	___	___	___	___	___	___
[j]	___	you	___	___	___	___	___	___	___	___	___
[h]	high	who	___	___	___	___	___	___	___	___	___

	reap	lip	ape	ripe	cap	roup	sip		rap		lope
[p]	reap	lip	ape	ripe	cap	roup	sip	—	rap	—	lope
[b]	—	—	Abe	—	cab	rube	—	babe	—	Bab	—
[t]	—	lit	—	write	—	—	—	—	—	—	—
[d]	read	—	—	—	—	—	—	—	—	—	—
[k]	reek	—	—	—	—	—	—	—	—	—	—
[g]	—	—	—	—	—	—	—	—	—	—	—
[č]	reach	—	—	—	—	—	—	—	—	—	—
[j]	—	—	—	—	—	—	—	—	—	—	—
[f]	reef	—	—	—	—	—	—	—	—	—	—
[v]	reeve	—	—	—	—	—	—	—	—	—	—
[θ]	wreath	—	—	—	—	—	—	—	—	—	—
[ð]	wreathe	—	—	—	—	—	—	—	—	—	—
[s]	Rhys	—	—	—	—	—	—	—	—	—	—
[z]	—	—	—	—	—	—	—	—	—	—	—
[š]	—	—	—	—	—	—	—	—	—	—	—
[ž]	—	—	—	—	—	—	—	—	—	—	—
[m]	ream	—	—	—	—	—	—	—	—	—	—
[n]	—	—	—	—	—	—	—	—	—	—	—
[ŋ]	—	—	—	—	—	—	—	—	—	—	—
[l]	reel	—	—	—	—	—	—	—	—	—	—
[r]	—	—	—	—	—	—	—	—	—	—	—

[i]	leak	feel	lead	——	——	beat	peel	meat	keyed	bead	——
[ɪ]	lick	fill	——	miss	kit	——	——	——	——	——	peer
[e]	lake	fail	——	——	——	——	——	——	——	——	——
[ɛ]	——	fell	——	——	——	——	——	——	——	——	——
[æ]	lack	——	——	——	——	——	——	——	——	——	——
[u]	Luke	fool	——	——	——	——	——	——	——	——	——
[ʊ]	look	full	——	——	——	——	——	——	——	——	——
[o]	——	foal	——	——	——	——	——	——	——	——	——
[ɔ]	——	fall	——	——	——	——	——	——	——	——	——
[ɑ]	lock	——	——	——	——	——	——	——	——	——	——
[a]	——	——	——	——	——	——	——	——	——	——	——
[ʌ]	luck	——	——	——	——	——	——	——	——	——	——
[ɜ(r)]	lurk	furl	——	——	——	——	——	——	——	——	——
[aɪ]	like	file	——	——	——	——	——	——	——	——	——
[aʊ]	——	foul	——	——	——	——	——	——	——	——	——
[ɔɪ]	——	foil	——	——	——	——	——	——	——	——	——
[ju]	——	fuel	——	——	——	——	——	——	——	——	——

3.6 MEDIAL CONSONANTS

For each of the following pairs of consonants, supply a contrastive pair of words which have the consonants as minimum distinctions in medial position. For example, for the pair [p]–[b] you might use *maple–Mabel* or *rippled–ribald*.

[p]–[b]	_____	[g]–[j]	_____
[t]–[d]	_____	[č]–[š]	_____
[k]–[g]	_____	[j]–[ž]	_____
[č]–[j]	_____	[θ]–[s]	_____
[f]–[v]	_____	[ð]–[z]	_____
[θ]–[ð]	_____	[s]–[š]	_____
[s]–[z]	_____	[z]–[ž]	_____
[š]–[ž]	_____	[m]–[n]	_____
[t]–[č]	_____	[n]–[ŋ]	_____
[d]–[j]	_____	[m]–[ŋ]	_____
[k]–[č]	_____	[r]–[l]	_____

3.7 EASILY CONFUSED CONSONANTS

Each of these words has been transcribed phonetically except that one or two sounds have been omitted. Circle the phonetic symbols which represent the missing sounds.

ether	[i__er]	[θ]	[ð]	Confucian	[kənfju__ən]	[š]	[ž]
either	[i__ər]	[θ]	[ð]	confusion	[kənfju__ən]	[š]	[ž]
bathe	[be__]	[θ]	[ð]	fishing	[fɪ__ɪŋ]	[š]	[ž]
bath	[bæ__]	[θ]	[ð]	vision	[vɪ__ən]	[š]	[ž]
other	[ʌ__ər]	[θ]	[ð]	allusion	[əlu__ən]	[š]	[ž]
author	[ɔ__ər]	[θ]	[ð]	Aleutian	[əlu__ən]	[š]	[ž]
northern	[nər__ərn]	[θ]	[ð]	composer	[kəmpo__ər]	[z]	[ž]
northeast	[nər__ist]	[θ]	[ð]	composure	[kəmpo__ər]	[z]	[ž]
thought	[__ɔt]	[θ]	[ð]	leisure	[li__ər]	[z]	[ž]
though	[__o]	[θ]	[ð]	pleaser	[pli__ər]	[z]	[ž]
faces	[fe__əz]	[s]	[z]	Caesar	[si__ər]	[z]	[ž]
phases	[fe__əz]	[s]	[z]	seizure	[si__ər]	[z]	[ž]
reason	[ri__ən]	[s]	[z]	fuchsia	[fju__ə]	[č]	[š]
recent	[ri__ənt]	[s]	[z]	future	[fju__ər]	[č]	[š]
rice	[raɪ__]	[s]	[z]	nature	[ne__ər]	[č]	[š]
rise	[raɪ__]	[s]	[z]	patient	[pe__ənt]	[č]	[š]
eraser	[ɪre__ər]	[s]	[š]	pleasure	[plɛ__ər]	[j]	[ž]
erasure	[ɪre__ər]	[s]	[š]	pledger	[plɛ__ər]	[j]	[ž]
mesher	[mɛ__ər]	[s]	[š]	virgin	[vɜr__ən]	[j]	[ž]
messer	[mɛ__ər]	[s]	[š]	version	[vɜr__ən]	[j]	[ž]
mason	[me__ən]	[s]	[š]	finger	[fɪ__ər]	[ŋ]	[ŋg]
nation	[ne__ən]	[s]	[š]	ringer	[rɪ__ər]	[ŋ]	[ŋg]

anger	[æ__ər]	[ŋ] [ŋg]	relinquish	[rɪlɪ__kwɪš]	[n] [ŋ]
hanger	[hæ__ər]	[ŋ] [ŋg]	tingle	[tɪ__gl]	[n] [ŋ]
languish	[læ__gwɪš]	[n] [ŋ]	tinkle	[tɪ__kl]	[n] [ŋ]

3.8 TRANSCRIPTION

dip	_____	pew	_____	shave	_____
deep	_____	teach	_____	tall	_____
shell	_____	path	_____	chuck	_____
shake	_____	yam	_____	prize	_____
fool	_____	pomp	_____	feud	_____
wool	_____	youth	_____	pig	_____
soap	_____	pull	_____	ebb	_____
saw	_____	thee	_____	moon	_____
job	_____	thing	_____	chaff	_____
pad	_____	glows	_____	tax	_____
hug	_____	verse	_____	they	_____
curt	_____	sedge	_____	woe	_____
wife	_____	cow	_____	hawk	_____
slouch	_____	soy	_____	town	_____
moist	_____	good	_____	judge	_____

3.9 MORE TRANSCRIPTION

through	_____	two	_____	wolf	_____
zinc	_____	ewe	_____	does	_____
wrong	_____	scald	_____	hour	_____
sign	_____	bunk	_____	choir	_____
psalm	_____	sigh	_____	of	_____
nerve	_____	clique	_____	once	_____
view	_____	ache	_____	tomb	_____
suite	_____	lose	_____	comb	_____
hymn	_____	loose	_____	bomb	_____
taunt	_____	siege	_____	gnaw	_____
build	_____	wrought	_____	wright	_____
beau	_____	plough	_____	folk	_____
flew	_____	move	_____	phlegm	_____
mule	_____	wove	_____	reign	_____
half	_____	dove	_____	corps	_____

3.10 TRANSCRIPTION: THE ENDINGS -ED AND -S

wished	_____	begged	_____	clapped	_____
headed	_____	bulged	_____	paved	_____
tried	_____	cloyed	_____	breathed	_____
heated	_____	talked	_____	shirred	_____
rowed	_____	crowded	_____	hanged	_____

combed	_____	dazes	_____	squabs	_____
gauged	_____	bridges	_____	juices	_____
squelched	_____	keeps	_____	says	_____
glimpsed	_____	ounces	_____	coughs	_____
housed	_____	words	_____	primes	_____
frothed	_____	suits	_____	scythes	_____
laughed	_____	knaves	_____	healths	_____
fixed	_____	limbs	_____	neighs	_____
styles	_____	hushes	_____	thanks	_____
watches	_____	pries	_____	tests	_____

3.11 *TRANSCRIPTION: VOWELS BEFORE* R

peer	_____	poor	_____	fur	_____
weird	_____	pour	_____	furry	_____
we're	_____	par	_____	hurt	_____
leery	_____	four	_____	hurry	_____
pair	_____	for	_____	purr	_____
there	_____	far	_____	per	_____
they're	_____	borne	_____	pyre	_____
care	_____	born	_____	hire	_____
carry	_____	barn	_____	higher	_____
ferry	_____	story	_____	flour	_____
lure	_____	sorry	_____	flower	_____
jury	_____	starry	_____	Moira	_____
Jewry	_____	mourning	_____	coyer	_____
your	_____	morning	_____	pure	_____
you're	_____	warning	_____	fewer	_____

3.12 *TRANSCRIPTION: VARIABLE PRONUNCIATIONS*

marry	_____	wash	_____	spread	_____
merry	_____	push	_____	shred	_____
Mary	_____	clash	_____	schnorkel	_____
candid	_____	beg	_____	pith	_____
candied	_____	egg	_____	with	_____
creak	_____	do	_____	wine	_____
creek	_____	due	_____	whine	_____
ketch	_____	dog	_____	squat	_____
catch	_____	hog	_____	what	_____
foot	_____	class	_____	bunion	_____
root	_____	aunt	_____	onion	_____
proof	_____	not	_____	grease	_____
roof	_____	naught	_____	greasy	_____
nut	_____	forest	_____	coil	_____
soot	_____	orange	_____	curl	_____

The nasals and the lateral [l] very commonly form syllables without the benefit of any vowel, for example, *Clapham* [klæpm], *rotten* [rɑtn], *bacon* [bekŋ], *model* [mɑdl]. Notice that a syllabic nasal may have a place of articulation different from that of its nonsyllabic equivalent: [bekən] and [bekŋ], [hæpən] and [hæpm]. This change in the nasal results from its assimilating to the position of the preceding stop.

Transcribe the following words with syllabic consonants. In some words the syllabic consonant is the only standard pronunciation; in others it is quite informal.

funnel _____	open _____	cabin _____
cotton _____	handle _____	reckon _____
rattled _____	making _____	seven _____
sudden _____	hoping _____	captain _____
people _____	lighten _____	slogan _____

An entire word, if it is weakly stressed, may be reduced to one syllabic consonant. Transcribe the middle word in each of these phrases as a syllabic consonant:

sweet and sour _____	up and back _____
bread and jam _____	scrub and polish _____
rag and cloth _____	keep them moving _____
back and forth _____	that will do _____

3.14 *PRIMARY STRESS*

Indicate the primary stress in each of these words by writing an accent mark over the vowel symbol (or over the first symbol of a digraph) thus: *sófa, abóut.*

abyss	ravage	gluttonous
almond	saloon	heresy
basket	surround	improvement
beguile	abolish	industry
decent	accredit	platinum
engaged	accrual	successor
figure	actual	adjustable
harangue	adornment	alternative
impose	animal	annually
infant	blamable	caressingly
ketchup	cavernous	circumference
laughter	cheerfully	consecutively
massage	collector	debauchery
message	detective	depositor
oblique	division	developable
organ	element	diminutively
preserve	fallacious	executive

fashionable	nominative	sensuousness
immediate	obtainable	servility
impermeable	parenthesis	tortuously

3.15 PRIMARY AND SECONDARY STRESS

Indicate the primary and secondary stresses with accent marks: ´ for primary; ` for secondary. The marks should be written over the vowel symbol of the stressed syllable.

backlash	iota	assimilation
cartoon	kangaroo	attitudinize
concourse	mayonnaise	communicative
foresee	panhandle	curiosity
good-by	pickpocket	depository
incest	represent	individual
lifelike	silverware	magnification
pulsate	varicose	memorialize
stockade	whatever	mystifyingly
technique	wrongdoer	philosophical
almighty	adversary	agreeability
attitude	aftereffect	authoritarian
barbaric	confidential	colorability
bumblebee	halfheartedly	contemptibility
casserole	heterodox	digestibility
chevalier	laudatory	expeditionary
dialogue	multiplicand	necessitarian
glorify	necessitate	superiority
heavyweight	orchestration	totalitarian
incorrect	pentameter	incorrigibility

3.16 TRANSCRIPTION WITH PRIMARY STRESS

Transcribe these words phonetically and indicate primary stress with a raised vertical mark at the beginning of the stressed syllable thus: [ˈsofə], [əˈbaʊt].

allow	_____	empty	_____	except	_____
arbor	_____	adorn	_____	produce	_____
baggy	_____	upon	_____	above	_____
seldom	_____	visit	_____	pleasure	_____
image	_____	command	_____	genial	_____
adjust	_____	comic	_____	mammoth	_____
oppose	_____	stomach	_____	receive	_____
martyr	_____	accept	_____	famishing	_____

successor	_____	intrude	_____	subtle	_____
parody	_____	angle	_____	epistle	_____
accessory	_____	entire	_____	arsenal	_____
negligence	_____	impose	_____	lexical	_____
sincerity	_____	include	_____	marginal	_____
synonymous	_____	python	_____	mechanical	_____
allege	_____	listen	_____	terminal	_____

3.17 MORE TRANSCRIPTION WITH PRIMARY STRESS

Transcribe phonetically and mark primary stress as in the preceding exercise.

conscience	_____	plumber	_____	pneumonia	_____
measure	_____	colonel	_____	appointed	_____
sugar	_____	houses	_____	beautiful	_____
righteous	_____	mortgage	_____	exactly	_____
indict	_____	sergeant	_____	anxiety	_____
business	_____	husband	_____	anxious	_____
pretty	_____	issue	_____	luxurious	_____
again	_____	hiccough	_____	election	_____
column	_____	soldier	_____	succulent	_____
romance	_____	enough	_____	vanquishable	_____
Utah	_____	either	_____	sequential	_____
woman	_____	mature	_____	parliament	_____
women	_____	linger	_____	Wednesday	_____
schism	_____	Lincoln	_____	government	_____
usual	_____	oblige	_____	columnist	_____

3.18 TRANSCRIPTION WITH PRIMARY AND SECONDARY STRESS

Transcribe phonetically; mark primary stress as in the preceding exercise and secondary stress with a lowered vertical mark thus: [ˈɛməˌnet].

drawback	_____	visionary	_____	obligation	_____
firetrap	_____	overgarment	_____	obligatory	_____
truncate	_____	collectivize	_____	application	_____
income	_____	elemental	_____	applicable	_____
furlong	_____	kaleidoscope	_____	operation	_____
locate	_____	mentholated	_____	operating	_____
undo	_____	preposition	_____	analog	_____
sauerkraut	_____	homeopath	_____	analogical	_____
amoral	_____	everybody	_____	consolidation	_____
chaotic	_____	communication	_____	consolidator	_____
envelope	_____	confirmatory	_____	migrate	_____
fingerprint	_____	acrimonious	_____	migration	_____
overreach	_____	localization	_____	migratory	_____
guarantee	_____	interrogative	_____	intellect	_____
absolute	_____	alliteration	_____	intellectual	_____

This diagram, a conventionalized cross section of the head, identifies some of the important organs used in producing speech.

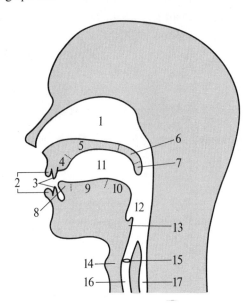

Identify each of the following organs by its number from the diagram above. These terms can be found in a desk dictionary.

_____ alveolar ridge	_____ nasal cavity	_____ dorsum or back of tongue
_____ epiglottis	_____ oral cavity	_____ trachea
_____ esophagus	_____ pharynx	_____ uvula
_____ hard palate	_____ teeth	_____ velum
_____ larynx	_____ apex or tip of tongue	_____ vocal cords
_____ lips	_____ blade or front of tongue	

3.20   *A CLASSIFICATION OF ENGLISH CONSONANTS AND VOWELS*

Complete these charts by writing the phonetic symbols in the appropriate boxes so as to show the place and manner of articulation for each sound. A dash in a box means that no English phoneme has that place and manner of articulation. Such sounds, however, do occur in other languages (for example, the Spanish voiced bilabial fricative in *haber*) and even in English, as allophonic variants (for example, the common labiodental nasal in *emphatic*). We need not be concerned with such seemingly exotic sounds when our purpose is the description of English phonemes, but they do exist.

Consonants   [b, d, f, h, k, l, m, n, p, r, s, t, v, w, z, g, j, ŋ, š, ž, č, ǰ, θ, ð]

To sort out [θ, s, š] and their voiced counterparts [ð, z, ž], observe where the tip and front of the tongue are positioned in pronouncing them. An interdental sound has the tongue tip just behind or between the teeth; an alveolopalatal sound has the tongue tip near the alveolar ridge and the front part of the tongue raised toward the hard palate.

The phoneme [h] has a great deal of variety in its place of articulation. It is sometimes called a fricative, but like [j] and [w] its manner of production is similar to that of the vowels. For convenience we may call it a velar semivowel.

| | | | PLACE OF ARTICULATION | | | | | |
| | | | *labial* | | *dental* | | | *velar* | |
			bilabial	labiodental	interdental	alveolar	alveolo-palatal	palatal	velar
MANNER OF ARTICULATION	*stops*	voiced		—	—		—	—	
		voiceless		—	—		—	—	
	affricates	voiced	—	—		—		—	—
		voiceless	—	—		—		—	—
	fricatives	voiced	—					—	—
		voiceless	—					—	—
	nasals			—			—		
	liquids	lateral	—	—	—		—	—	—
		retroflex	—	—	—		—	—	—
	semivowels			—	—	—	—		

Vowels [ɑ, a, æ, e, ɛ, ɜ, i, ɪ, o, ɔ, u, ʊ, ʌ, ə]

The vowels [ʌ], [ə], and [ɜ] are all mid-central, but [ʌ] is more open than the other two.

| | | FRONTNESS OF TONGUE | | |
		front	*central*	*back*
HEIGHT OF TONGUE	*high-close*		—	
	high-open		—	
	mid-close			
	mid-open			
	low			

Diphthongs or Glides [aɪ, aʊ, ɔɪ], and [ju] or [ɪu]

A diphthong is a combination of two vowels pronounced in a single syllable. The tongue moves from the position for the first vowel to that for the second vowel. The arrows in this diagram indicate the direction of movement. Write the phonetic symbol for each diphthong at the beginning of the appropriate arrow.

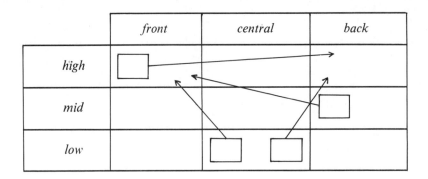

3.21 THE ARTICULATORY DESCRIPTION OF SOUNDS

Write the phonetic symbol for the sound that is being described:

voiceless bilabial stop ———
voiced labiodental fricative ———
voiced velar stop ———
voiceless affricate ———
voiced interdental fricative ———
high-close, front vowel ———
high-open, back vowel ———
low, central vowel ———

voiced alveolar fricative ———
alveolar nasal ———
lateral ———
bilabial semivowel ———
voiceless alveolopalatal fricative ———
mid-close, back vowel ———
mid-open, central vowel ———
low, back vowel ———

Give a phonetic description, like those above, for each of these sounds:

[t] ——————————————
[s] ——————————————
[ŋ] ——————————————
[j] ——————————————
[θ] ——————————————
[e] ——————————————
[u] ——————————————
[ɔ] ——————————————

[b] ——————————————
[ž] ——————————————
[j] ——————————————
[f] ——————————————
[k] ——————————————
[æ] ——————————————
[ɪ] ——————————————
[ɛ] ——————————————

3.22 THE PRODUCTION OF SPEECH SOUNDS

The diagrams in this exercise represent in conventionalized form the positions of the speech organs for certain English sounds. Notice the position of the velum, the lips, the tongue, and the vocal cords (a straight line indicates voicelessness, a jagged line indicates vibration and voice). For the vowels, a grid has been added to help in estimating the tongue's position.

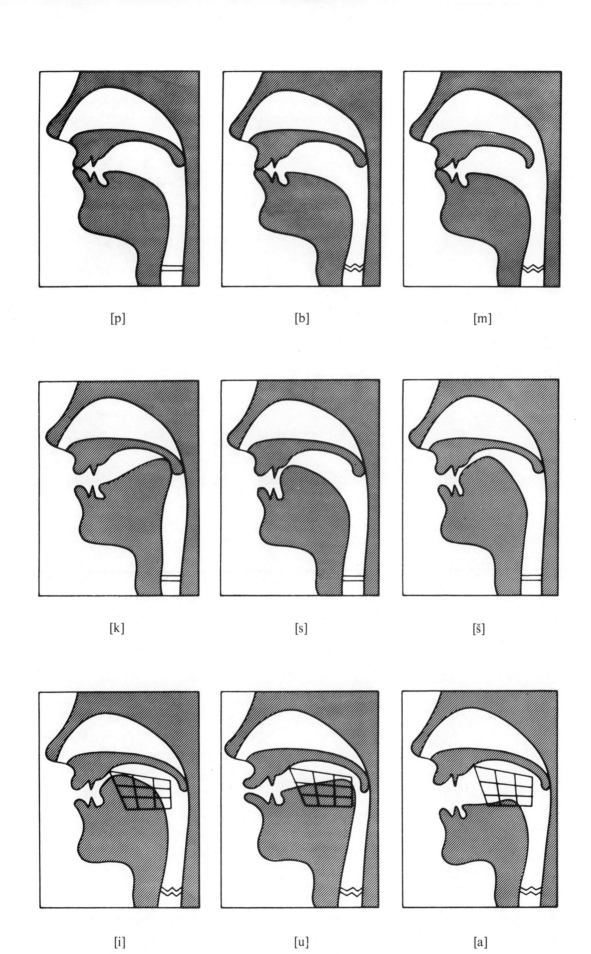

[p]   [b]   [m]

[k]   [s]   [š]

[i]   [u]   [a]

What sound is indicated by each of these diagrams?

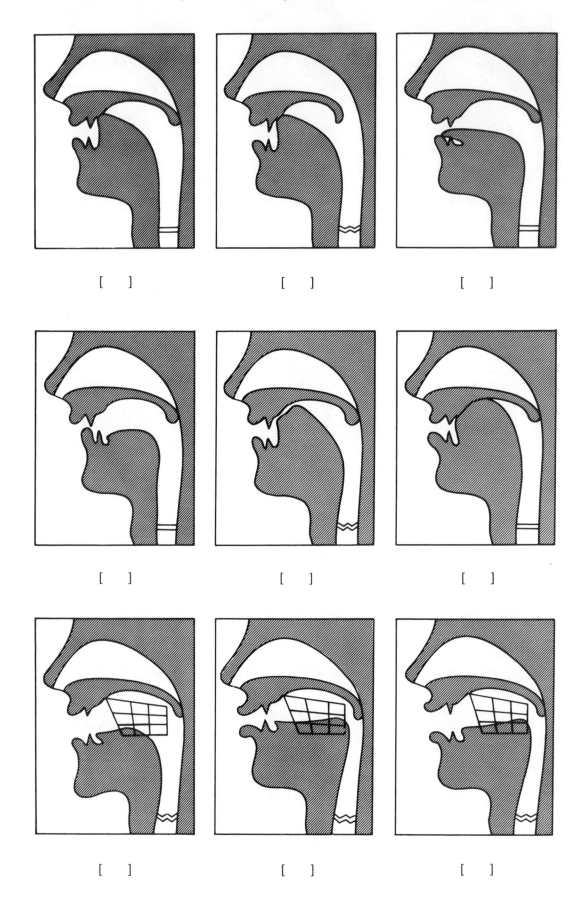

[   ]   [   ]   [   ]

[   ]   [   ]   [   ]

[   ]   [   ]   [   ]

Complete these diagrams by adding the velum, lips, tongue, and vocal cords to indicate the sounds called for.

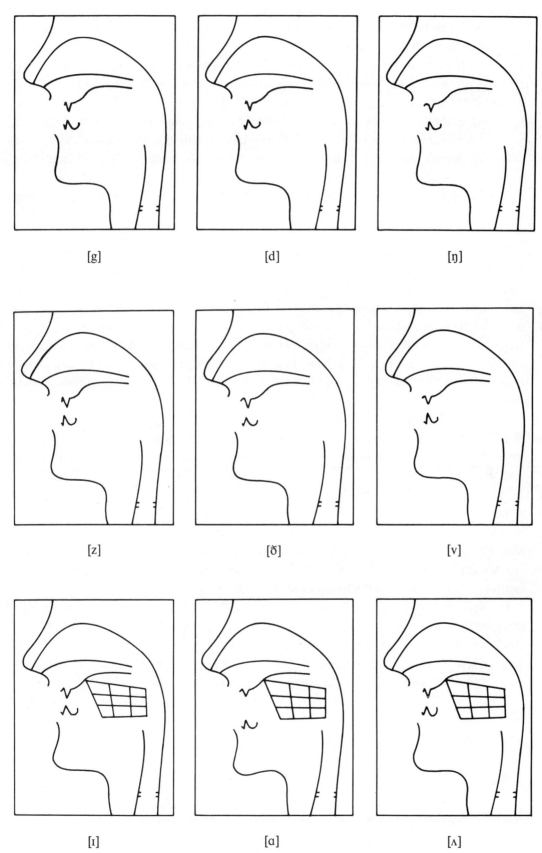

[g] [d] [ŋ]

[z] [ð] [v]

[ɪ] [ɑ] [ʌ]

The phoneme is the basic unit in the sound-system of a language. We may define the phoneme as a unit of sound which contrasts with other such units so as to be capable of distinguishing two utterances from each other. The word *hit*, phonetically [hɪt], is distinguished from *hip* [hɪp] by its final sound. The sounds [t] and [p] are different phonemes in English because the substitution of [p] for [t] in the word *hit* will change it into a different word. The sounds [i] and [ɛ] are also different phonemes because changing the [i] of *meet* [mit] to [ɛ] changes the word to *met* [mɛt]. In the word *leisure*, we may have either of these two vowel sounds, [ližər] or [lɛžər], with no difference in meaning. But even in the two pronunciations of this word, [i] and [ɛ] are different phonemes. As long as there are some utterances in the language which are kept apart by the contrast between [i] and [ɛ], the two sounds are different phonemes. We simply recognize that the word *leisure* has two phonemically different pronunciations. A difference in phonemes need not automatically change one utterance into another; it must merely be capable of doing so in some cases.

Consider again the word *hip*. There are a number of ways to pronounce this word. In one pronunciation, the lips remain firmly closed at the end of the [p] sound. Such a [p] is said to be "unreleased," and a special phonetic symbol may be used to write it: [hɪp˥]. In another pronunciation the lips are opened at the end of the [p] and a strong puff of air is ejected. Such a [p] is said to be "aspirated" and has its own phonetic symbol: [hɪpʰ]. These two [p] sounds are really quite different. You can see the difference between them if you will look in a mirror and say *hip* in the two ways described above. For the unreleased [p˥] the lips will be compressed together; for the aspirated [pʰ] the lips will close at the beginning of the [pʰ] and then part suddenly for the puff of air.

The difference between the two [p] sounds can also be detected if you will hold a lighted match about three inches in front of your mouth and repeat [hɪp˥] with unreleased [p˥] several times. The match flame may quaver slightly when you pronounce the first part of the word, but it should continue to burn. Then say [hɪpʰ] with aspiration and the flame will go out when it is hit by the puff of air at the end of the word.

The sounds [p˥] and [pʰ] are distinct from each other in the way they are made (closed lips versus open lips), in their effect on the air (as witnessed by the match flame), and in the impression they make on the human ear. With a little practice you can easily learn to distinguish the two sounds by ear so that you will know which one a speaker is saying even though you may not see his lips or have a match handy to hold in front of his mouth.

In English the two sounds, although phonetically different, are phonemically the same. You can learn to hear the difference between [hɪp˥] and [hɪpʰ], but there are no words or sentences in English which are distinguished in meaning by that difference in sound. In English [p˥] and [pʰ] are said to be allophones of the same phoneme. The word *allophone* comes from the Greek *allos*, meaning 'other,' and *phone*, meaning 'sound.' An allophone is a variant of a phoneme.

A phoneme may also be defined as a class of sounds which are phonetically similar to one another and which are in complementary distribution or in free variation. Notice the four key terms in this definition: *class of sounds*, *phonetically similar*, *complementary distribution*, and *free variation*. A phoneme is not a single sound, but rather a group of many different sounds. The phoneme /p/[2] is an abstraction, a set or class, which includes many objectively different

---

[2] Virgules indicate a strictly phonemic transcription. Square brackets indicate a phonetic transcription which may be "broad" (more or less phonemic) or may be "narrow" (allophonically detailed).

sounds, of which we have discussed two. An analogy may help. If you go into the library to borrow a book to while away your spare hours, you have your choice among mysteries, westerns, science fiction, historical novels, biography, and others. If you decide on a mystery novel, you have chosen a set or group of books. A mystery is not a single book, but an abstraction, a class which includes many individual and quite different books. It is no good saying to a librarian, "I'd like to check out the mystery novel, please." She is likely to respond, "*Which* mystery novel?" Your request implies that there is a single book to which the term can be applied. The librarian's response reminds you that "mystery novel" is not an individual item, but a class of similar items. Phonemes are roughly analogous to the classes of books: mysteries, westerns, biography, and so forth. Allophones are like the individual books: *The Butler's Revenge*, *The Screaming Blonde*, *The Inquisitive Corpse*, and so forth. Like any analogy, this one must not be pressed too far, but it may help illustrate what we mean by saying that a phoneme is a class of sounds. The phoneme /p/ is an abstraction, a class. The allophones [p⌐] and [pʰ] are individual members of that class.

The allophonic variants of a phoneme must also be phonetically similar to one another. To decide exactly how similar they must be is a highly technical matter. Nevertheless, everyone would agree that [p⌐] and [pʰ] are sufficiently similar to belong to the same phoneme, and everyone would probably agree that [p] and [i] are not sufficiently similar to belong to the same phoneme in any conceivable language. Here also the book analogy is roughly useful. We may be in some doubt about the classification of an imaginative life of King Henry VIII. Is it a historical novel or a biography? The decision would be difficult to make, but we can be quite sure the book is not a western.

In addition to being phonetically similar, the allophones of a phoneme must also be either in complementary distribution or in free variation. Let us first examine the second of these possibilities. We have already said that the word *hip* may be either [hɪp⌐] or [hɪpʰ]. Any word like *hip* which ends in the /p/ phoneme may have either the unreleased or the aspirated allophone. It makes no difference which one occurs. I may be more likely to use the aspirated variant when I am speaking slowly and distinctly and am making a conscious, even labored effort to make myself understood, but the message I am trying to communicate will be the same whichever [p] sound I use. I am free to choose between the two, and thus [p⌐] and [pʰ] are in free variation at the end of such words.

When we consider the beginning of a word like *pin*, however, the circumstances are quite different. Pin is always [pʰɪn], and never [p⌐ɪn]. At the beginning of a word before a vowel, [pʰ] occurs but [p⌐] never does. On the other hand, in a word like *kept*, where the phoneme /p/ occurs directly before a [t], we say only the unreleased [p⌐], never the aspirated [pʰ]. It is possible to pronounce the latter allophone in this position, but English speakers never do. Immediately before a [t], the only variety of /p/ to occur is the unreleased [p⌐]. Before a vowel only [pʰ] occurs, and before a [t], only [p⌐] occurs; neither allophone can appear in the territory of the other, and thus they are said to be in complementary distribution. Since [p⌐] and [pʰ] are in free variation in some positions and in complementary distribution in other positions, we must include both these concepts in our definition of the phoneme.

There are thus at least two different ways of looking at a phoneme. We can think of it in its function of distinguishing one utterance from another, or we can think of it as a class of similar sounds which never get in one another's way. If we don't mind being a bit redundant and not a little turgid, we can combine both these views into a single definition: A phoneme is a class of speech sounds which are phonetically similar to one another and which are in complementary distribution or in free variation with one another, which class contrasts with other such classes so as to permit one utterance to be distinguished from another.

The earlier exercise on contrastive sets illustrates how phonemes function to keep words apart. The remainder of this exercise is devoted to illustrating some important allophones of a few phonemes. The following list is in no way complete; it is merely typical. Try to hear the phonetic difference between the allophones of each phoneme, and then try to feel the different positions of the speech organs used in producing each sound. Since all English speakers do not make the same allophonic distinctions, you may find that you do not have all of the variants recorded here, but you should be able to recognize them in the speech of others with a little practice. Although you may not have enough information to do the job thoroughly, try to describe the environment or neighboring sounds that determine which allophone will occur. There will be some overlapping of environments because of free variation.

PHONEME	ALLOPHONE	KEY WORDS	ARTICULATORY DESCRIPTION	ENVIRONMENT
/t/	[tʰ]	*take* *scat!*	aspirated: a strong puff of air follows the [t]	
	[t˺]	*steak* *act*	unaspirated but released: the tongue tip is removed from the alveolar ridge without the puff of air	
	[t˺]	*outdoors* *dirt*	unreleased: the tongue tip stays on the alveolar ridge until the next sound is made or until there is a pause in speaking	
	[tˡ]	*battle*	lateral release: the tongue tip stays on the alveolar ridge, but the stop is released by lowering the sides of the tongue in preparation for the [l]	
	[tⁿ]	*cotton*	nasal release: the tongue tip stays on the alveolar ridge, but the stop is released by lowering the velum in preparation for the nasal	
	[ɾ]	*hitter* *rotted*	a flap: the tongue tip is quickly flicked against the alveolar ridge and the vocal cords are voicing	
	[ʔ]	*mutton* *bottle*	glottal stop: the vocal cords, instead of the tongue, shut off the air	
	[ʔ͡t]	*hit* *mutton*	simultaneous glottal stop and [t]	
/k/	[kʰ]	*kin* *look!*	aspirated: a strong puff of air follows the [k]	
	[k˺]	*skin* *back*	unaspirated but released: the dorsum of the tongue is removed from the velum without the puff of air	
	[k˺]	*act* *back*	unreleased: the tongue stays against the velum until the next sound is made or until there is a pause in speaking	

PHONEME	ALLOPHONE	KEY WORDS	ARTICULATORY DESCRIPTION	ENVIRONMENT
	[k<]	*keep* *cape* *cap*	palatal: the front of the tongue rises to the hard palate to make the stop	
	[k>]	*coop* *cope* *cop*	velar: the back of the tongue rises to the velum to make the stop	
/l/	[l]	*least* *look* *blind*	"clear": the tongue tip is against the alveolar ridge, the front and dorsum of the tongue slope downward	
	[l̥]	*please* *clime* *flew*	voiceless: like "clear" *l*, except that the vocal cords are not vibrating	
	[ɫ]	*full* *filling*	"dark": the tongue tip is against the alveolar ridge, and the dorsum of the tongue is raised toward the velum	
	[ɫ̩]	*able* *little*	syllabic: like "dark" *l*, but forms a syllable without any vowel	
	[lʷ]	*call* *silk*	velarized: the tongue tip is against the lower teeth, and the dorsum of the tongue touches the center of the velum	
/m/	[m]	*meet* *seem*	bilabial: the two lips meet to stop the air in the mouth	
	[ɱ]	*emphatic* *environs*	labiodental: the lower lip meets the upper teeth to stop the air in the mouth	
	[m̩]	*captain* (*cap'm*) *ribbon* (*rib'm*)	syllabic: the [m] forms a syllable without any vowel	
/z/	[z]	*zoo* *pleasing*	voiced and lenis: vocal cords are vibrating and the air stream is weak	
	[z̥]	*rise*	voiceless and lenis: the vocal cords are not vibrating but the air stream is still weak (cf. *rice* with voiceless and fortis or strongly articulated [s])	
/h/	[i̥]	*heat, heal*	voiceless [i]	
	[ɛ̥]	*hem, head*	voiceless [ɛ]	
	[ʊ̥]	*hook, hood*	voiceless [ʊ]	
	[o̥]	*home, hope*	voiceless [o]	
	[ɜ̥]	*hurt, her*	voiceless [ɜ]	
	[ḁ]	*hide, high*	voiceless [a]	

PHONEME	ALLOPHONE	KEY WORDS	ARTICULATORY DESCRIPTION
/e/[3]	[ĕ]	*chaotic*	quite short and pure
	[e] or [eɪ]	*mate* *make* *nape*	short, although not so short as the preceding; either pure or slightly diphthongized with a glide to [ɪ]
	[eɪˑ]	*made* *vague* *babe*	long: clearly diphthongized with an [ɪ] glide
	[ẽɪˑ]	*main* *vein*	nasalized: like the preceding allophone, but with the velum lowered for all or part of the vowel
	[eɪː]	*may* *nay* *bay*	very long with pronounced diphthongization

3.24 ANOTHER METHOD OF TRANSCRIBING ENGLISH VOWELS

The Trager-Smith phonemic transcription of English is mentioned on page 57 of *Origins and Development*. Because this style of transcription is widely used for current English, the student is likely to encounter it in his reading. The following table will show how the Trager-Smith analysis of English vowels correlates with the analysis used in Pyles's text and this workbook.

PYLES	T–S	EXAMPLES
[ɪ]	/i/	*it*, [ɪt], /it/; *sieve*, [sɪv], /siv/
[ɛ]	/e/	*elf*, [ɛlf], /elf/; *head*, [hɛd], /hed/
[æ]	/æ/	*at*, [æt], /æt/; *plaid*, [plæd], /plæd/
[ʊ]	/u/	*bull*, [bʊl], /bul/; *book*, [bʊk], /buk/
[ɑ]	/a/	*stop*, [stɑp], /stap/; *art*, [ɑrt], /art/
[ʌ]	/ə/	*sun*, [sʌn], /sən/; *young*, [jʌŋ], /yəŋ/
[ɜ]	/ə/	*urn*, [ɜrn], /ərn/; *bird*, [bɜrd], /bərd/
[ə]	/ə/	*gallop*, [ˈgæləp], /gǽləp/; *above*, [əˈbʌv], /əbə́v/
[ə]	/h/	as a replacement of final and preconsonantal [r] in the stressed syllables of *r*-less speech: *tour*, [tʊə], /tuh/; *beard*, [bɪəd], /bihd/
[i]	/iy/	*eat*, [it], /iyt/; *be*, [bi], /biy/
[e]	/ey/	*ape*, [ep], /eyp/; *great*, [gret], /greyt/
[aɪ]	/ay/	*buy*, [baɪ], /bay/; *height*, [haɪt], /hayt/
[ɔɪ]	/oy/	*oil*, [ɔɪl], /oyl/; *boy*, [bɔɪ], /boy/
[u]	/uw/	*ooze*, [uz], /uwz/; *two*, [tu], /tuw/
[o]	/ow/	*oats*, [ots], /owts/; *row*, [ro], /row/
[aʊ]	/aw/	*how*, [haʊ], /haw/; *house*, [haʊs], /haws/
[ju]	/yuw/	*feud*, [fjud], /fyuwd/; *cue*, [kju], /kyuw/
[ɔ]	/əh/	*ought*, [ɔt], /əht/; *law*, [lɔ], /ləh/
[a]	/æh/	as in eastern New England *ask*, [ask], /æhsk/; *half*, [haf], /hæhf/

[3] Some descriptions of English analyze this phoneme as /ej/ or /ey/; see page 57 of *Origins and Development* and exercise 3.24.

There are other differences between the two systems of transcription, but you can work them out if you have occasion to use the Trager-Smith system.

Transcribe each of these words twice, first according to Pyles's phonetic notation and again according to the Trager-Smith system.

	PYLES	T–S		PYLES	T–S
big	_____	_____	tie	_____	_____
beep	_____	_____	toy	_____	_____
less	_____	_____	vow	_____	_____
lace	_____	_____	fume	_____	_____
look	_____	_____	calf	_____	_____
loop	_____	_____	about	_____	_____
dud	_____	_____	gallon	_____	_____
burr	_____	_____	fear	_____	_____
mote	_____	_____	lure	_____	_____
raw	_____	_____	more	_____	_____
pop	_____	_____	harm	_____	_____
cap	_____	_____	bear	_____	_____

The Backgrounds of English

4.1 QUESTIONS FOR REVIEW AND DISCUSSION

1. Define the following terms:

   analogical change (analogy)
   sound change (sound shift)
   monosyllabic language
   agglutinative language
   incorporative language
   inflective language
   Indo-European (Proto-Indo-European)
   comparative linguistics
   inflection
   grammatical functions (for example,
      case, number, person, tense, mood,
      aspect, and so forth)
   word root
   affix (suffix, prefix, infix)
   stem
   thematic vowel

   athematic verb
   reconstruction (reconstructed form)
   cognate (cognate words)
   sound correspondences
   koine
   Vulgar Latin
   Romance languages
   Germanic (Pre-Germanic)
   preterit
   dental suffix
   strong and weak verbs
   strong and weak adjectives
   First Sound Shift (Grimm's Law)
   grammatical change (Verner's Law)
   Second (High German) Sound Shift
   rhotacism

2. To what extent can we explain why languages change? Consider the passage of time, geographical separation, and analogy as contributing factors.

3. What metaphors are commonly used to describe the connections that exist among languages?

4. Languages can be classified in two different ways. What are they?

5. What are some of the more important non-Indo-European language groups?

6. Summarize the contributions of Jones, Bopp, Rask, and Grimm to the comparative-historical study of Indo-European.

7. What linguistic features are shared by all Indo-European languages; that is, how are all Indo-European languages alike?

8. What is the special meaning in linguistics of an asterisk before a word?

9. What kinds of words are shared by all Indo-European languages?

10. On what kind of evidence do we base our conclusions about Indo-European culture and the original Indo-European homeland?

11. What are the main subgroups of Indo-European?

12. What is the distinction between *satem* languages and *centum* languages?

13. What linguistic features, shared by all Germanic languages, differentiate them from other branches of Indo-European?

4.2 *LANGUAGE TYPES*

The older and often imprecise classification of languages into four types (monosyllabic, agglutinative, inflective, and incorporative) has been greatly refined in recent years. Joseph H. Greenberg discusses the history of this four-way classification and suggests a number of indexes by which the type of a language can be determined quite precisely.[1] For a rough and ready classification, however, the four terms are still useful although linguists no longer use them to imply an evolutionary development in language. The following examples will illustrate the four types.

1. A *monosyllabic* or *isolating* language is one in which words tend to be one syllable long and invariable in form. They take no inflections or other suffixes. The function of words in a sentence is shown primarily by word order.

   CHINESE: Ni men ti hua wo pu tu tung.
   'I do not entirely understand your language.'

   Ni | men | ti | hua | wo pu | tu | tung
   you | plural | possessor | language | I | not | all | understand

2. An *agglutinative* language is one in which words tend to be made up of several syllables. Typically each word has a base or stem and a number of affixes. The affixes are quite regular; they undergo very little change regardless of what base they are added to.

   TURKISH: Babam kardeşime bir mektup yazdırdı.
   'My father had my brother write a letter.'

   Baba -m[2] kardeş -im[2] -e | bir mektup yaz -dır -dı
   father | my | brother | my | dative case | a | letter | write | cause to | past tense

3. *Inflective* languages are like agglutinative ones in that each word tends to have a number of suffixes. In an inflective language, however, the suffixes often show great irregularity in varying their shape according to the word-base to which they are added. Also, a single suffix tends to express a number of different grammatical concepts.

   LATIN: Arma virumque canō.
   'I sing about weapons and a man.'

   Arm -a | vir -um | -que
   weapon | neuter accusative plural | man | masculine accusative singular | and

   can -ō
   sing | first person singular present indicative

---

[1] "A Quantitative Approach to the Morphological Typology of Language," *International Journal of American Linguistics*, XXVI (1960), 178–94.

[2] *m* is used after vowels; *im*, after consonants.

4. An *incorporative* language is one in which the verb and the subject or object of a sentence may be included in a single word. What we would think of as the main elements of a sentence are joined in one word and have no independent existence.

ESKIMO: Qasuiirsarvigssarsingitluinarnarpuq.
         'Someone did not at all find a suitable resting place.'

Qasu	-iir	-sar	-vig	-ssar	-si	-ngit	-luinar
tired	*not*	*causing to be*	*place for*	*suitable*	*find*	*not*	*completely*

-nar	-puq
someone	*third person singular indicative mood*[3]

To which of the four types does each of these languages seem to belong?

1. Ya dumayu, chto eto samyĭ malen'kĭ iz vsekh gorodov Rossii.
   'I think that this is the smallest of all the cities of Russia.'

Ya	duma	-yu		chto	eto	sam
I	*think*	*first person singular present tense*		*that*	*this*	*most*

-yĭ	malen'k	-iĭ	iz
masculine nominative singular	*small*	*masculine nominative singular*	*out of*

vs	-ekh	gorod	-ov	Rossi	-i
all	*genitive plural*	*city*	*masculine genitive plural*	*Russia*	*feminine genitive singular*

TYPE: _____

2. Lâǹ-lâǹ dân-chúng học làm chính-trị.
   'Little by little the masses are learning to engage in politics.'

Lâǹ	lâǹ	dân	chúng	học	làm	chính	trị
time	*time*	*people*	*multitude*	*learn*	*make*	*government*	*rule*

TYPE: _____

3. La maljuna viro kreskigis malgrandan pomarbaron.
   'The old man cultivated a small apple orchard.'

La	mal-	jun	-a	vir	-o	kresk	-ig	-is	mal-
the	*un-*	*young*	*adjective*	*man*	*noun*	*grow*	*cause to*	*past tense*	*un-*

grand	-a	-n	pom	-arb	-ar	-o	-n
large	*adjective*	*accusative*	*apple*	*tree*	*collection*	*noun*	*accusative*

TYPE: _____

4. Ua mau ke[4] ea o ka 'aina i ka pono.
   'The life of the land is preserved in righteousness.'

Ua	mau	ke	ea	o	ka	'aina	i	ka	pono
perfect aspect	*constant*	*the*	*life*	*of*	*the*	*land*	*in*	*the*	*goodness*

TYPE: _____

---

[3] Suggestion: Read the gloss by starting at the end and working toward the beginning.
[4] *ke* occurs before words beginning with *e, a, o,* and *k; ka,* otherwise.

5. Tis ara houtos estin, hoti kai ho anemos kai hē thalatta hypakouei autōi?
   'Who then is this, that both the wind and the sea obey him?'

Ti   -s   ara   hout -os
who | masculine nominative singular | then | this | masculine nominative singular |

es   -tin   hoti   kai
be | third person singular present indicative | that | and |

h   -o   anem -os   kai
the | masculine nominative singular | wind | masculine nominative singular | and |

h   -ē   thalatt -a
the | feminine nominative singular | sea | feminine nominative singular |

hypakou -ei   aut   -ōi
obey | third person singular present indicative | same | masculine dative singular

TYPE: _____

6. Kahä'eisibäti.
   'He fractured his skull.'

Kah   -ä'ei -si   -bä   -ti
blow, strike | head | be in condition of | cause to | third person singular intransitive verb

TYPE: _____

The six languages above are Russian, Vietnamese, Esperanto, Hawaiian, Greek, and Arapaho.

The four language types are, of course, merely abstractions. No real language belongs entirely to any one type. For example, the English use of monosyllables like *to, for, when, not, must, the,* and *or,* and its reliance on word order to signal grammatical meaning would seem to make it a monosyllabic language. However the existence of paradigms like *ox, ox's, oxen, oxen's; show, shows, showing, showed, shown; good, better, best* is typical of inflective languages. Words like *activistic* which are built up by adding suffixes one by one to a stem (*act, active, activist, activistic*) are characteristic of agglutinative languages. And verb forms like *to baby-sit* or *horseback-riding* are the hallmark of an incorporative language. It is difficult to pigeonhole English, or for that matter most other languages, when we are using only four classifications. Greenberg's article, cited earlier, provides more than ten indexes that can be used in describing the type to which a language belongs. His first measurement is called the "index of synthesis," and is arrived at in this way: Take a passage written in the language you wish to type; the longer the passage, the more accurate the index will be. Count the number of words in the passage (W). Count the number of morphemes, that is, the smallest meaningful elements, in the passage (M). Divide the number of morphemes by the number of words (M/W). The result will be the index of synthesis. For example, the Chinese sentence we examined earlier has eight words; it also has eight morphemes. The index of synthesis is thus 8/8, or 1.00. The Turkish sentence has five words, but ten morphemes, as we see when the sentence is broken into its smallest meaningful units. The index of synthesis is 10/5, or 2.00. The Eskimo example is a single word, but it has ten morphemes. The index of synthesis is 10/1, or 10.00. The three samples we have just used to compute the index of synthesis for Chinese, Turkish, and Eskimo are far too short for reliable results, but they illustrate the process of figuring an index.

The index of synthesis for a language tells us on the average how many morphemes are present in each word. If our results for the three languages we examined were accurate, we could say that Chinese words have on the average one morpheme each, Turkish words have an average of two morphemes each, and Eskimo words have an average of ten morphemes each. However, as we have said, these samples are not adequate. For Eskimo especially our conclusion is highly suspect; we used only one word to figure the average, and an index of 10.00 is unbelievably high for any language.

A low index of synthesis, something approaching 1.00, tells us that the language is *analytic*. Monosyllabic languages are analytic. A higher index of synthesis, somewhere between 1.50 and 2.50, characterizes the language as *synthetic*. Agglutinative and inflective languages are both synthetic. A very high index of synthesis, something around 3.00 or above, identifies the language as *polysynthetic*. Incorporative languages are polysynthetic.

Now go back to the Latin sentence we used to illustrate an inflective language, and compute the index of synthesis for it.

Number of words in the sentence (W): _____

Number of morphemes in the sentence (M): _____

Number of morphemes divided by number of words (M/W) equals an index of: _____

The correct answer is 2.33 (round off the division to the second decimal place).

This single index is a very useful device for comparing languages. Here are four versions of the same Biblical passage in Latin, Old English, Middle English, and early Modern English. To assist you, the words have been divided by hyphens into their constituent morphemes. Words are separated from one another by spaces. Some words, for example *sawe* in the early Modern English passage, count as two morphemes. One morpheme is the basic meaning of the word, 'see'; the second morpheme is the meaning 'past time,' and is shown by the changed vowel sound. Such internal change is represented by the symbol $\emptyset$; $\emptyset$ should be counted as a separate morpheme. Compute the index of synthesis for each of the four passages and give your results in the space provided at the end of the exercise.

Latin

Moses aut-em pasce-ba-t ov-es Jethro co-gna-t-i su-i sac-er-dot-is Madian: cum-que min-a-sse-t greg-em ad in-ter-ior-a de-sert-i, ven-i-t ad mont-em De-i Horeb. Ap-par-ui-t-que e-i Dom-in-us in flamm-a ign-is de medi-o rub-i: et vide-ba-t quod rub-us arde-re-t, et non com-bure-re-t-ur. Dix-i-t ergo Moses: Vad-a-m, et vide-b-o vis-ion-em hanc-$\emptyset$ magn-am, qu-a-re-$\emptyset$ non com-bura-t-ur rub-us. Cerne-n-s aut-em Dom-in-us quod per-ge-re-t ad vide-nd-um, voca-vi-t e-um de medi-o rub-i, et a-i-t: Moses, Moses. Qu-i re-spond-i-t: Ad-su-m. At ill-e: Ne ap-propi-e-s, in-qu-i-t, huc: solv-e calc-e-ament-um de ped-ibus tu-is: loc-us enim, in qu-o sta-s, terr-a sanc-t-a es-t.

Old English

So$\eth$-lic-e Moyses heold-$\emptyset$ hy-s mæg-es sceap-$\emptyset$, þ-æs sacerd-es, on Madian; þ-æs nam-a wæ-$\emptyset$-s Iethro. And $\eth$a he draf-$\emptyset$ hi-s heord-e to inn-e-weard-um þ-am westen-e, he com-$\emptyset$ to God-es dun-e þe man Oreph nemn-eþ. And Drihten hi-m æt-eow-de on fir-es lig-e on-midd-an an-re bremel-þyrn-an, and he ge-seah-$\emptyset$ þæt s-eo $\eth$yrn-e barn-$\emptyset$ and n-æ-$\emptyset$-s for-burn-an. $\eth$a cwæ$\eth$-$\emptyset$ Moyses: Ic ga and ge-seo þ-a micl-an ge-sih-$\eth$-e, hw-i þ-eos þyrn-e ne sy-$\emptyset$ for-bærn-ed. So$\eth$-lic-e Drihten ge-seah-$\emptyset$ þæt he fer-de to ge-seo-nn-e; he clyp-ode of midd-re þ-ære bremel-þyrn-an, and cwæþ-$\emptyset$: Moyses! Moyses! And he and-wyr-de, and cwæþ-$\emptyset$: Her ic eo-m. And

77

he cwæþ-∅: Ne ge-nea-læc-e ðu hy-der; do þi-n ge-scy-∅ of ði-n-um fot-um: soþ-lic-e s-eo stow þe ðu on stent-st y-s hal-ig eorð-e.

Middle English

Moyses for-soþ fed-∅ þe schepe-∅ of Iethro, hi-s wyu-ys fader, þe prest of Madyan, and whenn he ha-d dreu-en þe flock to þe inn-er-mo-re part-y of desert, he comme-∅ to þe hyll of god, Oreb, and þe lord a-peer-id to hy-m in a flawme of fyre from þe mydyll of a bosche. And he sey3-∅ þat þe bosch wa-∅-s a-fyre, and wa-∅-s not bren-t. Þann say-d Moyses, "I schall go and see þis grete si3-t, why þe bosch i-s not bren-t." And þe lord by-hold-yng þat he 3e-de to see-n, clep-ed hy-m from þe mydyll of þe bosche and sey-þ, "Moyses, Moyses," þe which answer-d, "I a-m ny3." And he, "Ne come þou," he sei-þ, "no ne-rre hyþer, bot louse þou þi-n scho-ing frome þi-∅ fete-∅. The place for-soþ þat þou stond-is inne i-s a hol-y londe."

Early Modern English

Nowe Moses kep-t the flocke of Iethro hi-s father in law, the Priest of Midian: and hee led-∅ the flocke to the back-side of the desert, and came-∅ to the mountaine of God, even to Horeb. And the Angel of the Lord appear-ed un-to hi-m, in a flame of fire out of the mid-st of a bush, and he look-ed, and be-hold, the bush burn-ed with fire, and the bush wa-∅-s not con-sume-d. And Moses sai-de, I will nowe turne a-side, and see this great sigh-t, why the bush i-s not burn-t. And when the Lord sawe-∅ that he turn-ed a-side to see, God call-ed un-to hi-m out of the mid-st of the bush, and sai-d, Moses, Moses. And he sai-de, Here a-m I. And he sai-d, Drawe not nigh hither: put off thy-∅ shoo-es from off thy-∅ feete-∅, for the place where-on thou stand-est, is hol-y ground.

	LATIN	OLD ENGLISH	MIDDLE ENGLISH	MODERN ENGLISH
NUMBER OF WORDS				
NUMBER OF MORPHEMES				
INDEX OF SYNTHESIS				

Is Old English closer to Latin or to Modern English in its synthetic complexity?

_____

As measured by the synthetic complexity, did the greatest grammatical change in our language take place between Old and Middle or between Middle and Modern English?

_____

4.3 THE NON-INDO-EUROPEAN LANGUAGES (I)

This map shows the geographical distribution of non-Indo-European language groups with relation to Indo-European in the eastern hemisphere. Language groups in the western hemisphere are both more complex and less well defined. Complete the following key by writing the numbers from the map in the appropriate blanks.

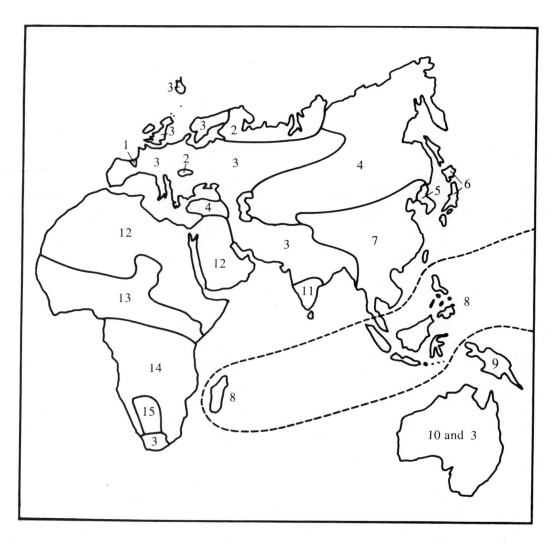

_____	Hamito-Semitic	_____	Malay-Polynesian
_____	Sudanese	_____	Australian
_____	Bantu	_____	Papuan
_____	Hottentot-Bushman	_____	Basque
_____	Dravidian	_____	Finno-Ugric
_____	Indo-Chinese	_____	Altaic
_____	Japanese	_____	Indo-European
_____	Korean		

4.4   *THE NON-INDO-EUROPEAN LANGUAGES (II)*

Within each group, match a language on the right with a related language on the left by writing the letter in the appropriate blank. There will be some unused letters and some unfilled blanks.

_____ Arabic	A. Bantu	_____ Aleut	A. Aramaic
_____ Finnish	B. Chinese	_____ Australian	B. Eskimo
_____ Korean	C. Geez	_____ Estonian	C. Lappish
_____ Malay	D. Hungarian	_____ Hebrew	D. Nahuatl
_____ Tibetan	E. Japanese	_____ Uto-Aztecan	E. Papuan

_____ Bantu	A. Ainu	_____ Basque	A. Bushman
_____ Coptic	B. Berber	_____ Chinese	B. Dravidian
_____ Indo-Chinese	C. Mongolian	_____ Ethiopic	C. Japanese
_____ Malay	D. Polynesian	_____ Hottentot	D. Manchu
_____ Turkish	E. Sudanese	_____ Osmanli	E. Phoenician

4.5 THE INDO-EUROPEAN HOMELAND

The accompanying map shows one possible location for the Indo-European homeland. The arrows are a family-tree diagram superimposed on the map; they do not trace the actual paths of migration from the original center. Complete the key on the map by filling the blanks with the appropriate numbers.

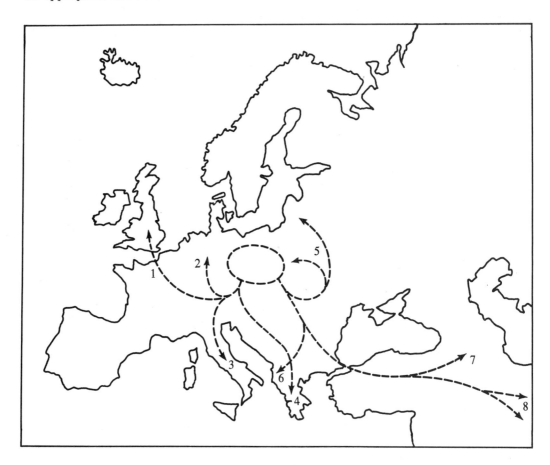

Branches of the Indo-European Family of Languages

_____ Indo-Iranian	_____ Hellenic	_____ Albanian	_____ Celtic
_____ Armenian	_____ Italic	_____ Balto-Slavic	_____ Germanic

4.6 THE MAIN DIVISIONS OF THE INDO-EUROPEAN GROUP (I)

The accompanying map shows the main Indo-European language groups and some important non-Indo-European languages of Europe and the Near East. Complete the key by writing the numbers in the appropriate blanks.

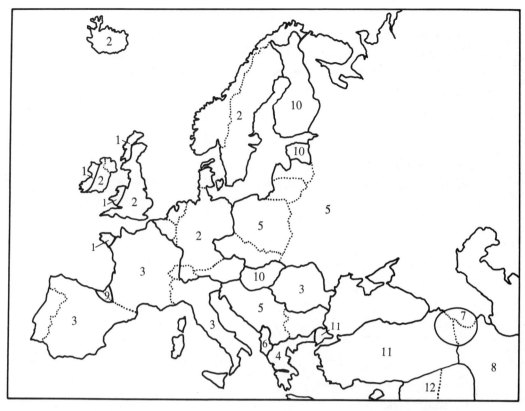

	Indo-European			Non-Indo-European	
_____ Indo-Iranian	_____ Hellenic		_____ Finno-Ugric	_____ Semitic
_____ Armenian	_____ Romance		_____ Altaic	_____ Basque
_____ Albanian	_____ Celtic			
_____ Balto-Slavic	_____ Germanic			

4.7 THE MAIN DIVISIONS OF THE INDO-EUROPEAN GROUP (II)

1. Here is a list of some Indo-European languages and dialects. Put an X in front of each language that is no longer spoken as a living tongue.

Aeolic	Flemish	Latin	Rhaeto-Romanic
Albanian	French	Lettish	Roumanian
Anglo-Norman	Frisian	Lithuanian	Sanskrit
Armenian	Galician	Little Russian	Scots Gaelic
Avestan	Gallic	Low German	Serbo-Croatian
Bengali	Gothic	Manx	Slovak
Breton	Great Russian	Modern Greek	Slovenian
Bulgarian	Gypsy	Norwegian	Sorbian
Catalan	High German	Oscan	Spanish
Cornish	Hindi	Pali	Swedish
Czech	Hindustani	Persian	Tocharian
Danish	Hittite	Pictish	Umbrian
Doric	Icelandic	Polish	Urdu
Dutch	Ionic-Attic	Portuguese	Walloon
English	Irish Gaelic	Provençal	Welsh
Faroese	Italian	Prussian	White Russian

2. Complete the following outline by writing in the names of the Indo-European languages from the list above. You should use this exercise to test yourself. First read Chapter IV in *Origins and Development*, and then try to complete the outline. Then check your work. When you have learned the classification of all of these languages, you should be able to construct a family-tree diagram like that on pages 80–81 of *Origins and Development*.

THE INDO-EUROPEAN LANGUAGES

I. *Satem* Languages

    A. Indo-Iranian

        1. Indic

        _____   _____   _____

        _____   _____

        _____   _____

        2. Iranian

        _____   _____

    B. _____

    C. _____

    D. Balto-Slavic

        1. Baltic

        _____   _____   _____

        2. Slavic

            a. East Slavic

        _____   _____   _____

            b. West Slavic

        _____   _____

        _____   _____

            c. South Slavic

        _____   _____   _____

II. *Centum* Languages

    A. Hellenic

    _____   _____

    _____   _____

    B. Italic

    _____   _____   _____

    _____   _____   _____

    _____   _____   _____

    _____   _____   _____

    _____   _____

C. Celtic

   1. _____

   2. Britannic

     _____   _____

     _____   _____

   3. Goidelic

     _____   _____   _____

D. Germanic

   1. _____

   2. North Germanic

     a. Western

       _____   _____   _____

     b. Eastern

       _____   _____

   3. West Germanic

     a. German

       (1) _____

       (2) Low

         (a) _____

         (b) Low Franconian

           _____   _____

     b. Anglo-Frisian

       _____   _____

E. _____

F. _____

4.8 *THE MAIN DIVISIONS OF THE INDO-EUROPEAN GROUP (III)*

In describing the historical development of a language group we have recourse to various metaphors and "models." One such metaphor is that of the family, by which we speak of the Indo-European *parent* language with its various *descendants*. Another metaphor is the botanical one, by which we speak of the Indo-European *stem* with its several *branches*. These two metaphors are often combined in a family-tree model of language like the diagram on pages 80–81 of *Origins and Development*.

The circular diagram that follows may, at first sight, look quite different from a family tree, but it is merely a somewhat different way of schematizing the same information. The blocks around the outer rim of the wheel represent important modern Indo-European languages and are so labeled. The interior blocks represent successively larger and older groupings of the various languages. The central point of the circle stands for Proto-Indo-European, the hub from which the linguistic spokes radiate. Complete this wheel diagram by labeling the remaining blocks with the names or numbers of the following language groups:

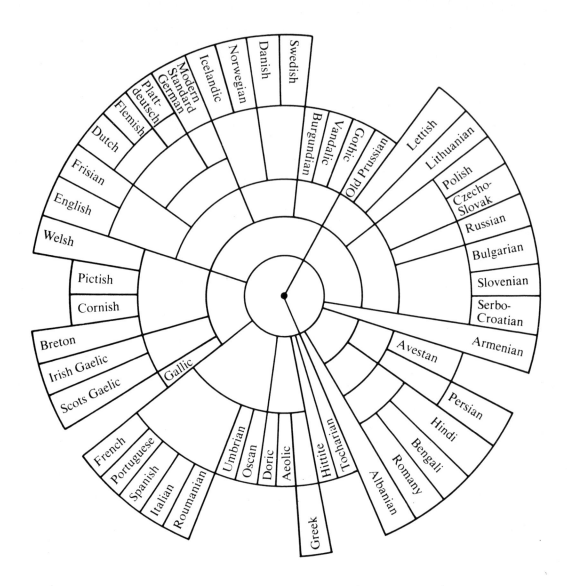

1. *Satem* languages	12. Baltic	23. East Slavic
2. *Centum* languages	13. East Germanic	24. West Slavic
3. Indo-Iranian	14. North Germanic	25. Eastern North Germanic
4. Balto-Slavic	15. West Germanic	26. Western North Germanic
5. Germanic	16. Britannic	27. German
6. Celtic	17. Gaelic	28. Anglo-Frisian
7. Italic	18. Latin	29. High German
8. Hellenic	19. Ionic-Attic	30. Low German
9. Indic	20. Sanskrit and Prakrits	31. Old Saxon
10. Iranian	21. Old Iranian	32. Old Low Franconian
11. Slavic	22. South Slavic	

1. All Indo-European languages share some words that are similar in form and meaning. We may confidently suppose that these words are the historical survivals of Indo-European roots. Both form and meaning may, of course, change with time. Thus the Indo-European *oinos* 'one' has changed its form in Latin *ūnus* and Gothic *ains*; and in Greek *oinē* 'one-spot on a die,' it has both changed its form and narrowed its meaning.

   To illustrate the common Indo-European vocabulary as it appears in the various languages of the group, we may consider the following lists of words, all of which are cited by Pyles on page 77 of *Origins and Development*. Compare the words with one another, observing similarities and differences.

	heart	*lung*	*head*	*foot*
OE	heorte	lungen	heafod	fot
Ger.	Herz	Lungen	Haupt	Fuss
ON	hjarta	lunga	haufoð	fotr
Goth.	hairto	leihts 'light'	haubiþ	fotus
Lat.	cordis	levis 'light'	caput	pedis
Gk.	kardia	elachus 'little'		podos
Russ.	serdtse	legkoe		(OSl.) podu 'ground'
Lith.	širdis	lengvas 'light'		pėda 'foot-track'
Ir.	cride	laigiu 'less'		
Skt.	hrd-	laghus 'light'	kapala 'cup, skull'	pad
IE	*kerd-	*le(n)gwh-	*kap-	*ped-

	night	*star*	*snow*	*sun*	*moon*
OE	niht	steorra	snaw	sunne	mona
Ger.	Nacht	Stern	Schnee	Sonne	Mond
ON	natt	stjarna	snær	sol, sunna	mani
Goth.	nahts	stairno	snaiws	sauil, sunno	mena
Lat.	noctis	stella	nivis	sol	mensis 'month'
Gk.	nuktos	aster	nipha	helios	men 'month'
Russ.	noch'		sneg	solntse	mesyats 'month'
Lith.	naktis		sniegas	saule	menuo
Ir.	nocht	(Br.) sterenn	snechte	(Br.) heol	mi 'month'
Skt.	naktam	star-	snih- 'sticky'	surya	mas- 'month'
IE	*nokt-	*ster-	*sn(o)igwh-	*sawel-	*menes-

	wind	*beech*	*corn*	*wolf*	*bear*
OE	wind	bece	corn	wulf	bera
Ger.	Wind	Buche	Korn 'rye'	Wolf	Bär
ON	vindr	bok	korn	ulfr	björn
Goth.	winds	boka 'letter'	kaurn	wulfs	
Lat.	ventus	fagus	granum 'a grain'	lupus	
Gk.	aer	phegos 'oak'	geron 'old man'	lukos	

	wind	beech	corn	wolf	bear
Russ.	veter		zerno	volk	berloga 'bear's den'
Lith.	vejas		žirnas 'pea'	vilkas	beras 'brown'
Ir.	(Br.) gwent		gran		
Skt.	vatas		jirna- 'worn out'	vrka-	bhallas
IE	*we-nt-	*bhago-	*grno-	*wlkwo-	*bheron-

	yoke	mead	weave	sew
OE	geoc	medu	wefan	siwian
Ger.	Joch	Met	weben	(OHG) siuwan
ON	ok	mjöðr	vefa	syja
Goth.	juk			siujan
Lat.	yugum			suere
Gk.	zugon	methu 'wine'	huphaino	kas-suo 'sew together'
Russ.	igo	med		shit'
Lith.	jungas	medus 'honey'	austi	siuti
Ir.	cuing	mid	figim	
Skt.	yugam	madhu- 'liquor'	urna-vabhi 'spider,' lit. 'wool-weaver'	siv-
IE	*yugo-	*medhu-	*webh-	*siu-

2. Below are lists of words from ten Indo-European languages and a list of their reconstructed Indo-European sources. Use the blank tables that follow to sort the words into cognate lists like the ones in the earlier part of this exercise.

Old English: broþor, dohtor, east, eax, fæder, full, hund, modor, nama, sunu, sweostor, toþ, widuwe

German: Achse, Bruder, Hund, Mutter, Name, Osten, Schwester, Sohn, Tochter, Vater, voll, Wittwe, Zahn

Old Norse: austr, broðir, dottir, faðir, fullr, hundr, moðir, namn, öxull, sunr, systir, tönn

Gothic: broþar, dauhtar, fadar, fulls, hunds, namo, sunus, swistar, tunþus, widuwo

Latin: aurora 'dawn,' axis, canis, dentis, frater, mater, nomen, pater, plenus, soror, vidua

Greek: axon, eos 'dawn,' huios, kuon, meter, odontos, onoma, pater, phrater, pleres, thugater

Russian: brat, doč', imya, mat', os', polnyǐ, sestra, suka 'bitch,' syn, vdova

Lithuanian: ašis, aušra 'dawn,' brolis, dantis, dukte, (OPruss.) emmens, mote 'woman,' pilnas, sesuo, sunus, šuo, (OPruss.) widdewu

Irish: (Br.) ahel, ainm, athir, brathir, cu, det, fedb, lan, mathir, siur

Sanskrit: aksa-, bhratar-, çvan-, dant-, duhitar-, matar-, naman-, pitar-, purna-, sunu-, svasar-, uşas 'dawn,' vidhava-

Indo-European: *aks-, *ausos-, *bhrater-, *dhughter-, *dont-, *ku(o)n-, *mater-, *nomen-, *pəter-, *plno-, *sunu-, *swesor-, *widhewa-

	father	mother	brother	sister	son
OE	_____	_____	_____	_____	____
Ger.	_____	_____	_____	_____	____
ON	_____	_____	_____	_____	____

	father	mother	brother	sister	son
Goth.	_____		_____	_____	_____
Lat.	_____	_____	_____	_____	
Gk.	_____	_____	_____	_____	_____
Russ.		_____	_____	_____	_____
Lith.		_____	_____	_____	_____
Ir.	_____	_____	_____	_____	_____
Skt.	_____	_____	_____	_____	_____
IE	_____	_____	_____	_____	_____

	daughter	widow	name	east	full
OE	_____	_____	_____	_____	_____
Ger.	_____	_____	_____	_____	_____
ON	_____		_____	_____	_____
Goth.	_____		_____	_____	_____
Lat.		_____	_____	_____	_____
Gk.	_____	_____	_____	_____	_____
Russ.	_____	_____	_____	_____	_____
Lith.	_____	_____	_____	_____	_____
Ir.		_____	_____		_____
Skt.	_____	_____	_____	_____	_____
IE	_____	_____	_____	_____	_____

	hound	tooth	axle
OE	_____	_____	_____
Ger.	_____	_____	_____
ON	_____	_____	_____
Goth.	_____	_____	
Lat.	_____	_____	_____
Gk.	_____	_____	_____
Russ.	_____		_____
Lith.	_____	_____	_____
Ir.	_____	_____	_____
Skt.	_____	_____	_____
IE	_____	_____	_____

3. For each of the following English words, find cognates in three or four other Indo-European languages. You can find the cognates in the *Oxford English Dictionary*, in W. W. Skeat's *An Etymological Dictionary of the English Language* (Oxford, 1879), or in C. D. Buck's *Dictionary of Selected Synonyms in the Principal Indo-European Languages* (Chicago, 1949).

acre _____

birch _____

bleat _____

blue _____

bright _____

comb _____

eat _____

fee _____
for _____
free _____
friend _____
give _____
have _____
mind _____
much _____
numb _____
oak _____
queen _____
right _____
that _____
thatch _____
thunder _____
town _____
tree _____
Tues(day) _____
what _____
wheel _____
wit _____
worth _____

4.10 COGNATE WORDS IN THE INDO-EUROPEAN LANGUAGES (II)

1. The following lists of the numbers 1 to 10 and 100 are from various Indo-European languages. The languages are grouped together according to the branch of the Indo-European family to which they belong. What similarities and differences can you find among the members of each branch? What similarities and differences are there among the various branches?

| Reconstructed Indo-European[5] | GERMANIC | | | | ARMENIAN | ALBANIAN |
	English	German	Dutch	Danish	Armenian	Albanian
*oinos	one	eins	een	en	mi	nji
*dwo	two	zwei	twee	to	erku	dy
*treies	three	drei	drie	tre	erek	tre
*kwetwor	four	vier	vier	fire	čork	katër
*penkwe	five	fünf	vijf	fem	hing	pesë
*s(w)eks	six	sechs	zes	seks	vec	gjashtë
*septm	seven	sieben	zeven	syv	evtn	shtatë
*okto	eight	acht	acht	otte	ut	tetë
*neun	nine	neun	negen	ni	inn	nând
*dekm	ten	zehn	tien	ti	tasn	dhiet
*kmtom	hundred	hundert	honderd	hundrede	hariur	qind

[5] The numbers show various "irregularities" in their phonological development. See the entry for *four* in the *Oxford English Dictionary* for the unexpected *f-* in Germanic languages. The number *five* has a similarly unexpected development in Italo-Celtic.

ITALIC				CELTIC		HELLENIC
Latin	*Italian*	*French*	*Spanish*	*Irish*	*Welsh*	*Greek*
ūnus	uno	un	uno	aon	un	heis
duo	due	deux	dos	dhá	dau	duo
trēs	tre	trois	tres	trí	tri	treis
quattuor	quattro	quatre	cuatro	ceithre	pedwar	tettares
quīnque	cinque	cinq	cinco	cúig	pump	pente
sex	sei	six	seis	sé	chwech	hex
septem	sette	sept	siete	seacht	saith	hepta
octō	otto	huit	ocho	ocht	wyth	oktō
novem	nove	neuf	nueve	naoi	naw	ennea
decem	dieci	dix	diez	deich	deg	deka
centum	cento	cent	ciento	céad	cant	hekaton

SLAVIC				BALTIC	IRANIAN	INDIC
Russian	*Polish*	*Bulgarian*	*Slovak*	*Lithuanian*	*Persian*	*Hindustani*
odin	jeden	edin	jeden	vienas	yek	ek
dva	dwa	dva	dva	du	do	do
tri	trzy	tri	tri	trys	se	tin
chetyre	cztery	četiri	štyri	keturi	cahar	char
pyat'	pięć	pet	pät'	penki	panj	panch
shest'	sześć	šest	šest'	šeši	shesh	chha
sem'	siedem	sedem	sedem	septyni	haft	sat
vosem'	osiem	osem	osem	aštuoni	hasht	ath
devyat'	dziewięć	devet	devät'	devyni	noh	nau
desyat'	dziesięć	deset	desat'	dešimt	dah	das
sto	sto	sto	sto	šimtas	sad	sau

2. The languages from which the following numbers come are also Indo-European. By comparing these lists with those above, you should be able to make a reasonable guess as to which branch of the Indo-European family each of these languages belongs. Write the name of the branch (Germanic, Armenian, Albanian, Italic, Celtic, Hellenic, Slavic, Baltic, Iranian, Indic) over each list.

	A	B	C	D	E	F
1	aon	jedinʉ	adzin	ains	ün	um
2	da	dʉva	dva	twai	deu	dois
3	tri	trije	try	þrija	trȳ	tres
4	ceithir	četyre	čatyry	fidwor	peswar	quatro
5	coig	pęti	piac'	fimf	pymp	cinco
6	sia	šesti	šesc'	saihs	whēgh	seis
7	seachd	sedmi	siem	sibun	seyth	sete
8	ochd	osmi	vosiem	ahtau	ēth	oito
9	naoi	deveti	dzieviac'	niun	naw	nove
10	deich	deseti	dziesiac'	taihun	dēk	dez
100	ced	sʉto	sto	taihuntehund	cans	cem

	G	H	I	J	K	L
1	un	ein	yek	un	jedan	an
2	dos	zwene	du	dos	dva	twegen
3	tres	dri	se	tres	tri	þry
4	quatre	fior	cwar	quatre	četiri	feower
5	cinc	finf	penj	cinc	pet	fif
6	seis	sehs	šest	sis	šest	syx
7	set	sibun	hewt	set	sedam	seofon
8	ueg	ahto	ešt	vuit	osam	eahta
9	nou	niun	no	nou	devet	nigon
10	detz	zehan	de	deu	deset	tyn
100	cent	zehanzo	sed	cent	sto	hundteontig

	M	N	O	P	Q	R
1	meg	eden	jeden	en	einn	ek
2	yergu	dva	dva	två	tveir	dui
3	yerek	tri	tři	tre	þrir	tin
4	čors	štiri	čtyři	fyra	fjorir	char
5	hing	pet	pět	fem	fimm	panch
6	vec	šest	šest	sex	sex	chhoe
7	yotə	sedem	sedm	sju	sjau	shat
8	utə	osem	osm	åtta	atta	at
9	innə	devet	devět	nio	niu	noe
10	dasə	deset	deset	tio	tiu	dosh
100	haryur	sto	sto	hundra	tiutigir	sho

3. Ten of the languages from which the following numbers come are Indo-European; the remaining eight are not. Distinguish the Indo-European languages from the non-Indo-European ones by writing *IE* or *non-IE* above each list.

	A	B	C	D	E	F
1	en	un	bir	jedyn	egy	ün
2	twene	doui	iki	dwaj	két	duos
3	thria	trei	üç	tři	három	trais
4	fiuwar	patru	dört	štyri	négy	quatter
5	fif	cinci	beş	pjeć	öt	tschinch
6	sehx	şase	altı	šěsć	hat	ses
7	sibun	şapte	yedi	sedm	hét	set
8	ahto	opt	sekiz	wosm	nyolcz	och
9	nigun	nouă	dokuz	dźewjeć	kilencz	nouv
10	tehan	zice	on	dźesać	tíz	dêsch
100	hunderod	sută	yüz	sto	száz	tschient

	G	H	I	J	K	L
1	nigen	mot	unan	mek	i	aeva
2	khoyar	hai	daou	yerku	liang	dva

90

3 ghorban	ba	tri	yerek	san	þrayo
4 durben	bon	pevar	čors	ssu	caþwaro
5 tabon	nam	pemp	hing	wu	panca
6 jirghoghan	sau	c'houec'h	vec	liu	xšvaš
7 dologhan	bay	seiz	yot	ch'i	hapta
8 naiman	tam	eiz	ut	pa	ašta
9 yisun	chin	nao	innə	chiu	nava
10 arban	muoi	dek	tas	shih	dasa
100 jaghon	tram	kant	haryur	pai	satem

	M	N	O	P	Q	R
1	ichi	hana	eka	yaw	eden	echad
2	ni	tul	dvau	daw	dva	shnayim
3	san	set	trayas	dree	tri	shlosha
4	shi	net	catur	tsaloor	četiri	arba'a
5	go	tasŏt	pañca	pindze	pet	chamishsha
6	roku	yŏsŏt	şaş	shpazz	šest	shishsha
7	shichi	ilgop	sapta	uwe	sedum	shiv'a
8	hachi	yŏdŏl	aşta	ate	osum	shmona
9	ku	ahop	nava	ne	devet	tish'a
10	ju	yŏl	daça	las	deset	'asara
100	hyaku	paek	çata	sulu	sto	mea

4.11 THE MAJOR CHANGES FROM INDO-EUROPEAN TO GERMANIC

All Germanic languages, in their oldest forms, share certain characteristics that distinguish them from other Indo-European languages. In *Origins and Development*, Pyles lists seven of these peculiarly Germanic features:

1. a two-tense verbal system
2. a dental suffix for the preterit tense
3. "strong" versus "weak" adjectives
4. a fixed stress accent
5. certain vowel changes
6. the First Sound Shift
7. a common distinctive vocabulary

Here are several examples of these Germanic characteristics. Forms from a Germanic language are listed together with parallel forms from a non-Germanic, but Indo-European, language. Compare the forms with one another and with the discussion in *Origins and Development*; then identify the Germanic characteristic which each example most clearly illustrates by writing the appropriate number, from 1 through 7, in the blank in the left margin.

———— *Old English:* micel guma 'a great man' *Latin:* magnus homo 'a great man'
se micela guma 'that great man' iste magnus homo 'that great man'
micele guman 'great men' magnī homines 'great men'
þā micelan guman 'those great men' istī magnī homines 'those great men'

_____ *Old English:* þorp 'town'   *Latin:* turba 'crowd'
             etan 'eat'   edō 'eat'
             īecan 'eke'   augeō 'increase'

_____ *Old English:* brū 'brow'   *Sanskrit:* bhrū 'brow'
             rēad 'red'   rudh-ira 'blood'
             gangan 'go' (cf. gangway)   janghā[6] 'heel, lower leg'

_____ *Old English:* mốdor 'mother'   singular nominative   *Greek:* mḗtēr 'mother'
             mốdor   singular genitive   mētrós
             mḗder   singular dative   mētrí
             mốdor   singular accusative   mētéra
             mốdor   plural nominative   mētéres
             mốdra   plural genitive   mētérōn
             mốdrum   plural dative   mētrási
             mốdor   plural accusative   mētéras

_____ *Old English:* brōþer 'brother'   *Latin:* frāter 'brother'
             bōc 'beech tree'   fāgus 'beech tree'
             mōdor 'mother'   māter 'mother'

_____ *Old English:* ic sēce 'I seek'   *Latin:* sagiō 'I perceive'
             ic sōhte 'I sought'   sagīvī 'I perceived'
             ic temme 'I tame'   domō 'I tame'
             ic temede 'I tamed'   domuī 'I tamed'

_____ *Gothic:* gasts 'stranger'   *Latin:* hostis 'stranger'
             nahts 'night'   nox 'night'
             gards 'garden'   hortus 'garden'

_____ *Old English:* sǣ 'sea'   *Greek:* thalassa 'sea'
        Dutch: zee   *Latin:* mare
        Modern German: See   *Russian:* more
        Old High German: sēo   *Irish:* muir
        Icelandic: sær   *Lithuanian:* jūra
        Danish: sö   *Hindustani:* samundar
        Swedish: sjö   *Old Persian:* drayah
        Gothic: saiws

_____ *Old English:* nefa 'nephew'   *Latin:* nepōs 'grandson'
             weorþan 'become'   vertō 'turn'
             hōre 'whore'   cāra 'dear one'

_____ *Old English:* ic dō 'I do, am doing, will   *Greek:* tithēmi 'I am placing'
             do'   thēsō 'I will place'
             ic dyde 'I was doing, did,   etithēn 'I was placing'
             have done'   ethēka 'I placed'
                                                 tethēka 'I have placed'

[6] The initial *j* is due to a sound change which is of no importance for Germanic languages.

1. The First Sound Shift occurred in five chronological steps. Each step was completed before the next began, so there was no overlapping or repetition of the changes. The following chart will summarize the five steps in the Shift. Steps 1, 2, 4, and sometimes 5 are collectively called Grimm's Law. Step 3 is called Verner's Law. Complete the chart by writing the appropriate phonetic symbol in each box.

STEP 1		
aspirated voiced stops		*voiced fricatives*
labial	$\longrightarrow$	
dental	$\longrightarrow$	
velar	$\longrightarrow$	

STEP 2		
voiceless stops	*see note*	*voiceless fricatives*
labial	$\longrightarrow$	
dental	$\longrightarrow$	
velar	$\longrightarrow$	

STEP 3		
voiceless fricatives	*see note*	*voiced fricatives*
labial	$\longrightarrow$	
dental	$\longrightarrow$	
velar	$\longrightarrow$	
sibilant	$\longrightarrow$	

STEP 4		
voiced stops		*voiceless stops*
labial	$\longrightarrow$	
dental	$\longrightarrow$	
velar	$\longrightarrow$	

STEP 5		
voiced fricatives	*see note*	*voiced stops*
labial	$\longrightarrow$	
dental	$\longrightarrow$	
velar	$\longrightarrow$	

NOTE: Under what conditions did step 2 *not* occur? _____
_____

Under what conditions did step 3 *not* occur?
_____
_____
_____

Under what conditions did step 5 occur? _____
_____
_____

2. Each of the following groups of consonants represents part of the Indo-European or Germanic sound system at one of six stages in its development. The six stages are (A) before the beginning of the First Sound Shift, (B)(C)(D)(E) between each step of that Shift, and (F) at the completion of the entire Shift. Letter the six stages (A) through (F) according to their proper chronological order.

STAGE _____

ƀ   ð   ʒ
p   t   k
f   þ   x
    z
    s

STAGE _____

ƀ   ð   ʒ
b   d   g
p   t   k
    s

STAGE _____

ƀ   ð   ʒ
b   d   g
f   þ   x
    z
    s

STAGE _____

bh   dh   gh
b   d   g
p   t   k
    s

STAGE _____

b   d   g
p   t   k
f   þ   x
    r
    s

STAGE _____

ƀ   ð   ʒ
b   d   g
f   þ   x
    s

3. The following pairs of cognate words illustrate the First Sound Shift. The first word in each pair is from a non-Germanic language (Latin unless noted otherwise); the second word is from a Germanic language (English unless noted otherwise). The words in each pair have come from the same Indo-European root but may have different suffixes; in a few examples, especially those showing the *b/p* correspondence, the paired words are not certain cognates, but they are possible ones. Supply the missing letters according to Grimm's Law (steps 1, 2, 4, and 5 of the Sound Shift). Note that *c* and *q* are spellings for [k].

In working this exercise, you must keep in mind the fact that the Indo-European aspirated voiced stops developed variously in the several daughter languages. You may find it useful to summarize those changes before proceeding to the cognate words.

DEVELOPMENTS OF INDO-EUROPEAN ASPIRATED VOICED STOPS				
Indo-European	*Sanskrit*	*Greek*	*Latin*	*Germanic*

(Skt.) bhan- 'declare' / _____an
(Skt.) dhāv- 'flow' / _____ew
(Skt.) vaha- 'road' / (OE) we_____'way'
pluvia 'rain' / _____low

(Gk.) thygatēr / _____aughter
canere 'sing' / _____en
augēre / e_____e
hiāre / (OE) _____eonian 'yawn'

trans / ____rough
cella 'hut' / ____all
labium / li____
domus 'house' / ____imber
gelu 'frost' / ____ool
____lōs / blossom
____ūmus 'smoke' / dust
____elvus / (OE) geolu 'yellow'
____aucus / few
____umēre 'swell' / thumb
____ursus 'running' / horse
sē____um 'tallow' / soap
____icere 'say' / teach
____lobus 'ball' / clue
(Gk.) graphein 'write' / ____arve
suādere 'persuade' / swee____
pānis 'bread' / ____ood
(Lith.) këmas 'village' / ____ome
(Gk.) pherō / ____ear
(Gk.) anchein 'strangle' / an____er
(Gk.) stembein / stam____

mortis 'death' / (OE) mor____or 'murder'
(Skt.) bhu- / ____e
tongēre 'know' / ____in____
(Gk.) pter- 'wing' / ____ea____er
trūdere 'push' / ____rea____
____ār 'grain' / barley
____ūcere 'lead' / tug
____oris / door
sca____ere 'scrape' / shape
va____is 'pledge' / wed
(Russ.) ____o 'up to' / to
(Russ.) sla____uii 'slack' / sleep
(Gk.) mē____anē 'means' / (OE) mæg 'may'
____luēre 'hear' / (OE) hlud 'loud'
____uter 'rotten' / foul
(Gk.) a____ōnia 'struggle' / ache
(Gk.) ____rēnos 'lamentation' / drone
____ollere 'bear' / (OE) þolian 'endure'
____ī____ī 'cleaved' / bite
____rē____ī / broke
(Gk.) ____le____ein 'weave' / (OHG) flahs 'flax'

4. The following pairs of cognate words illustrate Verner's Law (step 3 of the Sound Shift). Supply the missing letters.

caput / (Goth.) hau____iþ 'head'
(Gk.) plōtós 'swimming' / floo____
(Gk.) dekás / (Goth.) ti____us 'decade'
(Skt.) snusá / (OE) sno____u 'daughter-in-law'
centum / hun____red

se____tem / (Goth.) sibun 'seven'
cun____tārī 'tarry' / hang
(Skt.) -vr____āná 'turned' / (OE) worden 'become'
(Gk.) he____urá / (OE) sweger 'mother-in-law'
altiu____ / elder

4.13 THE HIGH GERMAN SOUND SHIFT

English and the Low German languages—Dutch, Flemish, and Plattdeutsch—differ from modern Standard German partly because Standard German has undergone a second or High German Sound Shift. English preserves the older common Germanic sounds which were changed in High German between the sixth and the eighth centuries.

Summarize in the following chart those parts of the Second Sound Shift which Pyles describes in Chapter IV of *Origins and Development*.[7]

---

[7] A complete statement of the High German Sound Shift would require some additional remarks about sounds and positions. The chart does, however, include the most important changes.

OLDER GERMANIC	HIGH GERMAN	
	after vowels	*otherwise*
p		
t		
k		——
d		

Below are some English and High German cognates which show sound correspondence according to the Second Sound Shift. Supply the missing letters.

ENGLISH	GERMAN	ENGLISH	GERMAN	ENGLISH	GERMAN
pan	____anne	boo____	Busse	bite	bei____en
grip	Gri____	sha____e	schaffen	plough	____lug
to	____u	____ath	Pfad	weaponless	wa____enlos
foot	Fu____	ri____e	reiten	heart	Her____
book	Bu____	hol____	Holz	fret	fre____en
door	____ür	re____on	rechnen	alike	glei____
pole	____ahl	ha____e	Hass	deed	____a____
tame	____ahm	o____en	offen	token	____ei____en
make	ma____en	floo____	Flut	plant	____lan____e
dream	____raum	shi____	Schiff	tide	____ei____

4.14 THE GERMANIC LANGUAGES ILLUSTRATED

The following selections are translations of the parable of the prodigal son (Luke xv. 11–24) in four early Germanic languages: Gothic, Old English, Old High German, and Old Norse. The Latin Vulgate text has been added for comparison. The Gothic, Old English, and Old High German versions are fairly close translations; with the help of a modern English translation and some imagination you should be able to make them out. The Old Norse version, however, is an unusually free and prolix rendering; therefore a gloss has been given for it.

Compare the translations with one another to discover similarities and differences among the Germanic languages.

Gothic

(11) Manne sums aihta twans sununs.   (12) Jah qaþ sa juhiza ize du attin: "Atta, gif mis sei undrinnai mik dail aiginis." Jah disdailida im swes sein.   (13) Jah afar ni managans dagans, brahta samana allata sa juhiza sunus jah aflaiþ in land fairra wisando, jah jainar distahida þata swes seinata libands usstiuriba.   (14) Biþe þan frawas allamma, warþ huhrus abrs and gawi

jainata, jah is dugann alaþarba wairþan.	(15) Jah gaggands gahaftida sik sumamma baurgjane jainis gaujis. Jah insandida ina haiþjos seinaizos haldan sweina.	(16) Jah gairnida sad itan haurne, þoei matidedun sweina, jah manna imma ni gaf.	(17) Qimands þan in sis qaþ: "Hwan filu asnje attins meinis ufarassau haband hlaibe, iþ ik huhrau fraqistna!	(18) Usstandands gagga du attin meinamma, jah qiþa du imma: 'Atta, frawaurhta mis in himin, jah in andwairþja þeinamma;	(19) ju þanaseiþs ni im wairþs ei haitaidau sunus þeins; gatawei mik swe ainana asnje þeinaize.'"	(20) Jah usstandands qam at attin seinamma. Nauhþanuh þan fairra wis-andan, gasahw ina atta is, jah infeinoda, jah þragjands draus ana hals is, jah kukida imma.	(21) Jah qaþ imma sa sunus: "Atta, frawaurhta in himin, jah in andwairþja þeinamma, ju þanaseiþs ni im wairþs ei haitaidau sunus þeins."	(22) Qaþ þan sa atta du skalkam seinaim: "Sprauto bringiþ wastja þo frumiston, jah gawasjiþ ina, jah gibiþ figgragulþ in handu is, jah gaskohi ana fotuns is,	(23) jah bringandans stiur þana alidan ufsneiþiþ, jah matjandans wisam waila,	(24) unte sa sunus meins dauþs was, jah gaqiunoda, jah fralusans was, jah bigitans warþ."

Old English

(11) Soðlice sum man hæfde twegen suna.	(12) Þa cwæð se gingra to his fæder: "Fæder, syle me minne dæl minre æhte þe me to gebyreþ." Þa dælde he him his æhte.	(13) Ða æfter feawum dagum, ealle his þing gegaderode se gingra sunu, and ferde wræclice on feorlen rice, and forspilde þar his æhta, lybbende on his gælsan.	(14) Ða he hig hæfde ealle amyrrede, þa wearð mycel hunger on þam rice, and he wearð wædla.	(15) Þa ferde he, and folgode anum burhsittendan men þæs rices.	Ða sende he hine to his tune þæt he heolde his swyn.	(16) Ða gewilnode he his wambe gefyllan of þam beancoddum, þe ða swyn æton, and him man ne sealde.	(17) Þa beþohte he hine, and cwæð: "Eala, hu fela hyrlinga on mines fæder huse hlaf genohne habbað, and ic her on hungre forwurðe!	(18) Ic arise, and ic fare to minum fæder, and ic secge him: 'Eala fæder, ic syngode on heofenas, and beforan þe;	(19) nu ic ne eom wyrðe þæt ic beo þin sunu nemned; do me swa anne of þinum hyrlingum.'"	(20) And he aras þa, and com to his fæder. And þa gyt þa he wæs feorr his fæder, he hyne geseah, and wearð mid mildheortnesse astyrod, and agen hine arn, and hine beclypte, and cyste hine.	(21) Ða cwæð his sunu: "Fæder, ic syngode on heofon, and beforan ðe; nu ic ne eom wyrþe þæt ic þin sunu beo genemned."	(22) Ða cwæþ se fæder to his þeowum: "Bringað raðe þone selestan gegyre-lan, and scrydað hyne, and syllað him hring on his hand, and gescy to his fotum,	(23) and bringað an fætt styric, and ofsleað, and uton etan, and gewistfullian,	(24) for þam þes min sunu wæs dead, and he geedcucode, he forwearð, and he is gemet."

Old High German

(11) Sum man habata zuuene suni.	(12) Quad tho ther iungoro fon then themo fater: "Fater, gib mir teil thero hehti, thiu mir gibure." Her tho teilta thia heht.	(13) Nalles after manegen tagon, gisamonoten allen ther iungoro sun elilentes fuor in uerra lantscaf, inti dar ziuuarf sina heht lebento uirnlustigo.	(14) Inti after thiu her iz al forlos, uuard hungar strengi in thero lantscefi, her bigonda tho armen.	(15) Inti gieng, inti zuoclebeta einemo thero burg-liuto thero lantscefi. Inti santa inan in sin thorf, thaz her fuotriti suuin.	(16) Inti girdinota gifullen sina uuamba fon siliquis, theo thiu suuin azzun, inti nioman imo nigab.	(17) Her tho in sih giuuorban quad: "Vvuo manege asnere mines fater ginuht habent brotes, ih uoruuirdu hier hungere!	(18) Arstantu, inti faru zi minemo fater, inti quidu imo: 'Fater, ih suntota in himil, inti fora thir;	(19) inti nibim iu uuirdig ginemnit uuesan thin sun; tuo mih so einan fon

thinen asnerin.'"   (20) Inti arstantanti quam zi sinemo fater. Mittiu thanne noh ferro uuas, gisah inan sin fater, inti miltida giruorit uuard, inti ingegin louffenti fiel ubar sinan hals, inti custa inan.   (21) Tho quad imo der sun: "Fater, ih suntota in himil, inti fora thir, iu nibim uuirdig ginemnit uuesan thin sun."   (22) Tho quad ther fater zi sinen scalcun: "Sliumo bringet thaz erira giuuati, inti giuuatet inan, inti gebet fingirin in sina hant, inti giscuohiu in fuozi, (23) inti leitet gifuotrit calb, inti arslahet, inti ezzemes, inti goumumes,   (24) uuanta theser min sun tot uuas, into arqueketa, foruuard, inti funtan uuard."

Old Norse

(11) Einn auðigr maðr atti tva sunu.   (12) En sa hinn yngri   sunr hans mælti til föður
A   rich   man had two sons.   And he this younger son of his said   to father

sins: "Faðir," sagði hann, "fa mer þann hlut   fjar   mins, er   til min telst   i
his Father   said   he   give me the portion of possessions my   which to me counts in

erfðum   millum var feðganna."   Sem faðir hans heyrði þetta, þa skipti hann hanum
inheritance among us father and sons. When father his   heard this   then divided he   to him

sinum hlut. (13) En hann varð þegar i brotto ok for langt i önnor land með sinum
his   portion. And he got at once away and went far to other lands with his

hlut, ok lifði þar folslega, eyddi fenu   öllu i fullifi sva snaplega, at um siðir
portion and lived there foolishly wasted substance all in foul life so brutishly that at last

hafði hann sjalfr alls ekki. (14) Ok fluttist þar fram með mykilli fatœkt, þviat i
had   he   himself at all nothing. And moved there from with great   poverty because at

þeim tima var mykit   uaran i þvi landi ok mykill sultr. (15) Ok kom hann ser   i
that time was great   dearth in the land and great   hunger.   And came he   himself into

fatœka   þjonustu með einum rikum   manni, en hann sendi hann til eins kotbœar, at
impoverished service with a   powerful man   and he   sent him   to a   farmstead that

hann skyldi gæta svina hans. (16) En hans vesöld vox sva mjök þar, at hann fystist
he   should watch swine his.   And his   misery grew so much there that he   desired

fyrir hungrs sakar at fylla kvið sinn af bauna skalmum ok stiklum, er   svinum var
for hunger's sake to fill belly his with bean pods   and thorns which to swine was

gefit til matar, ok fekk hann ser   þat til fœzlu, þviat engi   vildi gefa hanum
given as meat   and took he   himself that as food   because no one would give him

annat. (17) Ok hugleiddi hann þa, sjalfr, hversu folslega er   hann hafði farit með sinu
any other. And considered he   then himself how   foolishly that he   had   dealt with his

raði ok mæltist þa   við einn samann þessum orðum: "Faðir minn fœðir hversdaglega
life and spoke then to himself   in these words   Father my   feeds commonly

heima með ser   mykinn fjölda   leigumanna með gnogu brauði ok annarri vist œrinni,
at home with himself a great multitude of hired men with enough bread and other food enough

en ek svelt her af matleysi! (18) Ok þvi   skal ek skyndilega fara til föður mins ok
and I die here of starvation!   And therefore shall I quickly   go to father my and

biðja hann miskunnar með þessum orðum: 'Faðir, ek hefi syndgazt ok misgört   i moti
beg   him for mercy with these words Father I have sinned   and done amiss against

guði himneskum ok sva moti   þer;   (19) ok firir þvi em ek eigi verðr heðan ifra, at
god in heaven and also against thee   and therefore am I not worthy henceforth that

þu   haldir mik sva sem þinn sun; nu bið ek, at   þu gefir mer slikan rett i garði þinum
thou hold me thus as thy son now beg I that thou give me such   due in house thy

sem einum leigumanne þinum.'"   (20) Ok siðan   for   hann skyngilega ok kom til
as one of hired men thy.   And afterwards went   he   quickly   and came to

föður sins. Nu þegar sem faðir hans leit hann mjök fjarri komandi, þa sneri hann
father his. Now at once when father his saw him very far off coming   then turned he

þegar miskunn sinni til   hans ok rann at hanum ok tok höndum   sinum um   hals
at once mercy   his towards him and ran to him and held with hands his   about neck

hanum ok kysti hann með myklum fagnaði.⁸   (22) Ok mælti við þjonustumenn sina, er
his   and kissed him with great   delight.   And said to servants   his who

i hja   hanum varu: "Skyndið heim ok takit goða gangverju   með fögrum skom ok
close by him   were Hurry home and take good walking cloak with fair   shoes and

færið syni   minum ok gott fingrgull   dregit a hönd hanum ok sœmið hann,
bring to son my   and good gold finger-ring put   on hand his and honor him

(23) drepit ok einn feitan oxa; ver skulum hafa, i dag mykla veizlu ok fagnaðar   öl i
slay also a fat   ox we shall have to day great feast and for rejoicing ale at

heimkomu sunar mins,   (24) þviat ek hugða hann vera dauðan ok er hann nu lifs,
homecoming of son my   because I thought him to be dead and is he   now alive

þar sem hann hvarf   i brott ok er nu aptr kominn."
whereas he   vanished away and is now back come.

Latin

(11) Homo quidam habuit duos filios.   (12) Et dixit adolescentior ex illis patri: "Pater, da mihi portionem substantiae quae me contingit." Et divisit illis substantiam.   (13) Et non post multos dies, congregatis omnibus, adolescentior filius peregre profectus est in regionem longinquam, et ibi dissipavit substantiam suam vivendo luxuriose.   (14) Et postquam omnia consummasset, facta est fames valida in regione illa, et ipse coepit egere.   (15) Et abiit, et adhaesit uni civium regionis illius. Et misit illum in villam suam ut pasceret porcos.   (16) Et cupiebat implere ventrem suum de siliquis, quas porci manducabant, et nemo illi dabat.   (17) In se autem reversus, dixit: "Quanti mercenarii in domo patris mei abundant panibus, ego autem hic fame pereo!   (18) Surgam, et ibo ad patrem meum, et dicam ei: 'Pater, peccavi in caelum, et coram te;   (19) iam non sum dignus vocari filius tuus; fac me sicut unum de mercenariis tuis.'"   (20) Et surgens venit ad patrem suum. Cum autem adhuc longe esset, vidit illum pater ipsius, et misericordia motus est, et accurrens cecidit super collum eius, et osculatus est eum.   (21) Dixitque ei filius: "Pater, peccavi in caelum, et coram te, iam non sum dignus vocari filius tuus."   (22) Dixit autem pater ad servos suos: "Cito proferte stolam primam, et induite illum, et date annulum in manum eius, et calceamenta in pedes eius,   (23) et adducite vitulum saginatum, et occidite, et manducemus, et epulemur,   (24) quia hic filius mortuus erat, et revixit, perierat, et inventus est."

⁸ Verse 21 is lacking.

What words in each of the Germanic versions correspond to the Latin (or English) below?

	GOTHIC	OLD ENGLISH	OLD HIGH GERMAN	OLD NORSE
(11) homo 'man'				
duos 'two'				
filios 'sons'				
(12) adolescentior 'younger'				
patri 'to (his) father'				
pater 'father'				
(14) fames 'hunger'				
(15) porcos 'swine'				
(16) cupiebat 'desired'				
(17) panibus 'bread'				
ego 'I'				
fame 'in hunger'				
(18) caelum 'heaven'				
(19) filius 'son'				
(20) venit 'came'				
ad patrem suum 'to his father'				
(22) in manum eius 'on his hand'				
calceamenta 'shoes'				
(23) vitulum 'calf, young steer'				
(24) mortuus 'dead'				

The Old English Period (449–1100)

QUESTIONS FOR REVIEW AND DISCUSSION

1. Define the following terms:

grammatical gender	a-stems	grammatical change
natural gender	n-stems	preterit-present verbs
cases	ō-stems	anomalous verbs
nominative	mutation (umlaut)	enclitic
accusative	short syllable	personal endings
genitive	long syllable	indicative
dative	dual number	subjunctive
instrumental	gradation (ablaut)	imperative
"strong" declensions	preterit	finite forms
"weak" declensions	principal parts	nonfinite forms

2. What peoples inhabited the British Isles before the coming of the English?

3. According to Bede, what circumstances brought the Germanic tribesmen to Britain, and which tribes participated in the settlement of the island?

4. What was the Anglo-Saxon Heptarchy?

5. What was the influence of the Scandinavian settlement on the English language?

6. Which dialect of Old English was the standard language and from which dialect has Modern English descended?

7. What is the chief difference between the stress patterns of Old English and Modern English, and what historical events help to account for the difference?

8. What are the main differences in word order between Old English and Modern English?

9. From which Old English declension do the living noun inflections of Modern English derive?

10. How do the grammatical devices for indicating plurality in Old English and in Modern English differ?

11. What was the difference in use between the strong and weak forms of an Old English adjective?

12. What Old English adjective inflections have survived as living suffixes in Modern English?

13. What is the origin of Modern English adverbs without endings such as *deep, fast,* and *loud?*

14. What is the difference between mutation (umlaut) and gradation (ablaut)?

15. From what class of Old English verbs are the Modern English modal auxiliaries *shall, should, may, might, can, could, must,* and *ought* derived?

16. What distinctions in form, universal in Old English verbs, are preserved in Modern English only in the verb *to be*?

17. What is the Old English origin of the *y-* in Spenser's "A Gentle Knight was pricking on the plaine, / Ycladd in mightie armes and silver shielde"?

18. Old English differs from Modern English in the amount of inflection for nouns, adjectives, pronouns, and verbs. Name four or five other major differences between the linguistic systems of the two periods.

5.2 ANGLO-SAXON ENGLAND

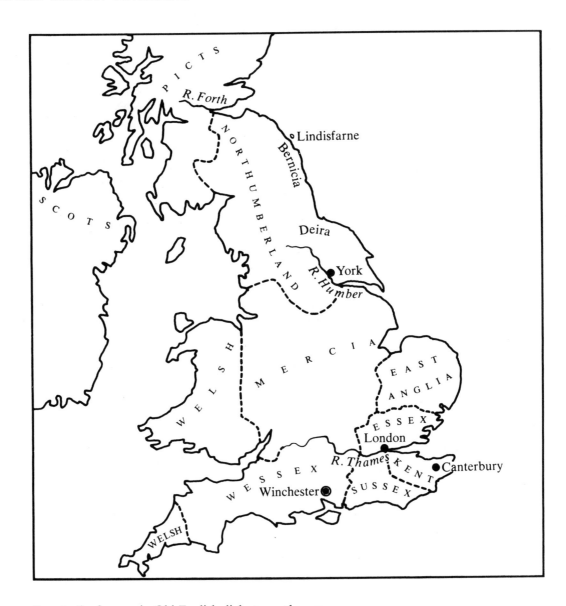

Locate the four main Old English dialects on the map.

ANGLIAN

Northumbrian

Mercian

West Saxon

Kentish

1. Summarize the rules for Old English stress on

   words without a prefix _____

   _____

   words with a prefix _____

   _____

   compounds _____

   _____

2. Indicate the primary stress of the following Old English words, all of which are without prefix, by placing a stress mark (′) over the stressed vowel.

cuman	'to come'	sweotol	'clear'
fēngon	'(they) took'	sweotolian	'to reveal'
reccere	'teacher'	spellian	'to relate'
dearnunga	'secretly'	lustfullic	'joyful'

3. Indicate the primary stress of the following Old English words by placing a stress mark (′) over the stressed vowel. Prefixes have been set off with hyphens to call attention to them.

on-fōn	'to receive'	be-sprecan	'to talk about'
and-fengness	'reception'	bī-spell	'proverb'
wið-sprecan	'to contradict'	be-cuman	'to happen'
wiðer-spræc	'contradiction'	be-cyme	'result'
of-þyncan	'to offend'	for-fōn	'to take away'
æf-þunca	'offense'	for-fang	'seizure'
to-cuman	'arrive'	ge-reccan	'to explain'
tō-cyme	'arrival'	ge-recedness	'interpretation'

4. Indicate the primary stress (′) and the secondary stress (`) of the following compounds by writing the appropriate marks over the stressed vowels. Compounds have been divided with hyphens. Some of the words have prefixes which you should recognize from the preceding question.

spell-boda	'messenger'	forfang-feoh	'reward for rescuing property'
god-spellere	'evangelist'	scīr-gerēfa	'shire reeve'
spræc-hūs	'senate house'	bebod-dæg	'appointed day'
man-cynn	'mankind'	gehāt-land	'promised land'
bōc-cræftig	'learned'	dǣd-cēne	'daring'
lof-geornost	'most eager for praise'	hēah-fæder	'patriarch'
hēah-burg	'capital city'	leorning-cniht	'disciple'
tungol-wītega	'astrologer'	mynster-mann	'monk'

103

5.4 THE PRONUNCIATION OF OLD ENGLISH: VOWELS

Old English had the following vowels:[1]

SPELLING	SOUND	SPELLING	SOUND	SPELLING	SOUND
a	[ɑ]	i	[ɪ]	y	[y]
ā	[ɑ:]	ī	[i:]	ȳ	[y:]
æ	[æ]	o	[ɔ]	ea	[æə]
ǣ	[æ:]	ō	[o:]	ēa	[æ:ə]
e	[ɛ]	u	[ʊ]	eo	[ɛə]
ē	[e:]	ū	[u:]	ēo	[e:ə]

1. Complete the following chart by filling in the phonetic symbols listed above to show the articulation of Old English vowels.

		FRONT UNROUNDED	FRONT ROUNDED	BACK
HIGH	long			
	short			
MID			DIPHTHONGS	
	long			
	short			
LOW	long			
	short			

2. Complete the following chart to show (a) the phonetic symbol for the Old English vowel, (b) the phonetic symbol for a typical Modern English development of the vowel, and (c) the typical spelling of the Modern English development. Complete columns (b) and (c) according to the Modern English key words.

---

[1] For the use of macrons in Old English spelling see *Origins and Development*, p. 107, n. 11. Other interpretations are possible for some of the sounds listed here; see *Origins and Development*, p. 107 and p. 109, n. 13. To pronounce [y:], say [i:] with your lips well-rounded, as though for [u:]; similarly, [y] is like [ɪ] with lip rounding as for [ʊ]. The colon is used in phonetic transcriptions to show that the preceding vowel is long.

	OLD ENGLISH			MODERN ENGLISH			
vowel	(a) phonetic symbol	key words		key words		(b) phonetic symbol	(c) typical spelling
a	[ɑ]	habban sadol	batt lamb	have saddle	bat lamb	[æ]	a
ā		hām tācen	gād pāl	home token	goad pole		
æ		þæt bæc	pæð mæst	that back	path mast		
ǣ		dǣl hǣlan	nǣdl mǣne	deal heal	needle mean		
e		settan rest	weddian denn	set rest	wed den		
ē		fēdan grēne	cēne mētan	feed green	keen meet		
i		sittan mist	timber rima	sit mist	timber rim		
ī		rīdan līf	tīma bī	ride life	time by		
o		moððe oft	pott botm	moth oft(en)	pot bottom		
ō		fōda nōn	gōd brōm	food noon	good broom		
u		sundor þus	wundor pullian	sunder thus	wonder pull		
ū		mūs dūne	nū ūt	mouse down	now out		
y		fyllan mynster	pytt þynne	fill minster	pit thin		
ȳ		mȳs hȳdan	fȳr hwȳ	mice hide	fire why		
ea		ceaf nearu	sleac fealu	chaff narrow	slack fallow		
ēa		bēatan lēaf	ēast stēap	beat leaf	east steep		
eo		geolu eolh	heofon seofon	yellow elk	heaven seven		
ēo		crēopan flēon	dēop bēo	creep flee	deep bee		

105

Old English had the following consonants:

SPELLING	SOUND	SPELLING	SOUND	SPELLING	SOUND
b	[b]	h	[h], [x][2]	s	[s], [z]
c, k	[k]	l	[l]	t	[t]
c	[č]	m	[m]	þ, ð	[θ], [ð]
d	[d]	n	[n], [ŋ]	w	[w]
f	[f], [v]	p	[p]	sc	[š]
g	[g], [ʒ][2]	r	[r]	cg	[j]
g	[j]				

Complete the following chart by filling in the symbols listed above so as to show the place and manner of articulation of Old English consonants. A review of the chart of Modern English consonants will help you complete this one, but you should note these points: To simplify the chart, [č] and [j] have been called stops although they might have been labeled affricates; although [ʒ] is a fricative it should be put with [g] among the stops for a reason we will presently see; similarly, [h] should be put with [x] as a fricative.

		LABIAL	DENTAL			VELAR	
			inter-dental	*alveolar*	*alveolo-palatal*	*palatal*	*velar*
STOPS	*voiceless*						
	voiced						
FRICATIVES							
NASALS							
LIQUIDS	*lateral*						
	retroflex or trill						
SEMIVOWELS							

[2] To pronounce [x] you may find one or more of the following techniques helpful: (1) Start to make the sound [k], but stop before the back of the tongue actually touches the roof of the mouth, and breathe out strongly; or make a [k] with light contact between the tongue and the roof of the mouth, and with the tongue still in that position, breathe out strongly; or (2) make an [š] sound, and while you are making it, force your tongue toward the back of your mouth; or (3) make the [hj] sound as in *hew* forcefully so that the [h] and [j] blend into a single sound, which will be the palatal version of [x]. Children sometimes use repeated [x]'s to represent the sound of a train engine. The sound [ʒ] is simply a voiced [x], so the simplest way to make it is to vibrate your vocal cords while making an [x], or try techniques (1) and (2) described above, but using [g] instead of [k] and [ž] instead of [š]. Or make a [w], unround your lips, and concentrate on producing a friction noise by slightly raising the back of your tongue. Children sometimes use a prolonged [ʒ] to represent the sound of an airplane engine.

Twelve of the consonant sounds listed in the preceding exercise are paired thus:

[f] / [v]   [θ] / [ð]   [s] / [z]   [g] / [ʒ]   [h] / [x]   [n] / [ŋ]

The sounds in each pair alternate in different environments. For example, [f] occurs in one set of positions and [v] occurs in a different set of positions. Neither [f] nor [v] normally turns up in any of the positions belonging to the other sound. Since the two labial fricatives alternate in this way, they are, as far as Old English is concerned, the same sound; that is, they are allophones of the same phoneme.

Examine the following words to determine the positions (environment) in which the sounds of each pair occur.

1. [f] / [v], [θ] / [ð], [s] / [z]

folc	[fɔlk]	'folk'	offrian	[ɔffrɪɑn]	'to offer'
þurh	[θʊrx]	'through'	moððe	[mɔθθɛ]	'moth'
sōna	[so:nɑ]	'immediately'	mæsse	[mæssɛ]	'mass'
fīf	[fi:f]	'five'	fīfel	[fi:vɛl]	'sea-monster'
bæð	[bæθ]	'bath'	baðu	[bɑðu]	'baths'
hūs	[hu:s]	'house'	māse	[mɑ:zɛ]	'titmouse'
fīfta	[fi:ftɑ]	'fifth'	ofnas	[ɔvnɑs]	'ovens'
fæst	[fæst]	'fast'	māðmas	[mɑ:ðmɑs]	'treasures'
hæpse	[hæpsɛ]	'hasp'	fæsl	[fæzl]	'progeny'

Which of the six sounds occur at the beginning of a word? _____

Which sounds occur at the end of a word? _____

Which sounds occur next to (either before or after) a voiceless consonant? _____

_____

Which sounds occur doubled? _____

Which sounds occur singly between vowels? _____

Which sounds occur singly between a vowel and a voiced consonant? _____

_____

Combine the answers to the preceding questions to make a concise rule which will state the environments of [v], [ð], [z] and of [f], [θ], [s]. _____

_____

_____

2. [g] / [ʒ]

gōd	[go:d]	'good'	sungen	[sʊŋgɛn]	'sung'
gēs	[ge:s]	'geese'	lagu	[lɑʒu]	'law'
grund	[grʊnd]	'ground'	āgan	[ɑ:ʒɑn]	'to own'
glæd	[glæd]	'glad'	swelgan	[swɛlʒɑn]	'to swallow'
gnorn	[gnɔrn]	'sad'	fuglas	[fuʒlɑs]	'fowls'
frogga	[frɔgga]	'frog'	sorg	[sɔrʒ]	'sorrow'
song	[sɔŋg]	'song'	bōg	[bo:ʒ]	'bough'

Which of the two sounds occurs initially? _____

Which sound occurs doubled? _____

Which sound occurs after *n* [ŋ]? _____

Which sound occurs between vowels? _____

Which sound occurs between consonant and vowel or between vowel and consonant?

_____

Which sound occurs finally? _____

Make a concise rule which will state the environments of [g] and of [ʒ]. _____

_____

_____

3. [h] / [x]

hund	[hʊnd]	'hound'	riht	[rɪxt]	'right'
hilt	[hɪlt]	'hilt'	brōhte	[bro:xtɛ]	'brought'
hāl	[hɑ:l]	'whole'	nīhsta	[ni:xstɑ]	'next'
hræfn	[hrævn]	'raven'	hlyhhan	[hlyxxɑn]	'to laugh'
hnutu	[hnʊtʊ]	'nut'	wealh	[wæəlx]	'foreigner'
hlāf	[hlɑ:f]	'loaf'	rūh	[ru:x]	'rough'
hwēol	[hwe:əl]	'wheel'	scōh	[šo:x]	'shoe'

Which of the two sounds occurs initially? _____

Which sound occurs between a vowel and a consonant? _____

Which sound occurs doubled? _____

Which sound occurs finally? _____

Make a concise rule which will state the environments of [h] and of [x]. _____

_____

_____

4. [n] / [ŋ]

singan	[sɪŋgɑn]	'sing'	mannes	[mɑnnɛs]	'man's'
drincan	[drɪŋkɑn]	'drink'	mōna	[mo:nɑ]	'moon'
gang	[gɑŋg]	'journey'	font	[fɔnt]	'font'
þanc	[θɑŋk]	'thought'	ende	[ɛndɛ]	'end'
nōn	[no:n]	'noon'	cylna	[kylnɑ]	'kilns'

Which of the two sounds occurs before [g]? _____

Which of the sounds occurs before [k]? _____

Which of the sounds occurs initially? _____

Which of the sounds occurs finally? _____

Which of the sounds occurs doubled? _____

Which of the sounds occurs between vowels? _____

Which of the sounds occurs between vowel and consonant or between consonant and vowel? _____ _____ _____

Make a concise rule which will state the environments of [n] and of [ŋ]. _____

_____

_____

5. Supply the missing sounds in these phonetic transcriptions. For some words you must add two sounds.

fæt	[____æt]	'vat'	weorð	[wɛər____]	'worth'
hæfde	[hæ____dɛ]	'had'	weorðan	[wɛər____an]	'to become'
hafoc	[hɑ____ək]	'hawk'	þorn	[____ɔrn]	'thorn'
of	[ə____]	'of'	oþþe	[ə____ɛ]	'or'
cræft	[kræ____t]	'skill'	wrīþan	[wri:____an]	'to twist'
pyffan	[py____an]	'to puff'	rīsan	[ri:____an]	'rise'

ēaster	[æ:ə＿＿＿tɛr]	'Easter'	hors	[＿＿＿ɔrs]	'horse'
missan	[mɪ＿＿＿ɑn]	'to miss'	lēoht	[le:ə＿＿＿t]	'light'
miltsian	[mɪlt＿＿＿ɪɑn]	'to pity'	feoh	[fɛə＿＿＿]	'cattle'
sylf	[＿＿＿ylf]	'self'	hnipian	[＿＿＿nɪpɪɑn]	'to droop'
rās	[rɑ:＿＿＿]	'arose'	beorht	[bɛɔr＿＿＿t]	'bright'
bōsm	[bo:＿＿＿m]	'bosom'	finger	[fɪ＿＿＿ɛr]	'finger'
plōg	[plo:＿＿＿]	'plow'	findan	[fɪ＿＿＿dɑn]	'to find
gold	[＿＿＿əld]	'gold'	sanc	[sɑ＿＿＿]	'sank'
boga	[bɔ＿＿＿ɑ]	'bow'	sunu	[su＿＿＿u]	'son'
glēo	[＿＿＿le:ə]	'mirth'	sunne	[su＿＿＿ɛ]	'sun'
burg	[bur＿＿＿]	'city'	lang	[lɑ＿＿＿]	'long'
belgan	[bɛl＿＿＿ɑn]	'to be angry'	scruncen	[šru＿＿＿ɛn]	'shrunken'

5.7 OLD ENGLISH SPELLING AND PRONUNCIATION

A perfectly alphabetical writing system has a distinct symbol for each of its consonant and vowel phonemes; each distinctive sound has only one symbol and each symbol represents only one such sound. Old English comes much closer to that ideal than does Modern English, but even Old English had some irrationalities in its spelling. The most troublesome of these are the letters *c* and *g*. Review in *Origins and Development*, pages 109–10, the discussion of the sounds represented by these two spellings; then examine the following words. Each group of words illustrates a typical position of the letters *c* and *g*; if the prehistoric form of the word is relevant, it is given as a reconstruction with the usual asterisk. For each group of words, decide whether *c* represents [k] or [č] and whether *g* represents [g] or [ʒ] or [j]. Write the appropriate phonetic symbol within the brackets.

c = [   ]
clif 'cliff'
cniht 'boy'
crisp 'curly'
cweorn 'mill'

g = [   ]
glæs 'glass'
gnorn 'sad'
grimm 'fierce'

c = [   ]
catt 'cat'
cōl 'cool'
cū 'cow'

g = [   ]
gāt 'goat'
gold 'gold'
guma 'man'

c = [   ]
ceaf 'chaff'
ceorl 'churl'
cīdan 'chide'
cyrran 'to turn'

g = [   ]
geard 'yard'
gē 'ye'
geolu 'yellow'
gimm 'gem'
gylp 'boast'

c = [   ]
cēlan 'to cool' < *kōljan
cȳ 'kine' < *kūiz

g = [   ]
gǣt 'goats' < *gātiz
gylden 'golden' < *guldīn

109

c = [   ]
āc 'oak'
brōc 'breech'
munuc 'monk'

g = [   ]
plōg 'plow'
burg 'city'

c = [   ]
pic 'pitch'
līc 'body'

g = [   ]
īg 'island'
bodig 'body'
þegnas 'thanes'
sægde 'said'

c = [   ]
ǣc 'oaks' <*ākiz
brēc 'breeches' <*brōkiz

g = [   ]
swēg 'sound' <*swōgijaz
byrg 'cities' <*burgiz

c = [   ]
nacod 'naked'
sūcan 'to suck'
bacan 'to bake'

g = [   ]
sagu 'saying'
swōgan 'to sound'
āgan 'to own'

c = [   ]
micel 'much'
bēce 'beech'
ræced 'building'

g = [   ]
sige 'victory'
drȳge 'dry'
segel 'sail'
nægel 'nail'

State a general rule for determining when c and g represent the velar sounds [k], [g], [ɣ] and when they represent the palatal sounds [č], [j]. _____

_____

_____

_____

_____

5.8 OLD ENGLISH TRANSCRIPTION

Write these Old English words in phonetic transcription:

fyxen 'vixen' _____
wīf 'woman' _____
wīfes 'woman's' _____
þēofas 'thieves' _____
bæð 'bath' _____
baðian 'to bathe' _____
sǣs 'seas' _____
nosu 'nose' _____
lȳs 'lice' _____
lūsa 'of lice' _____
hām 'home' _____

hring 'ring' _____
hlynsian 'to resound' _____
āhte 'owned' _____
eoh 'horse' _____
scēap 'sheep' _____
sceattas 'coins' _____
asce 'ash' _____
sceaft 'shaft' _____
brycg 'bridge' _____
oxa 'ox' _____
betwix 'between' _____

bazere	'baptist'	_____	dæges	'day's'	_____
weorc	'work'	_____	strang	'strong'	_____
cēosan	'choose'	_____	glōm	'darkness'	_____
cirice	'church'	_____	wōgan	'to woo'	_____
stycce	'piece'	_____	gnagan	'to gnaw'	_____
cuman	'to come'	_____	gīsl	'hostage'	_____
cycene	'kitchen'	_____	gyldan	'to yield'	_____
cēpan	'to keep'	_____	gyldan	'to gild'	_____
frignan	'to ask'	_____	genog	'enough'	_____
dæg	'day'	_____	hālig	'holy'	_____
dagas	'days'	_____	hālga	'saint'	_____

5.9 MUTATION OR UMLAUT

Mutation or umlaut is a change in the quality of a vowel resulting from its assimilation to a neighboring sound. The change took place in Old English during the prehistoric period.

1. The following words and their reconstructed sources will illustrate some mutations. Each historical form shows the result of umlaut in its first syllable.

lengest <*langista 'longest'   trymman <*trumjan 'to fortify'

gēs <*gōsiz 'geese'   yfel <*uƀil 'evil' (cf. Goth. ubil)

bēc <*bōki 'book (dat.)'   færþ <*fariþ 'goes' (cf. Goth. fariþ)

strengþu <*strangiþu 'strength'   synn <*sunjō 'sin'

fēdan <*fōdjan 'to feed' (cf. Goth. fōdjan)   hell <*hælju 'hell' (older haljō, cf. Goth. halja)

What sounds caused mutation? _____

_____

Why is the cause of mutation not clear in recorded Old English? _____

_____

2. In the following examples, the first word in each pair has a mutated vowel, and the second word is a related form with unmutated vowel.

ȳtemest 'outmost' / ūte 'outside'   secgan 'to say' / sægde 'said'

dehter 'daughter (dat.)' / dohtor 'daughter (nom.)'   frȳnd 'friends' / frēond 'friend'

gǣt 'goats' / gāt 'goat'   wyrþe 'worthy' / weorþ 'worth'

bæcþ 'bakes' / bacan 'to bake'   nȳr 'nearer' / nēah 'near'

hilpþ 'helps' / helpan 'to help'   yldra 'elder' / eald 'old'

All the vowels except the high front *i, ī, y, ȳ* and the front long *ē, ǣ* are subject to mutation. Short *a* has two mutations, depending on whether or not it is followed by a nasal consonant. Indicate the mutation of each of the following vowels.

FRONT VOWELS	DIPHTHONGS	BACK VOWELS
		ŭ _____
ĕ _____	ĕo _____	ð _____
		ă+n _____
ǣ _____	ĕa _____	ă _____

After you have compared these changes with the articulation chart of Old English vowels, describe the general direction in which vowels move when they are mutated. _____

3. In the following pairs, the first word has a mutated vowel omitted from its spelling, and the second word is a related form without mutation. Supply the missing vowel.

d_____man 'to judge' / dōm 'judgment'   m_____lt 'melts' / meltan 'to melt'
t_____nan 'to close' / tūn 'enclosure'   w_____tt 'goes' / wadan 'to go'
f_____nd 'enemies' / fēond 'enemy'   þ_____ccan 'to cover' / þæc 'thatch'
f_____llan 'to fill' / full 'full'   m_____rgen 'morning' / morgen 'morning'
h_____lan 'to heal' / hāl 'whole'   c_____pan 'to buy' / cēap 'price'
sc_____rtest 'shortest' / sceort 'short'   h_____rdan 'to harden' / heard 'hard'
m_____tan 'to meet' / mōt 'meeting'   m_____s 'mice' / mūs 'mouse'
str_____ngest 'strongest' / strang 'strong'   m_____st 'most' / mā 'more'

5.10 GRAMMATICAL GENDER

Examine the following phrases:

MASCULINE	FEMININE	NEUTER
se wīfmann 'the woman'	sēo hlæfdige 'the lady'	þæt wīf 'the woman'
se mete 'the food'	sēo reord 'the meal'	þæt ealu 'the ale'
se mōna 'the moon'	sēo sunne 'the sun'	þæt tungol 'the star'
se grund 'the ground'	sēo eorðe 'the earth'	þæt land 'the land'
se æppel 'the apple'	sēo bēan 'the bean'	þæt æg 'the egg'
se earm 'the arm'	sēo eaxl 'the shoulder'	þæt lim 'the limb'
þes wīfmann 'this woman'	þēos hlæfdige 'this lady'	þis wīf 'this woman'
þes grund	þēos eorðe	þis land
sum æppel 'a certain apple'	sumu bēan 'a certain bean'	sum æg 'a certain egg'
sum earm	sumu eaxl	sum lim
(Ic seah) sumne wīfmann	(Ic seah) sume hlæfdigan	(Ic seah) sum wīf
'(I saw) a certain woman'	'(I saw) a certain lady'	'(I saw) a certain woman'
(Ic seah) sumne æppel	(Ic seah) sume bēane	(Ic seah) sum æg
se mōna . . . hē is gōd	sēo sunne . . . hēo is gōd	þæt tungol . . . hit is gōd
'the moon . . . it is good'	'the sun . . . it is good'	'the star . . . it is good'
se mete . . . hē is gōd	sēo reord . . . hēo is gōd	þæt ealu . . . hit is gōd
se wīfmann . . . hēo is gōd	sēo hlæfdige . . . hēo is gōd	þæt wīf . . . hēo is gōd

1. Which of the following is the best indicator of the grammatical gender of an Old English noun? Which is the poorest indicator?

    meaning (sexual gender)
    the ending of the noun
    concord of adjective and noun
    concord of pronoun and noun

2. What is the gender of each of the italicized nouns?

sēo *ceaster* 'the city' _____

þæt *scip* 'the ship' _____

Ic seah sum *fæt* 'I saw a certain vessel' _____

se *tūn* 'the village' _____

sumu *lūs* 'a certain louse' _____

þes *blōstm* 'this blossom' _____

þis *lēaf* 'this leaf' _____

þēos *costung* 'this temptation' _____

Ic seah sume *bollan* 'I saw a certain bowl' _____

Ic seah sumne *disc* 'I saw a certain dish' _____

3. Translate these phrases into Old English:

the blossom _____

this moon _____

this ship _____

this sun _____

a certain meal _____

I saw a certain star. _____

I saw a certain arm. _____

4. What is the basis for determining the "gender" of a noun in Modern English, and how many "genders" do we have? How would you explain the gender relationship between noun and pronoun in these sentences?

"That's a lovely baby. What's its name?"

"You have a visitor in the lounge." "Who is it?"

"Somebody telephoned you." "What did they want?"

"I saw his new boat. She's a beauty."

"My car's nearly out of gas—fill 'er up."

5.11 INFLECTION OF NOUNS

Write the declension of these Old English nouns:

	a-DECLENSION, MASCULINE	*a*-DECLENSION, NEUTER	*ō*-DECLENSION, FEMININE
	grund 'ground' (like *hund*)	*gēar* 'year' (like *dēor*)	*talu* 'tale' (like *lufu*)
sing. nom.	_____	_____	_____
acc.	_____	_____	_____
gen.	_____	_____	_____
dat.	_____	_____	_____
plur. nom.	_____	_____	_____
acc.	_____	_____	_____
gen.	_____	_____	_____
dat.	_____	_____	_____

	n-DECLENSION, MASCULINE	*n*-DECLENSION, FEMININE	*u*-DECLENSION, MASCULINE
	nama 'name' (like *oxa*)	*sunne* 'sun' (like *belle*)	*wudu* 'wood' (like *sunu*)
sing. nom.	_____	_____	_____
acc.	_____	_____	_____
gen.	_____	_____	_____
dat.	_____	_____	_____
plur. nom.	_____	_____	_____
acc.	_____	_____	_____
gen.	_____	_____	_____
dat.	_____	_____	_____

	ATHEMATIC DECLENSION, MASCULINE	ATHEMATIC DECLENSION, FEMININE	*r*-DECLENSION, NEUTER
	fēond 'fiend, foe' (like *fōt*, but with mutation of *ēo* to *ȳ*)	*bōc* 'book' (like *brōc*)	*lamb* 'lamb' (sing. like *dēor*, pl. has -*r*- in all forms)
sing. nom.	_____	_____	_____
acc.	_____	_____	_____
gen.	_____	_____	_____
dat.	_____	_____	_____
plur. nom.	_____	_____	_____
acc.	_____	_____	_____
gen.	_____	_____	_____
dat.	_____	_____	_____

5.12 INFLECTION OF DEMONSTRATIVES AND ADJECTIVES

Write the declension of these phrases:

	se tila hlāford 'the good lord' (like *se dola cyning*)	*þæt tile sweord* 'the good sword' (like *þæt dole bearn*)	*sēo tile reord* 'the good meal' (like *sēo dole ides*)
sing. nom.	_____	_____	_____
acc.	_____	_____	_____
gen.	_____	_____	_____
dat.	_____	_____	_____
ins.	_____	_____	_____
plur. nom.	_____	_____	_____
acc.	_____	_____	_____
gen.	_____	_____	_____
dat.	_____	_____	_____

	til hlāford	*til sweord*	*tilu reord*
sing. nom.	_____	_____	_____
acc.	_____	_____	_____
gen.	_____	_____	_____
dat.	_____	_____	_____
ins.	_____	_____	_____
plur. nom.	_____	_____	_____
acc.	_____	_____	_____
gen.	_____	_____	_____
dat.	_____	_____	_____

5.13 *MODERN SURVIVALS OF OLD ENGLISH INFLECTION*

Some Old English inflectional endings have survived into Modern English and have actually increased in importance, that is, in the number of words to which they are added. Other inflections still survive, but only in petrified forms; they survive as dead museum pieces which illustrate earlier living endings. Each italicized word in the phrases below contains a modern survival of an Old English inflection. Match the modern forms with the Old English inflections listed on the right.

NOUNS

_____ The *boats* were floating by the dock.

_____ He found a *raven's* nest.

_____ They took a four-*day* trip.

_____ The *oxen* follow the plow.

_____ The *dormice* are hunting for food.

_____ He counted over eight *hundred*.

_____ The *deer* were plentiful.

_____ The *sheep* are in the pasture.

_____ These *kind* are oak trees.

_____ It *seldom* rains.

_____ The feast of the Annunciation is called *Lady* Day.

_____ Honeybun is five *foot* tall.

_____ There is hardly a man *alive*.

A. nominative-accusative plural ending *-as*

B. nominative-accusative plural ending *-an*

C. nominative-accusative plural ending *-ru*

D. nominative-accusative plural with mutation of the stem vowel

E. nominative-accusative plural identical in form with nominative-accusative singular

F. genitive singular ending *-es*

G. genitive singular without *-s*

H. genitive plural ending *-a*

I. dative singular ending *-e*

J. dative plural ending *-um*

(The next four italicized words have double inflection; each preserves two Old English inflectional changes. Identify both.)

_____ _____ a herd of beeves, fair oxen, and fair *kine*

_____ _____ They sewed fig leaves together, and made themselves *breeches*.

_____ _____ Jacob begat Judah and his *brethren*.

_____ _____ Suffer the little *children* to come unto me.

115

_____	a *colder* day	A. adverb formed with the suffix *-e*
_____	the *narrowest* margin	B. genitive singular used adverbially
_____	an *elder* son	C. adverb comparative ending *-or*
_____	the *eldest* daughter	D. adjective comparative ending *-ra*
_____	the *foremost* advocate	E. adjective superlative ending *-est* (from earlier *-ist*) with mutation
_____	*Mondays* they come home early.	F. adjective comparative ending *-ra* (from earlier *-ira*) with mutation
_____	And feed *deep*, deep upon her peerless eyes.	G. adjective superlative ending *-ost*
_____	He drives *slower* in town.	H. adjective double superlative ending
_____	He slept *days*.	
_____	She has a lot to do *besides*.	
_____	They called *once*.	
_____	Why livest thou, dead dog, a *lenger* day? (Spenser)	

5.14 *PRONOUNS*

For each of the Modern English pronouns, give the Old English word from which it developed, tell the case of the Old English source pronoun, and note whether the phonological development of the stressed vowel has been regular or irregular judging by what you discovered in exercise 5.4.

MODERN ENGLISH PRONOUN	OLD ENGLISH SOURCE	CASE OF OLD ENGLISH PRONOUN	PHONOLOGICAL DEVELOPMENT
I	ic	nominative	irregular
me			
mine			
we			
us			
our			
thou			
thee			
thine			
ye			
you			
your			
he			

MODERN ENGLISH PRONOUN	OLD ENGLISH SOURCE	CASE OF OLD ENGLISH PRONOUN	PHONOLOGICAL DEVELOPMENT
him			
his			
she			
her			
it			
(you tell) 'em			
who			
whom			
whose			
what			
why (adv.)			
that			
this			
those			

5.15   WEAK AND STRONG VERBS

1. The following verbs are cited in both their infinitive and their preterit singular forms. Mark weak verbs *W* and strong verbs *S*.

   _____ brengan–brōhte 'bring'   _____ hyngran–hyngrede 'hunger'
   _____ gifan–geaf 'give'   _____ lōcian–lōcode 'look'
   _____ habban–hæfde 'have'   _____ scīnan–scān 'shine'
   _____ hȳran–hȳrde 'hear'   _____ steppan–stōp 'step'
   _____ hōn–hēng 'hang'   _____ tæcen–tāhte 'teach'

2. Explain the difference in meaning and form between the modern verbs *drink* (pret. *drank*) and *drench* (pret. *drenched*). Other similar pairs are *fall* (*fell*) and *fell* (*felled*), *lie* (*lay*) and *lay* (*laid*), *sit* (*sat*) and *set* (*set*). _____
   _____
   _____
   _____

3. Explain why there is a difference between the stem vowel of the infinitive and that of the preterit in these verbs: *sēcan–sōhte* 'seek–sought,' *bycgan–bohte* 'buy–bought,' *þencan–þōhte* 'think–thought.' _____
   _____
   _____

4. Explain why there is a difference between the stem vowel of the infinitive and that of the preterit in these verbs: *rīdan–rād* 'ride–rode,' *teran–tær* 'tear–tore,' *frēosan–frēas* 'freeze–froze.' _____

_____

_____

_____

_____

5.16 *THE SEVEN CLASSES OF STRONG VERBS*

Strong verbs are characterized by a lack of the dental suffix in their preterit and by an internal vowel change (gradation or ablaut) between their present and preterit forms.

1. Strong verbs are conventionally divided into seven classes on the basis of what vowels occur in each of their four principal parts. List here the typical vowel series found in each of the classes.

CLASS	INFINITIVE	PRETERIT SINGULAR	PRETERIT PLURAL	PAST PARTICIPLE
I	_____	_____	_____	_____
II	_____ or _____	_____	_____	_____
III	_____	_____	_____	_____
	_____ or _____	_____	_____	_____
IV	_____	_____	_____	_____
V	_____	_____	_____	_____
	_____	_____	_____	_____
VI	_____	_____	_____	_____
VII		_____	_____	
		_____	_____	

2. Identify by number the class of each of these strong verbs. All four principal parts are given.

_____	bacan	bōc	bōcon	bacen	'bake'
_____	bēatan	bēot	bēoton	bēaten	'beat'
_____	beran	bær	bǣron	boren	'bear'
_____	bītan	bāt	biton	biten	'bite'
_____	blandan	blēnd	blēndon	blanden	'blend'
_____	blāwan	blēow	blēowon	blāwen	'blow'
_____	brēowan	brēaw	bruwon	browen	'brew'
_____	ceorfan	cearf	curfon	corfen	'carve'
_____	clēofan	clēaf	clufon	clofen	'cleave'
_____	climban	clamb	clumbon	clumben	'climb'
_____	cwelan	cwæl	cwǣlon	cwolen	'die' (cf. *quell*)
_____	cweðan	cwæð	cwǣdon	cweden	'say, quoth'
_____	delfan	dealf	dulfon	dolfen	'delve'
_____	drēosan	drēas	druron	droren	'fall' (cf. *dross* and *dreary*)
_____	drincan	dranc	druncon	druncen	'drink'

3. It is usually possible to recognize the class to which a strong verb belongs from its infinitive alone. Unless there are special irregularities, it is then possible to predict the other principal

parts, for all classes except class VII. All of the following verbs belong to classes I through VI and are regular. Write their remaining principal parts.

INFINITIVE	PRETERIT SINGULAR	PRETERIT PLURAL	PAST PARTICIPLE
begytan 'get'			
bīdan 'bide'			
bindan 'bind'			
būgan 'bow'			
cnedan 'knead'			
feohtan 'fight'			
flēotan 'float'			
glīdan 'glide'			
hrēowan 'rue'			
meltan 'melt'			
scafan 'shave'			
scēotan 'shoot'			
smēocan 'smoke'			
stelan 'steal'			
steorfan 'die'			
swellan 'swell'			
swimman 'swim'			
wascan 'wash'			
windan 'wind'			
wrecan 'wreak'			

5.17 INFLECTION OF VERBS

Hǣlan 'to heal' and *helpan* 'to help' are typical verbs, weak and strong respectively. Conjugate them in full. The imperative singular of both verbs is without ending; the imperative plural ends in *-að*.

PRINCIPAL PARTS	hǣlan, hǣlde, hǣled		helpan, healp, hulpon, holpen	
	PRESENT	PRETERIT	PRESENT	PRETERIT
INDICATIVE				
ic				
þū				
hē				
wē, gē, hī				
SUBJUNCTIVE				
ic, þū, hē				
wē, gē, hī				
IMPERATIVE				
þū				
gē				
PARTICIPLE				

119

The following passages illustrate Old English. The dialect of all the selections is basically West Saxon. You may notice some spelling variations and some differences in grammatical forms between these passages and the language described in *Origins and Development*. Such differences may be due to slight dialect variation, time lapse, or simply the predilections of different writers. In keeping with the practice of Old English scribes, macrons have been omitted.

The glosses which accompany the selections are generally word-for-word renderings of the Old English. They are inadequate as translations, but will help in reading the original.

Compare the passages with the description of Old English in *Origins and Development*. Note the peculiar features of Old English spelling, inflections, syntax, and vocabulary.

THE GOOD SAMARITAN

This version of the parable of the good samaritan (Luke x. 30–36) is from a late West Saxon translation of the Gospels.[3]

Sum   man ferde fram Hierusalem to Hiericho, and becom on   ða sceaðan; þa   hine
A certain man went from Jerusalem   to Jericho,   and came   upon the thieves;   they him

bereafodon and tintregodon hine, and forleton hine samcucene. Þa   gebyrode hit þæt
robbed   and tormented   him, and left   him half-alive. Then happened it that

sum   sacerd ferde on þam ylcan wege, and þa   he þæt geseah, he hine forbeah. And
a certain priest went on the same way, and when he that saw   he him passed by. And

eall swa se   diacon, þa   he wæs wið þa stowe and þæt geseah, he hyne eac forbeah. Ða
also   this deacon when he was at the place and that saw   he him also passed by. Then

ferde sum   Samaritanisc man wið hine; þa   he hine geseah, þa   wearð he mid
went a certain Samaritan   man by him; when he him saw   then became he with

mildheortnesse ofer hine astyred. Þa   genealæhte he, and wrað his wunda and on ageat
compassion   for him stirred up. Then drew near he, and bound his wounds and poured on

ele and win, and hine on hys nyten sette, and gelædde on his læcehus and hine lacnode; and
oil and wine, and him on his beast set,   and led   to his hospital and him medicated; and

brohte oðrum   dæge twegen penegas, and sealde þam læce,   and þus cwæð,
brought on the second day two   pennies, and gave to the doctor, and thus said,

"Begym   hys, and swa hwæt swa þu   mare to   gedest, þonne ic cume, ic hit forgylde
"Take care of him and whatsoever   thou more besides dost,   when I come, I it will repay

þe." Hwylc þara þreora þyncð þe   þæt sy   þæs   mæg   þe on   ða
thee." Which of the three   seems to thee that may be that one's neighbor who among the

sceaðan befeoll?
thieves fell?

THE VOYAGES OF OHTHERE AND WULFSTAN

King Alfred, desiring to promote learning in his kingdom after he had stemmed the Danish invasion, began the translation of several Latin works. One of these was Orosius's history of the world, which opens with a geographical survey of Asia, Africa, and Europe. Alfred

[3] James W. Bright, *The Gospel of Saint Luke in Anglo-Saxon* (Oxford, 1893).

supplemented the geography with an account of the travels of two Germanic sailors, Ohthere and Wulfstan, from which the following extracts are taken.[4]

The first passage describes a voyage made by Ohthere from his home on the northwest coast of Norway around the top of Scandinavia into the White Sea of modern Russia. This voyage was one of many being made by the Vikings. At about the same time other Northmen were settling Iceland and traveling to Greenland. In another hundred years they would arrive on the coast of North America. Ohthere's voyage, taking him into the unknown waters of the Arctic Ocean, was a feat of great daring for a ninth-century sailor.

Ohthere sæde his hlaforde, Ælfrede cyninge, þæt he ealra Norðmonna norþmest bude. He
Ohthere told his lord, Alfred the king, that he of all Northmen northmost dwelt. He

cwæð þæt he bude on þæm lande norþweardum wiþ þa Westsæ.[5] He sæde þeah þæt land
said that he dwelt in the land northward by the West Sea. He said although the land

sie[6] swiþe lang norþ þonan, ac hit is eal weste, buton on feawum stowum
is very long northward thence, yet it is all waste, except that in a few places

styccemælum wiciað Finnas, on huntoðe on wintra, and on sumera on fiscaþe be þære sæ.
here and there encamp Finns, for hunting in winter, and in summer for fishing in the sea.

He sæde þæt he æt sumum cirre wolde fandian hu longe þæt land norþryhte læge, oþþe
He said that he at one time wanted to find how far that land due north lay, or

hwæðer ænig mon be norðan þæm westenne bude. Þa for he norþryhte be þæm
whether any man on the north of the wasteland dwelt. Then went he due north along the

lande; let him ealne weg þæt weste land on ðæt steorbord, and þa widsæ on ðæt
land; he kept all the way the waste land on the starboard, and the open sea on the

bæcbord þrie dagas. Þa wæs he swa feor norþ swa þa hwælhuntan firrest faraþ. Þa
larboard for three days. Then was he as far north as the whale hunters farthest go. Then

for he þagiet norþryhte swa feor swa he meahte on þæm oþrum þrim dagum gesiglan. Þa
went he still due north as far as he might in the next three days sail. Then

beag þæt land þær eastryhte, oþþe seo sæ in on ðæt lond, he nysse hwæðer; buton he
bent the land there due east, or the sea in on the land, he knew not which; but he

wisse ðæt he ðær bad westanwindes and hwon norþan, and siglde ða east
knew that he there awaited a west wind and somewhat from the north, and sailed then east

be lande swa swa he meahte on feower dagum gesiglan. Þa sceolde he ðær bidan
along the land as far as he might in four days sail. Then must he there await

ryhtnorþanwindes, for ðæm þæt land beag þær suþryhte, oþþe seo sæ in on ðæt land, he
a due north wind, because the land bent there due south, or the sea in on the land, he

nysse hwæþer. Þa siglde he þonan suðryhte be lande swa swa he mehte on fif dagum
knew not which. Then sailed he thence due south near land as far as he might in five days

gesiglan. Ða læg þær an micel ea up in on þæt land. Þa cirdon hie up in on ða ea,
sail. Then lay there a great river up into the land. Then turned they up into the river,

---

[4] Henry Sweet, ed., *King Alfred's Orosius* (EETS OS 79; London, 1883).
[5] That is, 'the Norwegian Sea.'
[6] *ie* is an early Old English diphthong, replaced in the classical period by *y* or *i*.

for þæm hie ne dorston forþ bi þære ea siglan for unfriþe, for þæm ðæt land wæs eall
because they did not dare past   the river sail   for hostility, because the land was all

gebun   on oþre   healfe þære eas. Ne mette he ær   nan gebun   land, siþþan he
inhabited on the other side   of the river. Nor had met he before any inhabited land, since   he

from his agnum ham for. Ac him   wæs ealne weg   weste land on þæt steorbord,
from his own   home came. But for him it was all   the way waste land on the starboard,

butan   fiscerum and fugelerum and huntum, and þæt wæron eall Finnas; and him   wæs
except for fishers   and fowlers   and hunters, and they were all Finns; and for him it was

a   widsæ   on ðæt bæcbord.
ever open sea on the larboard.

Wulfstan's voyage carried him through the Baltic Sea to a region he calls Eastland. Wulfstan was not only a traveler but also something of an anthropologist as the following passage about life and death among the Estonians will show.

Þæt Estland is swyðe mycel, and þær bið swyðe manig burh, and on ælcere byrig bið
The Eastland[7] is very   large, and there are very   many towns, and in each   town is

cyningc. And þær bið swyðe mycel hunig and fiscað; and se cyning and þa ricostan men
a king. And there is very   much honey and fishing; and the king   and the richest men

drincað myran meolc, and þa unspedigan and þa þeowan drincað medo. Þær bið swyðe
drink mare's milk, and the poor   and the slaves   drink   mead. There is very

mycel gewinn betweonan him. And ne   bið ðær nænig ealo gebrowen mid Estum,   ac
much strife[8] between   them. And neither is there any   ale brewed   by Estonians, but

þær bið medo genoh. And þær is mid   Estum   ðeaw,   þonne þær bið man dead,
there is mead enough. And there is among Estonians a custom, when   there is a man dead,

þæt he lið inne   unforbærned mid his magum and freondum monað, ge hwilum
that he lies indoors unburned   with his kinsmen and friends   a month, and sometimes

twegen; and þa kyningas, and þa oðre heahðungene men, swa micle lencg swa hi   maran
two;   and the kings,   and the other high-ranking men, as   much longer as   they more

speda habbað, hwilum   healf gear þæt hi   beoð unforbærned, and licgað bufan
wealth have,   sometimes [it is] half a year that they are   unburned,   and lie   above

eorðan on hyra husum. And ealle þa hwile þe þæt lic bið inne, þær sceal beon gedrync
ground in their houses. And all   the while that the body is   within, there must be   carousal

and plega, oð ðone dæg þe hi   hine forbærnað. Þonne þy ylcan dæge þe hi   hine to
and sports, until the day that they him burn.   Then   the same day that they him to

þæm ade beran wyllað, þonne todælað hi   his feoh,   þæt þær to lafe   bið æfter þæm
the pyre will bear,   then   divide   they his property, what there as remnant is   after the

gedrynce and þæm plegan, on fif oððe syx,   hwylum   on ma,   swa swa þæs
carousal and the sports, into five or   six [parts], sometimes into more, as   the

feos   andefn bið.   Alecgað   hit ðonne forhwæga on anre mile þone mæstan dæl
property's amount may be. They place it then   away   one mile (the largest portion)

[7] That is, 'Estonia.'
[8] That is, either 'war' or 'contests'; the word is ambiguous.

fram þæm tune,   þonne oðerne, ðonne þæne þriddan, oþþe hyt eall aled bið on   þære
from the dwelling, then   another, then the third,   until it all is laid out within the

anre mile; and sceall beon se læsta dæl   nyhst þæm tune   ðe se deada man on lið.
one mile; and must be   the least portion nearest the   dwelling that the dead man lies in.

Ðonne sceolon beon gesamnode ealle ða menn ðe swyftoste hors habbað on þæm lande,
Then must   be   gathered   all   the men that swiftest horses have   in the   land,

forhwæga on fif milum oððe on syx milum fram þæm feo.   Þonne ærnað hy   ealle
about   five miles or   six miles from the property. Then run   they all

toweard þæm feo;   ðonne cymeð se man se þæt swiftoste hors hafað to þæm ærestan
toward the property; then   comes the man who the swiftest horse has to the first

dæle   and to þæm mæstan, and swa ælc æfter oðrum, oþ hit bið eall genumen; and se
portion and to the   greatest, and so each after another, until it is all taken;   and he

nimð þone læstan dæl   se nyhst þæm tune   þæt feoh   geærneð. And þonne rideð
takes the least   portion who next to the dwelling the property reaches. And then   rides

ælc hys weges mid ðan feo,   and hyt motan habban eall;   and for ðy   þær
each his way with the property, and it they may keep   entirely; and therefore in that place

beoð þa swiftan hors ungefoge dyre.
are the swiftest horses excessively dear.

THE COMING OF THE ENGLISH

St. Bede describes the coming of the English to Britain in his *Historia Ecclesiastica Gentis Anglorum* (A.D. 731). Although it was written in Latin, the *History* was translated into Old English during the reign of King Alfred. The passage below is taken from that Old English version.[9]

Þa gesomnedon hi   gemot   and þeahtedon and ræddon, hwæt him   to donne
Then gathered   they[10] an assembly and deliberated and counseled, what for them to do

wære,   hwær him   wære   fultum to secanne to gewearnienne and to wiðscufanne
might be, where for them might be help   to be sought to avoid   and to shove back

swa reðre hergunge and swa gelomlicre   þara norðþeoda. And þa   gelicode him
such fiercer raids   and such more frequent ones of the north people. And then it pleased them

eallum mid   heora cyninge, Wyrtgeorn wæs   haten, þæt hi Seaxna   þeode
all   together with their king   (Vortigern he was called) that they the Saxons' people

ofer   þam sælicum dælum him   on fultum gecygdon and geladedon. Þæt cuð   is þæt
beyond the   sea   parts to them in aid   should call and invite.   It   known is that

þæt mid Drihtnes mihte gestihtad wæs, þæt yfell wræc   come   ofer ða wiþcorenan,
that by God's   might arranged was, that evil punishment should come upon the rejected ones,

swa on þam ende þara wisena sweotolice ætywed is.
as in the end of the events clearly   shown is.

[9] Thomas Miller, ed., *The Old English Version of Bede's Ecclesiastical History of the English People* (EETS OS 95; London, 1890).

[10] The Britons.

Ða wæs ymb feower hund wintra and nigon and feowertig fram ures Drihtnes
Then it was about four hundred years and nine and forty after our Lord's

menniscnysse, þæt Martianus casere rice onfeng and VII gear hæfde. Se wæs
incarnation, that Marcian Caesar the kingdom[11] received and seven years held. He was

syxta eac feowertigum fram Agusto þam casere. Ða Angel þeod and Seaxna wæs
the sixth and forty from Augustus the Caesar. The Angle people and the Saxons' was

gelaðod fram þam foresprecenan cyninge, and on Breotone com on þrim myclum scypum;
invited by the foresaid king, and into Britain came in three great ships;

and on eastdæle þyses ealondes eardungstowe onfeng þurh ðæs ylcan cyninges
and in the east part of this island a dwelling place received through the same king's

bebod, þe hi hider gelaðode, þæt hi sceoldan for heora eðle compian and
decree, who them hither invited, that they should for their native land strive and

feohtan. And hi sona compedon wið heora gewinnan, þe hi oft ær
fight. And they immediately fought with their enemies, who them[12] often before

norðan onhergedon; and Seaxan þa sige geslogan. Þa sendan hi ham
from the north had harassed; and the Saxons the victory won. Then sent they home

ærenddracan and heton secgan þysses landes wæstmbærnysse, and Brytta
a messenger and commanded [him] to report this land's fruitfulness, and the Britons'

yrgþo. And hi þa sona hider sendon maran sciphere strengran wighena; and
cowardice. And they then immediately hither sent a larger fleet of stronger warriors; and

wæs unoferswiðendlic weorud, þa hi togædere geþeodde wæron. And him Bryttas
it was an invincible host, when they together joined were. And them the Britons

sealdan and geafan eardungstowe betwih him þæt hi for sibbe and hælo heora
granted and gave a dwelling place among them that they for the peace and safety of their

eðles campodon and wunnon wið heora feondum, and hi him andlyfne and are
native land might fight and struggle with their enemies, and they them sustenance and revenue

forgeafen for heora gewinne. Comon hi of þrim folcum, ðam strangestan Germanie, þæt
allowed for their labor. Came they of three peoples, the strongest of Germany, that

of Seaxum and of Angle and of Geatum. Of Geata fruman syndon Cantware, and
of Saxons and of Angles and of Jutes. Of Jutish origin are Kent-men, and

Wihtsætan; þæt is seo ðeod þe Wiht þæt ealond oneardað. Of Seaxum, þæt is of
Wight-settlers; that is the people that Wight the island inhabit. Of Saxons, that is from

ðam lande þe mon hateð Ealdseaxan, coman Eastseaxan and Suðseaxan and
the land that one calls Old Saxons, come East Saxons and South Saxons and

Westseaxan. And of Engle coman Eastengle and Middelengle and Myrce and eall
West Saxons. And of Angles come East Angles and Middle Angles and Mercians and all

Norðhembra cynn; is þæt land ðe Angulus is nemned, betwyh Geatum and
the Northumbrians' race; [it] is the land that Angeln is named, between Jutes and

11 The Roman Empire.
12 The Britons.

124

Seaxum; is   sæd of   þære tide þe hi   ðanon gewiton oð   to dæge, þæt hit weste
Saxons; [it] is said from the   time that they thence departed until today,   that it   deserted

wunige. Wæron ða ærest heora   latteowas and heretogan twegen gebroðra Hengest and
remains. Were   the first of their leaders   and war-chiefs two   brothers Hengest and

Horsa. Hi   wæron Wihtgylses suna, þæs   fæder wæs Witta haten, þæs   fæder wæs Wihta
Horsa. They   were   Wihtgils' sons, whose father was Witta called, whose father was Wihta

haten, and þæs   Wihta fæder   wæs Woden nemned; of ðæs strynde monigra mægða
called, and of that Wihta the father was Woden named; of that stock   many   tribes'

cyningcynn fruman   lædde. Ne wæs ða   ylding to þon þæt hi   heapmælum coman maran
royal family [its] origin takes. Nor was then delay before   they in droves   came, more

weorod of þam ðeodum, þe we ær   gemynegodon. And þæt folc,   ðe hider com, ongan
bands of those peoples that we before mentioned.   And that people that hither came, began

weaxan and myclian to þan swiðe, þæt hi   wæron on myclum ege   þam   sylfan
to wax and multiply so   much that they were   a great   terror to the very

landbigengan ðe hi   ær   hider laðedon   and cygdon.
natives   that them before hither had invited and called.

Æfter þissum hi   þa   geweredon to sumre   tide wið Pehtum, þa   hi   ær
After this   they then were allied for a certain time with the Picts, whom they before

þurh gefeoht feor   adrifan. And þa wæron Seaxan   secende intingan and
through battle far away had driven. And then were   the Saxons seeking cause   and

towyrde   heora gedales wið Bryttas. Cyðdon   him openlice and sædon, butan
opportunity for their breaking with the Britons. They informed them openly   and said   unless

hi   him maran andlyfne   sealdon, þæt hi   woldan him sylfe   niman and hergian,
they them more sustenance gave,   that they would for themselves take   and plunder

þær hi   hit findan mihton. And sona   ða beotunge dædum   gefyldon: bærndon
where they it find   might. And immediately the threat   with deeds fulfilled: they burned

and hergedon and slogan fram eastsæ   oð westsæ;   and him nænig wiðstod. Ne wæs
and harried   and slew from the east sea to the west sea; and them none withstood. Nor was

ungelic wræcc   þam ðe iu   Chaldeas bærndon Hierusaleme weallas and ða
unlike the vengeance to that when formerly the Chaldees burned   Jerusalem's walls   and the

cynelican getimbro mid fyre fornaman for ðæs Godes folces   synnum.
royal   building with fire destroyed for   God's people's sins.

THE ANGLO-SAXON CHRONICLE

The *Anglo-Saxon Chronicle* was an annual record of important events. The exact date of its origin is unknown, but it was probably first compiled during the reign of King Alfred. Thereafter it was continued at various monasteries so that there are several different versions of the *Chronicle*. The last entry, describing the death of King Stephen and the election of a new Abbot of Peterborough, is for the year 1154. The most remarkable thing about the *Chronicle* is that it was written in English at a time when other historical writings throughout Europe were composed exclusively in Latin. The extracts printed below are all taken from the Peter-borough Chronicle (Bodleian MS. Laud 636).[13]

Brittene igland is ehta hund   mila lang and twa hund   brad, and her sind
[PROLOGUE]   *Britain island is eight hundred miles long and two hundred broad, and here are*

on þis iglande fif geþeode: Englisc and Brytwylsc   and Scyttisc   and Pyhtisc and
in this island five languages: English and British-Welsh[14] and Scottish[15] and Pictish and

Bocleden.   Erest weron bugend   þises landes Brittes; þa coman of Armenia and
book-Latin.[16] First were   inhabitants of this land   Britons; they came from Armenia[17] and

gesætan suðewearde Bryttene ærost . . . .
settled southern   Britain first.

An. CCCC.XLIX. Her   Martianus and Ualentinus onfengon rice   and rixadon VII.
A.D. *449*   *Here[18] Marcian and Valentinian received the kingdom and ruled   7*

winter, and on heora dagum gelaðode Wyrtgeorn Angelcin   hider, and hi þa comon
years, and in their days invited Vortigern English people hither, and they then came

on þrim ceolum hider to Brytene . . . .
in three ships   hither to Britain.

An. D.XCVI. Her Gregorius papa   sende to Brytene Augustinum mid wel manegum
A.D. *596[19]*   *Here Gregory the Pope sent to Britain Augustine with very many*

munucum, þe Godes word Engla   þeoda godspellodon.
monks,   who God's word to English people preached.

An. DCC.LXXXVII. Her . . . comon ærest III. scipu Norðmanna of   Hereðalande, and
A.D. *787* [789][20]   *Here   came first 3 ships of Northmen from Hörthaland, and*

þa se gerefa þær to rad, and hi   wolde drifan to þes cininges tune, þy he nyste
then the reeve there to rode, and them wished to force to the king's manor, for he knew not

hwæt hi wæron, and hine man ofsloh þa. Ðæt wæron þa erestan scipu Deniscra   manna
what they were, and him one slew then. Those were the first ships of Danish men

þe Angelcynnes   land gesohton.
that English people's land sought.

An. DCC.XCIII. Her wæron reðe   forebecna cumene ofer Norðanhymbra land, and þæt
A.D. *793*   *Here were terrible foresigns come over Northumbrians' land, and the*

folc earmlice   bregdon; þæt wæron ormete ligræscas, and wæron geseowene fyrene
people wretchedly terrified; they were intense lightnings and were   seen   fiery

---

[13] Benjamin Thorpe, ed., *The Anglo-Saxon Chronicle, According to the Several Original Authorities* (London, 1861).

[14] The Peterborough Chronicle has *Brittisc* and *Wilsc*; the scribe mistook the compound noun as two words, thus increasing the language names to six. The correct *Brytwylsc* is found in the Worcester Chronicle.

[15] That is, 'Erse.'

[16] That is, 'Latin as a learned tongue.'

[17] An error resulting from a misreading of Bede, who says *fram Armoricano* 'Armorica or Brittany.'

[18] That is, 'now, in this year.'

[19] Augustine left Rome in 596 and arrived in England in 597.

[20] The dates in the *Chronicle* are occasionally mistaken; they are corrected in brackets.

dracan on þam lyfte fleogende. Ðam   tacnum sona   fyligde mycel hunger, and litel
dragons in the air flying.   On the tokens immediately followed great hunger, and a little

æfter þam þæs   ilcan geares on VI Id. Ianr. earmlice   heþenra   manna hergung adiligode
after that in the same year   on January 8   wretchedly the heathen men's harrying destroyed

Godes cyrican in Lindisfarena ee   þurh   reaflac and mansleht . . . .
God's church in Lindisfarne   island[21] through plunder and manslaughter.

An. DCC.XCIIII. Her . . . þa hæðenan on   Norðhymbrum   hergodon, and Ecgferðes
A.D. *794   Here   the heathens among the Northumbrians harried,   and Ecgferth's*

mynster   æt Donemuðe   berefodon . . . .
monastery at Donmouth [Jarrow]   plundered.

An. DCCC.LXV. Her sæt   se hæþene here on Tenet and genam frið wið
A.D. *865   Here camped the heathen army in Thanet and made   peace with*

Cantwarum, and Cantware heom feoh   beheton wið þam friðe, and on þam feohbehate
Kentmen,   and Kentmen them money promised for the peace, and for the   money-promise

se here hine on niht up bestæl, and oferhergode ealle Cent eastewarde.
the army itself at night up stole,   and overran   all   Kent eastward.

An. DCCC.LXXI. Her . . . feng   Ælfred Æþelwulfing . . . to West   Seaxna rice,
A.D. *871   Here   succeeded Alfred Ethelwulf's son   to the West Saxons' kingdom,*

and þæs ymb I. monað gefeaht Ælfred cining   wið   ealne þone here litle   werede
and after that 1 month fought Alfred the king against all   the army with a little force

æt Wiltune, and hine lange on dæg   geflymde,   and þa Deniscan ahton
at Wilton, and it   far   into the day put to flight, and the Danish   owned

wælstowe   geweald . . . .
the slaughter-place's control.[22]

An. DCCC.LXXVIII. Her . . . Ælfred cyning . . . gefeaht wið ealne   here, and hine
A.D. *878   Here   Alfred the king   fought with the whole army, and it*

geflymde,   and him æfter rad oð þet geweorc, and þær sæt   XIIII niht,   and þa
put to flight, and after it   rode to the fortress, and there camped 14   nights, and then

sealde se here him gislas   and myccle aðas, þet hi of   his rice   woldon,   and him
gave   the army him hostages and great   oaths, that they from his kingdom would [go], and him

eac geheton   þet heora cyng fulwihte onfon wolde, and hi   þæt gelaston . . . .
also they promised that their king baptism receive would, and they that did.

An. DCCCC.I. Her gefor   Ælfred cyning, VII Kl. Nouembris, and he heold þet
A.D. *901 [899] Here passed away Alfred the king, October 26,   and he held the*

rice   XXVIII wintra and healf gear . . . .
kingdom 28   winters and a half year.

[21] *Lindisfarena ea* 'Lindisfarne,' lit. 'Lindisfare people's water.'
[22] That is, 'Alfred's small force repelled the Danish army throughout the day, but the Danes finally won the battle.'

An. DCCCC.XCI.   Her   wæs Gypeswic gehergod, and æfter þam swyðe raðe   wæs
A.D. *991*   *Here was Ipswich   harried,   and after that very   quickly was*

Brihtnoð ealdorman   ofslægen æt Mældune, and on þam geare man gerædde þæt man
Byrhtnoth the ealdorman slain   at Maldon,   and in this year one   decided that one

geald   ærest gafol   Deniscum mannum for þam mycclan brogan þe   hi   worhton be
yielded first tribute[23] to Danish men   for the great   terror that they caused   along

þam særiman; þæt wæs ærest X. þusend   punda . . . .
the   sea coast; it   was first   10 thousand pounds.

An. DCCCC.XCIIII.   Her   on þisum geare com Anlaf and Swegen to Lundenbyrig on
A.D. *994*   *Here in this   year   came Olaf and Svein   to London town on*

Natiuitas   Sancte Marie mid IIII and hundnigontigum scipum, and hi   þa on þa burh
the Nativity of St.   Mary with 4   and ninety   ships,   and they then   the town

festlice   feohtende wæron . . . .
continuously attacking were.

Millesimo. XVII.   Her on þisum geare feng   Cnut cyning to eall Angelcynnes
1017   *Here in this   year succeeded Cnut the king to all the English people's*

rice . . . and þa   toforan Kl. Aug. het   se cyng feccan   him Æðelredes lafe
kingdom and then before August 1 commanded the king to be brought him Ethelred's widow

þes   oðres cynges him   to cwene, Ricardes dohtor.
(*this other king's*) *for him as queen (Richard's daughter).*

Millesimo. XLI.   Her forðferde   Hardacnut cyng   æt Lambhyðe on VI. Idus Iun. and
1041 [1042]   Here passed away Harthacnut the king at Lambeth   on June 8,   and

he wæs cyng ofer eall Englaland twa gear buton X. nihtum, and he is bebyrged on ealdan
he was king over all England   two years less   10 nights,   and he is buried   in the old

mynstre on Winceastre mid Cnute cynge   his fæder; and ear þan þe he bebyrged wære, eall
minster at Winchester with Cnut the king his father; and before   he buried   was,   all

folc   geceas Eadward to cynge on Lundene, healde   þa hwile þe   him God
the people chose Edward   as king   at London,   may he rule the while that him God

unne . . . .
grants.

Millesimo. XLII.   Her   wæs Æðward gehalgod   to cyng on Winceastre on Æster dæg mid
1042 [1043]   Here was Edward   consecrated as king at Winchester on Easter day with

mycclum wurðscipe . . . and raðe   þæs   se cyng let   geridan   ealle þa land þe
great   honor   and quickly after that the king caused to be seized all   the lands that

his modor ahte   him to handa,   and nam of   hire eall þæt heo ahte   on golde and on
his mother owned into his own hands, and took from her   all   that she owned in gold   and in

seolfre and on unasecgendlicum þingum forþan heo hit heold to feste wið hine.
silver   and in indescribable   things   because she it held   too firmly from him.

[23] That is, 'it was first decided to pay tribute.'

Millesimo. LXVI. On þissum geare man halgode   þet mynster   æt Westmynstre on
1066   *In this   year they consecrated the monastery at Westminster on*

Cyldamæsse dæg, and se cyng Eadward forðferde   on Twelfta mæsse æfen, and hine mann
Childermas   day, and the king Edward   passed away on Epiphany   eve, and him they

bebyrgede on Twelftan mæssedæg innan þære niwa halgodre   circean on Westmynstre, and
buried   on Epiphany day   within the   newly consecrated church at Westminster, and

Harold eorl   feng   to Englalandes cynerice swa swa se cyng hit him geuðe,   and eac
Harold the earl succeeded to England's   realm   as   the king it him promised, and also

men hine þærto gecuron . . . and þa hwile   com Willelm eorl   upp æt Hestingan, on
men him thereto chose   and meanwhile came William the earl up   at Hastings   on

Sancte Michaeles mæssedæg, and Harold com norðan,   and him wið gefeaht ear þan þe
St.   Michael's massday,   and Harold came from the north, and with him fought before

his here come eall,   and þær he feoll, and his twægen gebroðra, Gyrð and Leofwine, and
his army came entirely, and there he fell, and his two   brothers Gurth and Leofwine, and

Willelm þis land geeode and com to Westmynstre, and Ealdred arcebiscop   hine to cynge
William this land occupied and came to Westminster, and Ealdred the Archbishop him as king

gehalgode . . . .
consecrated.

CÆDMON'S HYMN

The following poem, "Cædmon's Hymn," is the oldest known example of Old English religious poetry. Although Cædmon was an early northern poet, the hymn is given here in a West Saxon version, in keeping with the form of Old English described in *Origins and Development*. Since the position of stress is especially important in Old English poetry, accent marks have been added. The story of Cædmon and his poem can be found in Bede's *Ecclesiastical History of the English People*, 4, xxiv.

Nú   sculon   hérigean   héofonrìces   Wéard,
Now shall [we][24] praise   heaven-kingdom's Guardian,

Métodes méahte   and his módgeþánc,
[the] Creator's might   and his heart-thought,

wéorc   Wúldorfæder: swa he wúndra   gehwǽs,
[the] works [of the] Glory-father: how he [of] wonders [of] each

éce   Drýhten,   ór   onstéalde.
[the] eternal Lord,   [the] beginning established.[25]

He ǽrest sceóp   éorðan   béarnum
He first   shaped   [for] earth's children

héofon to hrófe,   hálig   Scýppend;
heaven as [a] roof,   [the] holy Creator;

[24] That is, 'we are bound to.'
[25] That is, 'how he, the eternal Lord, established the beginning of every wonder.'

þa míddangéard,	mónncỳnnes Wéard,
then [a] middle-dwelling[26]	*mankind's Guardian,*
éce Drýhten,	ǽfter téode
[the] eternal Lord,	*afterwards prepared*
fírum fóldan,	Fréa ǽlmìhtig.
[for the] men [of] earth,	*[the] Lord almighty.*

PARABLES

Translate the following series of parables. Most of the words are easily recognizable or have occurred in the previous selections. The passage, which has been slightly regularized in spelling, is from James W. Bright's edition of *The Gospel of Saint Luke in Anglo-Saxon* (Oxford, 1893). Vowel length is marked.

Ðā sǣde hē him sum bīspell, Sǣgst þu, mæg sē blinda þone blindan lǣdan? hū ne feallaþ hī bēgen on þone pytt?

Nis sē leorning-cniht ofer þone lārēow; ælc bið fulfremed, gif hē is swylce his lārēow.

Hwȳ gesyhst þū þā egle on þīnes brōþor ēagan, and ne gesyhst þone bēam on þīnum ēagan?

And hū miht þū secgan þīnum brēþer, Brōþor, lǣt þæt ic ātēo þā egle of þīnum ēagan, and þū sylf ne gesyhst þone bēam on þīnum āgenum ēagan? Ēalā līcetere, tēoh ǣrest þone bēam of þīnum ēagan, and þonne þū gesyhst þæt ðū ātēo þā egle of þīnes brōðor ēagan.

Nis gōd trēow þe yfelne wæstm dēð; nē nis yfel trēow gōdne wæstm dōnde.

Ælc trēow is be his wæstme oncnāwen; nē hī of þornum fīc-æppla ne gaderiaþ, nē wīn-berian on gorste ne nimað.

Gōd man of gōdum gold-horde his heortan gōd forðbringð; and yfel man of yfelum gold-horde yfel forðbringþ: sōðlīce sē mūð spicð swā sēo heorte þencð.

Hwȳ clypie gē mē Drihten, Drihten, and ne dōð þæt ic ēow secge?

VOCABULARY

bēgen 'both'	*līcetere* 'hypocrite'
nis, contraction of *ne* and *is*	*wæstm* 'fruit'
lārēow 'teacher'	*dōn* 'to do, make, produce'
fulfremman 'to fulfill, perfect'	*fīc* 'fig'
swylce 'as, like'	*berie* 'berry'
egl 'mote'	*niman* 'to take'
(a)tēon 'to draw out'	*clypian* 'to call'
ēalā 'oh'	

[26] That is, 'the earth.'

The Middle English Period
(1100–1500)

6.1 *QUESTIONS FOR REVIEW AND DISCUSSION*

1. Define the following terms:

Norman	vocalization	leveling (merging)
Anglo-Norman	off-glides	inorganic *-e*
elision	lengthening	syncope (syncopation)
unrounding	shortening	analogy (analogical form)
monophthongization (smoothing)	open syllable	verbal noun
diphthongization	closed syllable	

2. Summarize the historical events of the Norman Conquest.

3. What was the chief influence of the Conquest on the English language?

4. Which variety of Middle English became the standard dialect and when did it become the literary standard?

5. Compare the vowel system of Old English with that of Middle English as they are shown in the two vowel charts. What additions, losses, and rearrangements took place between the two periods?

6. Make a similar comparison of the consonant systems of the two periods.

7. Which sound change between Old and Middle English had the most far-reaching effect on the language?

8. What is the chief difference between Old and Middle English grammar?

9. Did word order and function words increase or decrease in importance during the Middle English period?

10. What factors contributed to the loss of grammatical gender in Middle English?

11. How did English acquire a device for indicating plurality independent of case?

12. What grammatical category of number was lost from the Middle English personal pronouns?

13. The traditional seven classes of strong verbs survived in Middle English, but what factors began to disturb their orderly arrangement?

14. What was the origin of the verbal ending *-ing*?

15. What is the chief difference in word order between Middle and Modern English?

16. What caused the decline of French as the language of the governing classes in England?

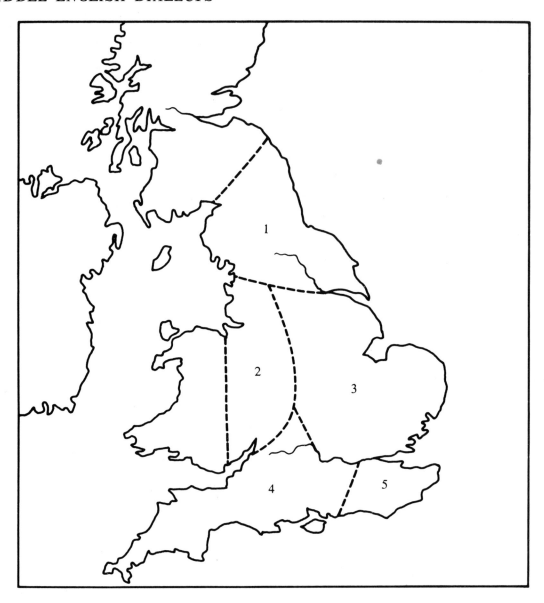

1. List the main Middle English dialect areas according to the numbers on the map.

    1 _____   4 _____
    2 _____   5 _____
    3 _____

2. In the *Reeve's Tale* Chaucer has two clerics—university students—who had come originally from the north of England. Their dialogue is full of northernisms, which Chaucer's London audience doubtlessly found highly comic. In the blanks write the standard London or East Midland forms of the italicized words. You will find it easier to identify the forms if you have read all of Chapter VI in *Origins and Development*.

    _____   "Hou *fares* thy faire doghter and thy wyf?" (4023)

                        "By God, right by the hopur wil I stand,"
    _____   Quod John, "and se howgates [how] the corn *gas* in.
                        Yet saugh I never, by my fader kyn,
    _____   How that the hopur wagges *til* and fra." (4036–39)

_____ "I is as ille a millere as *ar* ye." (4045)

_____ "What, *whilk* way is he geen [gone]?" he gan to crie. (4078)

_____ "A wilde fyr upon *thair* bodyes falle!" (4172)

_____ "I is thyn awen clerk, *swa* have I seel [bliss]!" (4239)

"Myn heed is toty [dizzy] of my swynk [work] to nyght,

_____ That *makes* me that I ga nat aright." (4253–54)

3. From what dialect did each of the following forms enter standard English?

build (OE byldan) _____   kirk (cf. church, OE cyrice) _____

bury [bɛri] (OE byrgan) _____   them (cf. 'em) _____

busy (OE bysig) _____   vat (OE fæt)[1] _____

door (OE duru) _____   vixen (OE fyxen) _____

hale (cf. whole, OE hāl) _____   weevil (OE wifel) _____

4. What were the main differences between London speech and the other dialects of Middle English? _____

_____

_____

_____

_____

_____

6.3 *THE PRONUNCIATION OF MIDDLE ENGLISH: CONSONANTS*

Middle English had the following consonants:[2]

COMMON SPELLING	SOUND	COMMON SPELLING	SOUND	COMMON SPELLING	SOUND
b	[b]	m	[m]	y, ȝ	[j]
d	[d]	n	[n], [ŋ]	z, s	[z]
f	[f]	p	[p]	ch	[č]
g	[g]	r	[r]	gh, ȝ, h	[x]
h	[h]	s, c	[s]	sh, sch	[š]
j (i), g	[j]	t	[t]	th, þ	[θ]
k, c, q	[k]	v (u)	[v]	th, þ	[ð]
l	[l]	w, u	[w]		

Complete the following chart by filling in the symbols listed above to show the place and manner of articulation of the Middle English consonants. To simplify the chart [č] and [j] have been classed as stops. In spite of the customary spelling differences between [h] and [x], they were probably still variants of the same phoneme; put them both in the spot appropriate for [x].

---

[1] Cf. "Wherefore art thou red in thine apparel, and thy garments like him that treadeth in the winefat?" Isa. lxiii. 2 (Authorized Version).

[2] There were a good many other spellings less common than those cited here; for example, [š] could also be spelled *ssh*, *ss*, or *s* in various parts of England. In the writing system, *x* was also used in its modern value [ks]. Do not confuse it with the same letter used as a phonetic symbol.

		LABIAL	DENTAL			VELAR	
			inter-dental	*alveolar*	*aveolo-palatal*	*palatal*	*velar*
STOPS	*voiceless*						
	voiced						
FRICATIVES	*voiceless*						
	voiced						
NASALS							
LIQUIDS	*lateral*						
	retroflex or trill						
SEMIVOWELS							

6.4 THE PRINCIPAL CONSONANTAL CHANGES

In *Origins and Development*, Pyles lists eight consonantal changes which occurred during the Middle English period:

1. loss of [h] before [l], [n], and [r]
2. [ʒ] > [w] after [l] or [r]
3. loss of [w] between consonant and back vowel
4. loss of final [č] in unstressed syllables
5. loss of medial [v]
6. prefix [gə] > [ɪ], (*i-, y-*)
7. Southern voicing of initial [f], [s], and [θ]
8. loss of final [n] in many unstressed syllables

Identify the change which each of these Middle English words illustrates by writing the appropriate number, from 1 through 8, before the word. For many of the words you will find it necessary to compare the Middle English with the corresponding Old English form to determine what change has occurred. You can find the Old English form in the etymology given for the word in any good dictionary. The modern form of the word is given in parentheses whenever it differs from the Middle English spelling.

_____ alsō	_____ laughen (laugh)	_____ sorwe (sorrow)
_____ ēve	_____ lōthely (loathly)	_____ swelwen (swallow)
_____ hō (who)	_____ maide (maid)	_____ thong
_____ I	_____ neyen (neigh)	_____ vāne
_____ icleped (yclept)	_____ ō (a)	_____ ynogh (enough)
_____ lādy	_____ rāven	_____ zinne (sin)
_____ larke (lark)	_____ ring	

The preceding exercise was concerned with eight of the more important consonantal changes of the Middle English period, but there were other changes affecting Middle English consonants. You can discover some of these additional changes by examining the words listed here.
(1) Determine the pre-Middle English form of each word (Old English, Old French, Old Norse).
(2) Describe the consonantal change which seems to have affected each group of words. Each group is intended to illustrate a single consonantal change.

MIDDLE ENGLISH	PRE-MIDDLE ENGLISH	DESCRIPTION OF THE CONSONANTAL CHANGE
A. elle 'ell'	_____	
kill 'kiln'	_____	
mille 'mill'	_____	
B. kindred	_____	
thunder	_____	
jaundice	_____	
spindle	_____	
C. glistnen 'glisten'	_____	
listnen 'listen'	_____	
against	_____	
bihēste 'behest'	_____	
D. hemp	_____	
noumpere 'umpire'	_____	
comfort	_____	
E. strenkth 'strength'	_____	
lenkth 'length'	_____	
F. shambles	_____	
slumbren 'slumber'	_____	
thimble	_____	
empty	_____	
G. lemman 'leman'	_____	
wimman 'woman'	_____	
Lammasse 'Lammas'	_____	
H. wurshipe 'worship'	_____	
Sussex	_____	
Norfolk	_____	
I. best	_____	
laste 'last'	_____	
Wessex	_____	
blosme 'blossom'	_____	
J. answerien 'answer'	_____	
gospelle 'gospel'	_____	
gossib 'gossip'	_____	

135

MIDDLE ENGLISH	PRE-MIDDLE ENGLISH	
K. ēch 'each'	_____	
suche 'such'	_____	
which	_____	
L. coom 'comb'	_____	
dum 'dumb'	_____	
lam 'lamb'	_____	
M. birien 'bury'	_____	
bisy 'busy'	_____	
hōly	_____	
silly	_____	
N. aukward 'awkward'	_____	
craul 'crawl'	_____	
hauk 'hawk'	_____	
O. bird	_____	
thirde 'third'	_____	
bright	_____	
through	_____	
wrighte 'wright'	_____	
P. adder	_____	
apron	_____	
auger	_____	
neute 'newt'	_____	
nones 'nonce'	_____	

The changes illustrated above are typical of some general tendencies which have operated at various times in the history of our language. These tendencies are described by the following six terms. Match the terms with the changes A through P by writing the appropriate letters in the blank before each term.

_____ ARTICULATIVE INTRUSION: the addition of a new sound produced by the speech organs as they move from the position for one sound to that for another or to silence (for example, *once* [wʌns] pronounced as [wʌnts] or [wʌnst]; *film* pronounced [ˈfɪləm]).

_____ PARTIAL ASSIMILATION: a change in pronunciation such that one sound becomes more like a neighboring sound (for example, *have to* pronounced [ˈhæftu]).

_____ COMPLETE ASSIMILATION: a change in pronunciation such that two sounds become identical; one of the two sounds may simply disappear (for example, *cupboard* pronounced [ˈkʌbərd]).

_____ VOCALIZATION: the conversion of a consonant into a vowel or the absorption of a consonant by a neighboring vowel (for example, the regional pronunciation of *fear* as [fɪə] or of *bulb* as [bʌ:b]).

_____ METATHESIS: the inversion of two sounds (for example, *apron* pronounced either [ˈeprən] or [ˈepərn]).

_____ JUNCTURE LOSS OR DISPLACEMENT: a shift in the boundary between syllables so that a sound formerly in one syllable comes to be in another (for example, *at all* pronounced like *a tall*).

Because the Middle English period lasted for some four hundred years and included several strikingly different dialects of our language, no single description of the sounds of Middle English can cover all the varieties of the language which the student may encounter. The treatment of Middle English sounds in this exercise concerns itself with Chaucer's language, since he is the Middle English writer who is most read. In his dialect, these vowels occur:

SPELLING	SOUND	SPELLING	SOUND	SPELLING	SOUND
a	[a][3]	o	[ɔ]	au, aw	[aʊ]
a, aa	[a:]	o, oo	[ɔ:]	ai, ay, ei, ey	[æɪ][4]
e	[ɛ], [ə]	o, oo	[o:]	eu, ew	[ɛʊ]
e, ee	[ɛ:]	u, o	[ʊ]	eu, ew, u	[ɪʊ]
e, ee, ie	[e:]	ou, ow	[u:]	oi, oy	[ɔɪ]
i, y	[ɪ]			ou, ow	[ɔʊ]
i, y	[i:]			oi, oy	[ʊɪ]

Notice that Middle English spelling was a less accurate record of pronunciation than Old English spelling had been. Complete the following charts by filling in the symbols listed above to show the articulation of Middle English vowels.

SIMPLE VOWELS

			FRONT	CENTRAL	BACK
HIGH	long			——	
	short			——	
MID	long	close		——	
		open		——	
	short			——	
LOW	long		——		——
	short		——		——

[3] The exact sound of this vowel is uncertain; it may have been [ɑ] or [æ]. The symbol [a] is used here as a compromise. The same uncertainty exists for the corresponding long vowel.

[4] The exact quality of this diphthong is doubtful; it represents a combination of two older diphthongs, [aɪ] and [ɛɪ]. Many modern Chaucerians pronounce it [æɪ], the symbol used here. There are some similar doubts about the quality of several other diphthongs.

DIPHTHONGS

Classify the diphthongs according to the position of their initial element. The arrows indicate the direction of the second element in the diphthong.

	FRONT	CENTRAL	BACK
HIGH	→	——	←
MID	↗	——	↖ ↑
LOW	↑	↗	——

Complete the following chart to show (a) the phonetic symbols for the Old English sounds from which the Middle English vowel developed, (b) the phonetic symbol for the corresponding Modern English vowel, and (c) the typical spelling of the Modern English development of the vowel. You can get all of this information from the key words.

The complete history of the Middle English vowels is quite complex because it involves many minor sound changes and borrowings between dialects. However, when you have completed this chart, you will have a list of the Middle English vowels with their main sources and future developments.

OLD ENGLISH SOURCES		MIDDLE ENGLISH		MODERN ENGLISH DEVELOPMENT		
key words	(a) phonetic symbol	vowel	key words	key words	(b) phonetic symbol	(c) typical spelling
sacc bæc sceal		[a]	sak bak shal	sack back shall		
talu æcer		[a:]	tale aker	tale acre		
bedd seofon		[ɛ]	bed seven	bed seven		
clǣne[5] dǣl[5] bēam stelan		[ɛ:]	clene deel beem stelen	clean deal beam steal		
gēs slǣp[5] sēoþan		[e:]	gees sleep sethen	geese sleep seethe		

[5] See *Origins and Development*, pp.147–48.

OLD ENGLISH SOURCES		MIDDLE ENGLISH			MODERN ENGLISH DEVELOPMENT	
key words	*(a) phonetic symbol*	*vowel*	*key words*	*key words*	*(b) phonetic symbol*	*(c) typical spelling*
fisc lim hyll cynn		[ɪ]	fish lym hil kyn	fish limb hill kin		
hrīm wīf hȳdan mȳs		[i:]	rim wyf hiden mys	rime wife hide mice		
frogga cocc		[ɔ]	frogge cok	frog cock		
hām bāt wā þrote		[ɔ:]	hoom boot wo throte	home boat woe throat		
gōs mōna gōd		[o:]	goos mone good	goose moon good		
full bucca sunne cuman		[ʊ]	ful bukke sonne comen	full buck sun come		
mūs brū		[u:]	mous brow	mouse brow		
lagu clawu aht		[aʊ]	lawe clawe aught	law claw aught		
hægl dæg segl weg eahta		[æɪ]	hail day seil wey eighte	hail day sail way eight		
lǣwede fēawe cnēow		[ɛʊ]	lewed fewe knew	lewd few knew		
nīwe Tīwesdæg		[ɪu]	newe Tuesdai	new Tuesday		
No OE source; from OF development of Lat. [au]: OF joie < Lat. gaudia OF cloistre < Lat. claustra		[ɔɪ]	joy cloistre	joy cloister		

OLD ENGLISH SOURCES		MIDDLE ENGLISH		MODERN ENGLISH DEVELOPMENT		
key words	(a) *phonetic symbol*	*vowel*	*key words*	*key words*	(b) *phonetic symbol*	(c) *typical spelling*
snāw āgen dāh grōwan boga dohtor brohte		[ɔu]	snow owen dough growen bowe doughter broughte	snow own dough grow bow daughter brought		
No OE source; from OF development of Lat. [u] and [ō]: OF joindre < Lat. jungere OF poison < Lat. pōtio		[ui]	joinen poysen	join poison		

6.7 *THE LENGTHENING AND SHORTENING OF VOWELS*

Vowels were lengthened during the late Old English period or in early Middle English times

1. before certain consonant sequences and
2. in open syllables.

They were shortened

3. in closed syllables before two or more consonants,
4. in unstressed syllables, and
5. in a syllable followed by two unaccented syllables.

Which of the five conditions listed above accounts for the vowel length of the first syllable in each of the following words? Write the appropriate number before the word.

_____ abīden 'abide'	_____ dōre 'door'	_____ pound
_____ āker 'acre'	_____ evere 'ever'	_____ stiropes 'stirrups'
_____ arīsen 'arise'	_____ fedde 'fed'	_____ sutherne 'southern'
_____ asken 'ask'	_____ feeld 'field'	_____ tāle
_____ bēren 'bear'	_____ ground	_____ the
_____ bētel 'beetle'	_____ hōlden 'hold'	_____ today
_____ bēver 'beaver'	_____ hōpe	_____ us
_____ blosme 'blossom'	_____ husbonde 'husband'	_____ wepenes 'weapons'
_____ Christmasse 'Christmas'	_____ kīnde 'kind'	_____ wimmen 'women'
_____ cōld	_____ naddre 'adder'	_____ wōmb

The results of the lengthening and shortening of vowels in Middle English words like *hiden–hidde* or *wīs–wisdom* can still be seen in their Modern English developments, although now the vowels differ primarily in quality rather than in length. For each of the following Modern

English words, which have developed from Middle English forms with long vowels, supply a related word which has developed from a form with a short vowel. For example, *five* might be matched with *fifty*, *fifteen*, or *fifth*.

bathe	_____	dear 'beloved'	_____	lead 'guide'	_____
bleed	_____	deep	_____	mead 'grassland'	_____
break	_____	glaze	_____	shade	_____
clean	_____	goose	_____	shoe	_____
creep	_____	heal	_____	white	_____

6.8 THE LEVELING AND LOSS OF UNSTRESSED VOWELS

Unstressed vowels had a special development, different from that of stressed vowels. In unstressed syllables the following changes occurred:[6]

1. [a], [ɛ], [ɔ], [ʊ] merged as [ə], spelled *e*;
2. final [n], including that which had replaced earlier [m] by analogy, was lost;
3. final [ə] was lost; and
4. nonfinal [ə] in inflectional endings was lost.

Thus Old English *leornodon* '(they) learned' passed through the following stages: [lɛrnədən] (change 1), [lɛrnədə] (change 2), [lɛrnəd] (change 3), [lɛrnd] (change 4), although the spelling usually preserved a silent *e* before the *d*, as it still does in *learned*. Similarly, *locode* '(he) looked' became [lo:kədə] (change 1), [lo:kəd] (change 3), [lo:kt] (change 4). Note that with the loss of nonfinal [ə], the [d] unvoiced after voiceless consonants, but the usual spelling remained *looked*.

Similarly trace the development of each of the following words. If a change is not applicable, write *n/a* in the corresponding blank.

	1.	2.	3.	4.
lufodon '(they) loved'	_____	_____	_____	_____
hopodon '(they) hoped'	_____	_____	_____	_____
clǣnsodon '(they) cleansed'	_____	_____	_____	_____
endoden '(if they) ended'	_____	_____	_____	_____
betācnoden '(if they) betokened'	_____	_____	_____	_____
answarod 'answered (past part.)'	_____	_____	_____	_____
sāwon '(they) saw'	_____	_____	_____	_____
stōdon '(they) stood'	_____	_____	_____	_____
standan 'to stand'	_____	_____	_____	_____
springan 'to spring'	_____	_____	_____	_____
gladosta 'gladest'	_____	_____	_____	_____
strengesta 'strongest'	_____	_____	_____	_____
stapoles 'pillar's'	_____	_____	_____	_____
stapolas 'pillars'	_____	_____	_____	_____
gyrdelas 'girdles'	_____	_____	_____	_____

[6] For a discussion of these changes, including limitations and approximate chronology, see *Origins and Development*, pp. 151–52, 156–57.

6.9 MIDDLE ENGLISH TRANSCRIPTION

Write these Middle English words in phonetic transcription. Unstressed *e* at the end of a word is phonetically [ə]. The modern development is given as a gloss when there is possible ambiguity.

flat	_____	now	_____	ye 'ye'	_____
glad	_____	boot 'boot'	_____	ye 'eye'	_____
nest	_____	boot 'boat'	_____	gyse 'guise'	_____
shin	_____	cook	_____	shoo 'shoe'	_____
top	_____	hoom 'home'	_____	doute 'doubt'	_____
broth	_____	dool 'dole'	_____	wood 'wood'	_____
cuppe	_____	doten 'dote'	_____	wood 'woad'	_____
love	_____	fode 'food'	_____	theme	_____
wolf	_____	strete 'street'	_____	gaude	_____
synne	_____	lene 'lean'	_____	grey	_____
fable	_____	felen 'feel'	_____	main	_____
caas 'case'	_____	dreem 'dream'	_____	rowen 'row'	_____
pipe	_____	wreken 'wreak'	_____	sought	_____
hyden 'hide'	_____	weep	_____	lawe	_____
cloud	_____	sete 'seat'	_____	rein 'rain'	_____

6.10 MIDDLE ENGLISH SPELLING AND PRONUNCIATION

Middle English spelling was less perfectly alphabetical than Old English spelling had been. The letter *o* alone could be used to spell four different vowels—[ə], [ɔ:], [o:], [ʊ]—and as part of a digraph it could help to spell four more—[u:], [ɔʊ], [ɔɪ], [ʊɪ]. Yet Middle English orthography can be pronounced with reasonable accuracy on the basis of four clues:

1. the spelling of the Middle English word,
2. the pronunciation of the modern development (provided the word still exists),
3. the spelling of the modern development (with the same obvious provision), and
4. the etymology of the Middle English word.

The four clues are listed in the order of their usefulness, but to apply them you must have a firm mastery of the information on pages 144–49 of *Origins and Development* and in exercises 6.3 and 6.6. For example, to pronounce the word *boon* as in the line "We stryve as dide the houndes for the boon," we can note first that the *oo* spelling indicates a long vowel, either [ɔ:] or [o:]. The modern development *bone* [bon] indicates by both its sound and its spelling that the Middle English vowel must have been [ɔ:]. Finally, if we happen to know that the Old English source of the word was *bān*, we can be confident that the Middle English was [bɔ:n]. If the reason for these observations is not clear to you, review the discussions mentioned above.

There will, of course, still be much uncertainty. Some words, like *halwes* 'shrines' have not survived into Modern English. Others, like *seeke* 'sick' have survived, but in a different form. Also the diphthongs [ɔɪ] and [ʊɪ] were usually spelled alike in Middle English, and their modern developments are both spelled and pronounced alike; they can be distinguished only by their etymology, which a beginning student is unlikely to know. The same difficulty exists for the diphthongs [ɛʊ] and [ɪʊ]. Nevertheless, a mastery of the pronunciation and spelling correspondences between Middle and Modern English will allow you to read Chaucer's language with a fair degree of accuracy.

1. Write each of these phonetically transcribed words in one possible Middle English spelling:

[parfɪt] 'perfect'	_____	[me:tə]	_____
[ma:t] 'dead'	_____	[mɛ:tə]	_____
[bɛllə]	_____	[fo:l]	_____
[kru:dən]	_____	[grɔ:pən]	_____
[dɔggə]	_____	[wri:ðən]	_____
[rʊdɪ]	_____	[wæɪvən]	_____
[gnɔʊən]	_____	[nɔɪzə]	_____
[θɔʊx]	_____	[pʊɪnt]	_____
[hwɪč]	_____	[hɪu] 'hue'	_____
[knɪxt]	_____	[hɛʊən] 'to hew'	_____

2. An examination of the following passages from the *Canterbury Tales* will make apparent both the uses and the limitations of pronunciation clues. The phonetic transcriptions represent a fairly conservative pronunciation of Middle English; some of the words might have been written differently because there is not complete agreement among scholars about Chaucer's pronunciation.[7]

GENERAL PROLOGUE, ll. 1–27

Whan that Aprille with hise shoures soote	hwan θat ˈa:prɪl wɪθ hɪs ˈšu:rəs ˈso:tə
The droghte of March hath perced to the roote	θə dru:xt ɔf marč haθ ˈpɛ:rsəd to: θə ˈro:tə
And bathed every veyne in swich licour	and ˈba:ðəd ˈɛv(ə)rɪ væɪn ɪn swɪč lɪˈku:r
Of which vertu engendred is the flour;	ɔf hwɪč vɛrˈtɪu ɛnˈǰɛndrəd ɪs θə flu:r
Whan Zephirus eek with his swete breeth	hwan ˈzɛfɪrʊs e:k wɪθ hɪs ˈswe:tə brɛ:θ
Inspired hath in every holt and heeth	ɪnˈspi:rəd haθ ɪn ˈɛv(ə)rɪ hɔlt and hɛ:θ
The tendre croppes, and the yonge sonne	θə ˈtɛndrə ˈkrɔppəs and θə ˈjʊŋgə ˈsʊnnə
Hath in the Ram his half[e] cours yronne,	haθ ɪn θə ram hɪs ˈhalvə ku:rs ɪˈrʊnnə
And smale foweles maken melodye,	and ˈsmalə ˈfu:ləs ˈma:kən ˌmɛləˈdi:ə
That slepen al the nyght with open eye—	θat ˈsle:pən al θə nɪxt wɪθ ˈɔ:pən ˈi:ə
So priketh hem nature in hir corages—	sɔ: ˈprɪkəθ hɛm naˈtɪur ɪn hɪr kuˈra:ǰəs
Thanne longen folk to goon on pilgrimage[s],	θan ˈlɔŋgən fɔlk to: gɔ:n ɔn ˌpɪlgrɪˈma:ǰəs
And Palmeres for to seken straunge strondes,	and ˈpalm(ə)rəs fɔr to: ˈse:kən ˈstraunǰə ˈstrɔndəs
To ferne halwes kowthe in sondry londes	to: ˈfɛrnə ˈhalwəs ku:θ ɪn ˈsʊndrɪ ˈlɔndəs
And specially from every shires ende	and ˈspɛsjallɪ frəm ˈɛv(ə)rɪ ˈši:rəs ˈɛndə
Of Engelond to Caunturbury they wende	ɔf ˈɛŋgələnd to: ˈkauntərbri: θæɪ ˈwɛndə
The hooly blisful martir for to seke	θə ˈhɔ:lɪ ˈblɪsful ˈmartɪr fər to: ˈse:kə
That hem hath holpen whan þat they were seeke.	θat hɛm haθ ˈhɔlpən hwan θat θæɪ wɛ:r ˈse:kə
Bifil that in that seson on a day,	bɪˈfɪl θat ɪn θat ˈsɛ:zun ɔn ə dæɪ
In Southwerk at the Tabard as I lay	ɪn ˈsuðərk at θə ˈtabard as i: læɪ
Redy to wenden on my pilgrymage	ˈrɛ:dɪ to: ˈwɛndən ɔn mi: ˌpɪlgrɪˈma:ǰə
To Caunterbury with ful devout corage,	to: ˈkauntərbri: wɪθ ful dəˈvu:t kuˈra:ǰə
At nyght were come in to that hostelrye	at nɪxt wɛ:r kum ɪn to: θat ˌɔstəlˈri:ə
Wel nyne and twenty in a compaignye	wɛl ni:n and ˈtwɛntɪ ɪn ə ˌkumpæɪˈni:ə
Of sondry folk by aventure y-falle	ɔf ˈsʊndrɪ fɔlk bi: ˌavənˈtɪur ɪˈfallə
In felaweshipe, and pilgrimes were they alle	ɪn ˈfɛlauˌšɪp and ˈpɪlgrɪm(ə)s wɛ:r θæɪ ˈallə
That toward Caunterbury wolden ryde.	θat ˈto:ward ˈkauntərˌburɪ ˈwo:ldən ˈri:də

[7] Unstressed syllables and words are particularly susceptible to changes. For example, final *s* and *th* in unstressed syllables may have been voiced; *th* in unstressed words like *the, that,* and *there* may have been voiced; initial *h* in unstressed words like *him, hem, hir* was probably silent; unstressed words like *I* and *to* probably had short vowels. For the pronunciation of schwa in final syllables, see *Origins and Development*, pp. 156–57.

But first I pray yow, of youre curteisye,	but first i: præi ju: of ju:r ˌkurtæɪˈziːə
That ye narette it nat my vileynye,	θat je: naˈrɛt ɪt nat mi: ˌvɪlæɪˈniːə
Thogh that I pleynly speke in this mateere,	θoux θat i: ˈplæɪnlɪ spɛːk ɪn θɪs maˈteːrə
To telle yow hir wordes and hir cheere,	to: ˈtɛllə ju: hɪr ˈwɔrdəs and hɪr ˈčeːrə
Ne thogh I speke hir wordes proprely.	nə θoux i: spɛːk hɪr ˈwɔrdəs ˈprɔprəˌliː
For this ye knowen al so wel as I,	fər θɪs je: ˈknɔuən al sɔ: wɛl as i:
Who so shal telle a tale after a man,	hwo: sɔ: šal tɛl a ta:l ˈaftər a man
He moote reherce as ny as evere he kan	he: mo:t rəhɛːrs as ni: as ˈɛvər he: kan
Everich a word, if it be in his charge,	ˈɛv(ə)rɪč a wɔrd if ɪt be: ɪn hɪz ˈčarǰə
Al speke he never so rudeliche or large,	al spɛːk he: ˈnɛvər sɔ: ˈrɪudəlɪč ər ˈlarǰə
Or ellis he moot telle his tale untrewe,	ər ˈɛllɪs he: mo:t tɛl hɪs ta:l unˈtrɛuə
Or feyne thyng, or fynde wordes newe.	ər ˈfæɪnə θɪŋg ər ˈfiːndə ˈwɔrdəs nɛuə
He may nat spare, al thogh he were his brother;	he: mæɪ nat spa:r al θoux he: wɛːr hɪs ˈbroːðər
He moot as wel seye o word as another.	he: mo:t as wɛl sæɪ ɔ: wɔrd as aˈnoːðər
Crist spak hym self ful brode in hooly writ,	kri:st spak hɪmˈsɛlf ful brɔ:d ɪn ˈhɔ:lɪ wrɪt
And wel ye woot no vileynye is it.	and wɛl je: wɔ:t nɔ: ˌvɪlæɪˈniː ɪs ɪt
Eek Plato seith, who so kan hym rede,	e:k ˈplaːtɔ ˈsæɪθ ˈhwo: sɔ: kan hɪm ˈreːdə
"The wordes moote be cosyn to the dede."	θə wɔrdəs mo:t be: ˈkuzɪn to: θə ˈdɛːdə

THE WIFE OF BATH'S PROLOGUE, ll. 469–80

But, lord crist! whan that it remembreth me	but lɔ:rd kri:st hwan θat ɪt rəˈmɛmbrəθ me:
Upon my yowthe, and on my jolitee,	uˈpɔn mi: ju:θ and ɔn mi: ˌǰɔlɪˈte:
It tikleth me aboute myn herte roote.	ɪt ˈtɪkləθ me: aˈbu:t mi:n ˈhɛrtə ˈro:tə
Unto this day it dooth myn herte boote	unˈto: θɪs dæɪ ɪt do:θ mi:n ˈhɛrtə ˈbo:tə
That I have had my world as in my tyme.	θat i: hav had mi: wurld as ɪn mi: ˈtiːmə
But Age, allas! that al wole envenyme,	but a:ǰ alˈlas θat al wɔl ˌɛnvəˈniːmə
Hath me biraft my beautee and my pith.	haθ me: bɪˈraft mi: ˈbɛute: and mi: pɪθ
Lat go, fare wel! the devel go therwith!	lat gɔ: fa:r wɛl θə ˈdɛvəl gɔ: θe:rˈwɪθ
The flour is goon, ther is namoore to telle;	θə flu:r ɪs gɔ:n θe:r ɪs naˈmɔ:r to: ˈtɛllə
The bren, as I best kan, now moste I selle;	θə brɛn as i: bɛst kan nu: mo:st i: ˈsɛllə
But yet to be right myrie wol I fonde.	but jɛt to: be: rɪxt ˈmɪrɪ wəl i: ˈfɔ:ndə
Now wol I tellen of my fourthe housbonde.	nu: wəl i: tɛllən of mi: fourθ huzˈbɔ:ndə

CHAUCER'S RETRACTION

Now preye I to hem alle that herkne this litel tretys or rede, that if ther be any thyng in it that liketh hem, that therof they thanken oure lord Jhesu crist, of whom procedeth al wit and al goodnesse. And if ther be any thyng that displese hem, I preye hem also that they arrette it to the defaute of myn unkonnynge, and nat to my wyl, that wolde ful fayn have seyd bettre if I hadde had konnynge. For oure boke seith, "al that is writen is writen for oure doctrine," and that is myn entente. Wherfore I biseke yow mekely for the mercy of god, that ye

nu: præi i: to: hɛm al θat ˈhɛrknə θɪs ˈlɪtəl ˈtrɛːtɪs ər rɛ:d θat if θe:r be: ˈanɪ θɪŋg ɪn ɪt θat ˈliːkəθ əm θat ˈθe:rɔf θæɪ ˈθaŋkən u:r lɔ:rd ˈǰe:zu kri:st of hwo:m prɔˈse:dəθ al wɪt and al ˈgo:dnɛs and if θe:r be: ˈanɪ θɪŋg θat dɪsˈplɛ:z əm i: præɪ əm ˈalsɔ: θat θæɪ aˈrɛt ɪt to: θə dəˈfaut of mi:n unˈkunnɪŋg and nat to: mi: wɪl θat wəld ful fæɪn hav sæɪd ˈbɛttrə if i: had had ˈkunnɪŋg fər u:r bo:k sæɪθ al θat ɪs ˈwrɪtən ɪs ˈwrɪtən fər u:r ˈdɔktri:n and θat ɪs mi:n ɛnˈtɛnt ˈhwe:rfər i: bɪˈse:k ju: ˈme:kəlɪ fər θə ˈmɛrsɪ of gəd θat je: præɪ fər me: θat kri:st hav ˈmɛrsɪ ɔn me: and

preye for me that crist have mercy on me and for-
yeve me my giltes, and namely of my translacions
and enditynges of worldly vanitees, the whiche I
revoke in my retraccions.

fərˈjɛːv meː miː ˈgɪltəs and ˈnaːməlɪ ɔf miː
tranzˈlaːsɪɔnz and ɛnˈdiːtɪŋgəs ɔf ˈwʊrldlɪ ˈvanɪˌteːs
θə hwɪč iː rəˈvɔːk ɪn miː rəˈtraksɪɔnz.

6.11 *THE REDUCTION OF INFLECTIONS*

The number of inflectional distinctions which had existed in Old English was strikingly diminished in Middle English. The decrease in endings was due partly to the merger of unstressed
vowels and partly to the operation of analogy. The declension of the adjective in Old and Middle
English is illustrated below. Write *S* before each Old English form that developed into the
corresponding Middle English form by regular sound change, and *A* before each form that
was lost through analogy.

	OLD ENGLISH						MIDDLE ENGLISH
	MASC.		NEUT.		FEM.		
STRONG							
sing. nom.	_____	smæl	_____	smæl	_____	smalu	smal
acc.	_____	smælne	_____	smæl	_____	smale	
gen.	_____	smales	_____	smales	_____	smælre	
dat.	_____	smalum	_____	smalum	_____	smælre	
ins.	_____	smale	_____	smale	_____	smælre	
plur. nom.-acc.	_____	smale	_____	smalu	_____	smala	smale
gen.			_____	smælra			
dat.			_____	smalum			
WEAK							
sing. nom.	_____	smala	_____	smale	_____	smale	smale
acc.	_____	smalan	_____	smale	_____	smalan	
gen.-dat.	_____	smalan	_____	smalan	_____	smalan	
plur. nom.-acc.			_____	smalan			smale
gen.	_____	smælra /	_____	smalena			
dat.			_____	smalum			

NOTE: The loss of final nasals in unstressed syllables must have been the result of both sound
change and analogy. First a sound change began to operate whereby nasals were lost when they
were followed by a consonant but were retained when they were followed by a vowel; the resulting fluctuation can be seen in the two forms of the indefinite article, *a bird* but *an owl*.
Almost immediately, however, analogy came into play to eliminate the final nasal completely
in adjective endings and to restore it generally in the endings of strong past participles like
eaten and of noun plurals like *oxen*.

The effect of leveling, whether phonological or analogical, was to eliminate all differences
of case and gender from the adjective and to eliminate the distinction of number from the weak
forms of the adjective. What effects did leveling have on the Middle English noun and verb?

_____

_____

6.12 *THE INFLECTION OF NOUNS AND ADJECTIVES*

1. Write the following phrases in Middle English. All of the nouns are declined alike according to the usual Middle English pattern. The adjectives, however, vary; see *Origins and Development*, page 153.

VOCABULARY

the 'the'	*free* 'noble'	*lord* 'lord'
oold 'old'	*long* 'long'	*wyf* 'wife'
hethen 'heathen'	*feend* 'fiend'	*yeer* 'year'

PHRASES

_____	old fiend	_____	heathen lord
_____	old fiend's	_____	heathen lord's
_____	old fiends	_____	heathen lords
_____	the old fiend	_____	the heathen lord
_____	the old fiend's	_____	the heathen lord's
_____	the old fiends	_____	the heathen lords
_____	noble wife	_____	long year
_____	noble wife's	_____	long year's
_____	noble wives	_____	long years
_____	the noble wife	_____	the long year
_____	the noble wife's	_____	the long year's
_____	the noble wives	_____	the long years

2. Explain the origin of each of the following doublets:

brothers _____

brethren _____

latter _____

later _____

older _____

elder _____

3. Explain the vowel difference between the singular *chīld* and the plural *children*.

_____

_____

4. In his description of the Knight in the *Canterbury Tales*, Chaucer wrote, "His hors were goode." Did the Knight have one horse or more than one, and how can you tell? (The verb is no help; it might be either a plural or a subjunctive singular.) _____

_____

6.13 *PERSONAL PRONOUNS*

Write the declensions of the Middle English personal pronouns. The four cases of the personal pronoun are the nominative, the objective, the adjectival genitive (as in "That is *my* book"), and the pronominal genitive (as in "That is *mine*"). Mark forms which are not East Midland (Chaucerian) with an asterisk (*). Mark forms borrowed from Scandinavian with a dagger (†). Mark new analogical forms with a double dagger (‡). The first person singular has been done.

	FIRST PERSON SINGULAR			FIRST PERSON PLURAL	
nom.	Ī, ich, ik*		nom.	_____	
obj.	mē		obj.	_____	
adj. gen.	mī, mīn		adj. gen.	_____	
pron. gen.	mīn		pron. gen.	_____	

	SECOND PERSON SINGULAR			SECOND PERSON PLURAL	
nom.	_____		nom.	_____	
obj.	_____		obj.	_____	
adj. gen.	_____		adj. gen.	_____	
pron. gen.	_____		pron. gen.	_____	

	THIRD PERSON SINGULAR MASCULINE			THIRD PERSON PLURAL	
nom.	_____		nom.	_____	
obj.	_____		obj.	_____	
adj. gen.	_____		adj. gen.	_____	
pron. gen.	_____		pron. gen.	_____	

	THIRD PERSON SINGULAR FEMININE			THIRD PERSON SINGULAR NEUTER	
nom.	_____		nom.	_____	
obj.	_____		obj.	_____	
adj. gen.	_____		adj. gen.	_____	
pron. gen.	_____		pron. gen.	_____	

6.14 DEMONSTRATIVE PRONOUNS

The Old English demonstratives consisted in part of these forms:

NOMINATIVE SINGULAR		NOMINATIVE PLURAL	INSTRUMENTAL SINGULAR
masc.	*sē* 'the, that'; *þes* 'this'	*þā* 'the, those'; *þās* 'these'	*þē* 'by the, that'
fem.	*sēo* *þēos*		
neut.	*þæt* *þis*		

Middle English had the following forms. Indicate which Old English form each developed from, and explain any irregularities in the development.

singular			
and plural	*the*	_____	
		_____	
singular	*that*	_____	
plural	*thō*	_____	
	thōs	_____	
singular	*this*	_____	
plural	*thēse*	_____	
	thise	_____	

Notice how the italicized pronouns are used in the following quotations from Chaucer.[8]

Who herd ever of swich a thyng or now? (D 2229)

"*Who* artow [art thou]?" "It am I, Absolon." (A 3766)

Who hath no wyf he is no cokewold. (A 3152)

Who so first cometh to the mille first grynt [grinds]. (D 389)

Who that is moost vertuous alway .... Taak hym for the grettest gentil man. (D 1113)

"To *whom*?" quod he. (G 304)

My lady, *whom* I love and serve. (A 1143)

The sighte of hire, *whom that* I serve. (A 1231)

Whos is that faire child that stondeth yonder? (B 1018)

Of him *whos* I am all, whil I may dure. (Venus 6)

Syk lay the goode man *whos that* the place is. (D 1768)

This carpenter answerde, "*What* seystow [sayest thou]?" (A 3490)

What is bettre than a good womman? (B 2298)

Whan folk in chirche had yeve [given] him *what* hem leste [pleased them], He wente his wey. (D 1735)

Ne every appul that is fair at eye Ne is nat good, *what so* men clappe [chatter] or crye. (G 965)

But God woot [knows] *what that* May thoughte in hire herte. (E 1851)

Which was the mooste fre [noble], as thynketh yow? (F 1622)

Thise riotoures thre, of *which* I telle. (C 661)

Alle thinges *whiche that* I have sayd. (D 2245)

He *which that* hath no wyf, I hold hym shent [ruined]. (E 1320)

Smale houndes hadde she *that* she fedde. (A 146)

Taak heede of every word *that* I you seye. (E 475)

To me, *that* am thy cosyn and thy brother. (A 1131)

Thou hast nat doon *that* I comanded thee. (D 2041)

The fruit of this matiere is *that* I telle. (B 411)

1. What pronouns, simple and compound, does Middle English use as

    interrogatives _____
    indefinite relatives (introducing noun clauses) _____
    _____
    relatives (introducing adjective clauses) _____
    _____

2. Describe one difference between Middle English and contemporary English in their use of *which.* _____
   _____

3. Describe three differences between Middle English and contemporary English in their use of *that.* _____
   _____
   _____
   _____
   _____

[8] Following each quotation the source is identified by the customary abbreviation.

The principal parts of many Old English strong verbs survived in Middle English with no changes other than those resulting from the regular sound shifts affecting all words. The following Old English verbs, typical of the seven strong classes, had such regular development. By applying what you have already studied about sound and spelling changes you should be able to predict their Middle English forms. Write the Middle English developments; mark all long vowels with a macron and use the hook to show open ẹ̄ [ɛ:] and ọ̄ [ɔ:].

	OLD ENGLISH	MIDDLE ENGLISH		OLD ENGLISH	MIDDLE ENGLISH
CLASS I	'write'		CLASS IV	'bear'	
	wrītan	_____		beran	_____
	wrāt	_____		bær	_____
	writon	_____		bǣron[9]	_____
	writen	_____		boren	_____
CLASS II	'cleave'		CLASS V	'knead'	
	clēofan	_____		cnedan	_____
	clēaf	_____		cnæd	_____
	clufon	_____		cnǣdon[9]	_____
	clofen	_____		cneden	_____
CLASS III	'bind'		CLASS VI	'shake'	
	bindan	_____		scacan	_____
	band	_____		scōc	_____
	bundon	_____		scōcon	_____
	bunden	_____		scacen	_____
	'melt'		CLASS VII	'know'	
	meltan	_____		cnāwan	_____
	mealt	_____		cnēow	_____
	multon	_____		cnēowon	_____
	molten	_____		cnāwen	_____
	'warp'			'let'	
	weorpan	_____		lǣtan[9]	_____
	wearp	_____		lēt	_____
	wurpon	_____		lēton	_____
	worpen	_____		lǣten	_____

6.17   *INFLECTION OF VERBS*

The Middle English weak verb *hẹ̄len* 'to heal' and strong verb *helpen* 'to help' are typical developments of their Old English counterparts. Conjugate them in full, using the endings characteristic of the Midland dialects. The imperative endings are regular developments of the Old English forms.

[9] The stem vowel was *ā* in West Germanic.

PRINCIPAL PARTS	hēlen, hēlde, hēled		helpen, halp, hulpen, holpen	
	PRESENT	PRETERIT	PRESENT	PRETERIT
INDICATIVE				
Ī	_____	_____	_____	_____
thōu	_____	_____	_____	_____
hē	_____	_____	_____	_____
wē, yē, they	_____	_____	_____	_____
SUBJUNCTIVE				
I, thōu, hē	_____	_____	_____	_____
wē, yē, they	_____	_____	_____	_____
IMPERATIVE				
thōu	_____		_____	
yē	_____		_____	
PARTICIPLE				
	_____	_____	_____	_____

6.18 *MIDDLE ENGLISH ILLUSTRATED*

The following passages illustrate Middle English through a period of some three hundred years. The first selection preserves many of the inflections characteristic of Old English; the last selection is hardly distinguishable from early Modern English. Some dialect variation is also represented in the passages. The translations which accompany most of the texts scarcely do literary justice to their originals, but they will serve as glosses.

Compare the passages with one another. Note significant differences among them and any characteristics which help to date them as early or late Middle English.

Observe the spelling, inflections, word order, and vocabulary.

THE PETERBOROUGH CHRONICLE

The *Anglo-Saxon Chronicle* was continued at Peterborough for almost a century after the Norman Conquest. The passage reproduced here was written about the middle of the twelfth century. The text is based on Benjamin Thorpe's *The Anglo-Saxon Chronicle, According to the Several Original Authorities* (London, 1861), corrected by readings from Dorothy Whitelock's *The Peterborough Chronicle: The Bodleian Manuscript Laud Misc. 636* ("Early English Manuscripts in Facsimile," Vol. IV [Copenhagen, 1954]). Abbreviations have been silently expanded.

Millesimo. C. XXXV.   On þis gære for se king Henri ouer sæ æt te   Lammasse. and ðat
1135   In this year went the King Henry over sea at the Lammas,   and that

oþer dei þa   he lai an slep in   scip. þa þestrede þe dæi ouer al landes. and
second day while he lay and slept in [the] ship then darkened the day over all lands, and

uuard þe sunne suilc als it uuare   thre niht ald mone. an sterres abuten him at middæi.
became the sun   such as it were [a] three night old moon and stars about it   at midday.

Wurþen men suiðe ofuundred   and ofdred. and sæden ðat   micel þing sculde
Became men greatly filled with wonder and afraid   and said   that [a] great thing should

cumen herefter. sua   dide. for þat ilc   gær warth þe king ded. ðat oþer   dæi efter
come   hereafter; so [it] did, for that same year was   the King dead the second day after

Sanct Andreas massedæi on Normandi. Þa   þestre[den] sona   þas landes. for
Saint   Andrew's mass-day in Normandy. Then darkened   immediately   these lands, for

æuric man sone   ræuede oþer   þe mihte. Þa   namen his sune and his frend. and
every man immediately robbed another who might.[10] *Then took   his son   and his friends and*

brohten his lic   to Engleland. and bebiriend in Redinge. God   man he wes. and micel æie
brought his body to England   and burying   at Reading. [A] good man he was, and much awe

wes of him. durste nan man misdon wið   oðer   on his time. Pais he makede   men and
was of him; durst no   man misdo   against another in his time. Peace he made [for] man and

dær.   Wua sua bare his byrthen   gold and sylure. durste nan man sei to him naht   bute
beast. Who so   bore his burden [of] gold and silver, durst no   man say of him naught but

god. Enmang þis   was his nefe   cumen to Engleland. Stephne de blais. and com to
good. Among   this[11] *was his nephew come   to England,   Stephen de Blois, and came to*

lundene. and te lundenisce folc him underfeng. and senden efter þe ærcebiscop Willelm
London, and the London   folk him received   and sent   after the archbishop William

curbuil. and halechede   him to kinge on midewintre dæi. On þis kinges time wes al unfrið.
Corbeil, and   consecrated him as king on midwinter   day. In this king's time was all strife

and yfel. and ræflac. for agenes him risen sona   þa   rice   men þe wæron swikes.
and evil and robbery, for against him rose at once those powerful men that were   traitors.

THE CHRONICLE OF ROBERT OF GLOUCESTER

Histories enjoyed a great popularity during the Middle Ages; the so-called *Metrical Chronicle of Robert of Gloucester*, edited by William Aldis Wright (London, 1887), was written about 1300 by three men, only one of whom has been identified by name. Wright said of this chronicle, "As literature, it is as worthless as twelve thousand lines of verse without one spark of poetry can be." Although it is rimed in an undistinguished doggerel, the work is linguistically interesting. The eleven lines printed here express an oft-repeated sentiment.

Þus com   lo engelond in to normandies hond
Thus came, lo, England into Normandy's hand,

& þe normans ne couþe speke þo   bote hor owe speche
and the Normans   could speak then only their own speech,

& speke french as hii dude atom   & hor children   dude also teche
and spoke French as they did   at home and their children [they] did   also teach,

So þat heiemen of þis lond þat of hor blod come
so that nobles   of this land, who of their blood come,

Holdeþ alle þulke   speche þat hii of   hom nome
keep   all that same speech that they from them took.[12]

[10] That is, 'every man who might immediately robbed another.'
[11] That is, 'at this time.'
[12] That is, 'which they inherited from them.'

151

Vor bote a man conne frenss me telþ of him lute
For unless a man knows French, one accounts him little.

Ac lowe   men holdeþ to engliss & to hor owe speche ȝute
But humble men hold   to English and to their own speech yet.

Ich wene   þer ne beþ in al þe world contreyes none
I   believe there are in all the world countries none

Þat   ne holdeþ to hor owe speche bote engelond one
that [do] not hold   to their own speech but England alone;

Ac wel me wot uor to conne boþe wel it is
but well one knows, to know both, well it is;[13]

Vor þe more þat a mon can   þe more wurþe he is.
for the more that a man knows, the more worth he is.

THE ANCRENE RIWLE

The *Ancrene Riwle* (rule for anchoresses) is a guide to the religious life written for three sisters of good family, who had determined to retire from the world and to lead lives of holy solitude. The book gives them advice about their devotions, about moral questions, temptations, penance, and about numerous small domestic matters. The subject is hardly a promising one, but the treatment is so refreshingly unorthodox that readers continue to discover the *Riwle* with pleasure and surprise. The selection printed here is based on James Morton's *The Ancren Riwle* (London, 1853); more recent editions have been published by the Early English Text Society. In West Midland dialect, it was composed probably in the late twelfth century.

Eue heold ine parais   longe tale mid te neddre, and told hire   al þat lescun þat
Eve held in paradise [a] long talk with the serpent, and told him[14] *all that lesson that*

God hire hefde ilered, and Adam, of þen epple; and so þe ueond þurh   hire word,
God her had   taught and Adam of the apple; and so the fiend   through her words

understond anonriht hire wocnesse, and ivond   wei touward hire of hire uorlorenesse.
understood at once   her weakness and found [a] way toward   her for her ruin.

Vre lefdi, Seinte Marie, dude al anoðer wise: ne tolde heo þen engle none tale; auh askede
Our lady, Saint Mary,   did all another way: told she the angel no   tale, but asked

him   þing scheortliche þat heo   ne kuðe. Ye, mine leoue sustren, uoleweð ure
him [the] thing briefly   that she [did] not know. Ye, my   dear sisters, follow   our

lefdi and nout þe kakele Eue. Vorþi   ancre,   hwat se heo beo, alse muchel ase
lady and not the cackling Eve. Therefore [an] anchoress, what so she be, as   much   as

heo euer con and mei, holde   hire   stille: nabbe heo   nout   henne kunde. Þe
she ever can and may, [should] keep her[self] still: [let] her have not [a] hen's nature. The

hen hwon heo haueð ileid, ne con buten kakelen. And hwat biyit heo þerof?   Kumeð þe
hen when she has   laid, cannot but   cackle. And what gets she from that? Comes the

coue   anonriht and reueð hire   hire eiren, and fret   al þat of hwat heo schulde
chough at once   and robs her [of] her eggs and devours all that from which she should

13 That is, 'but it is well-known that it is good to know both.'
14 Literally, 'her'; a survival of grammatical gender from Old English, in which adders were feminine.

uorð bringen hire cwike briddes: and riht also þe luðere coue   deouel   berð awei
bring forth   her live birds; and just so the evil   chough, [the] devil, bears away

urom þe kakelinde ancren,   and uorswoluweð al þat god þat heo istreoned   habbeð,
from the cackling anchoress and swallows up   all that good that she has brought forth,

þat schulden ase briddes beren ham   up touward heouene, yif hit nere   icakeled.
that should   as birds bear them[selves] up toward heaven, if it were not cackled.[15]

Þe wreche   peoddare more noise he makeð to yeien his sope, þen a riche mercer
The wretched peddler   more noise he makes to hawk his soap, than a rich mercer [does for]

al his deorewurðe ware. To sum gostliche monne þat ye beoð strusti uppen ase ye
all his expensive   wares. Of some spiritual man   that ye are trustful upon as ye

muwen beon of hit, god is   þat ye asken   red,   and salue þat he teche ou
may   be   of it,[16] good is [it] that ye ask [for] advice and remedy that he teach you

to yeines fondunges, and ine schrifte   scheaweð him gif he wule iheren ower greste, and
against temptations, and in confession show   him, if he will hear, your greatest and

ower lodlukeste   sunnen; uor þi þat him areowe   ou; and þurh   þe bireaunesse
your most loathsome sins   in order that it may pity him you[17] and through the pity

crie   Crist inwarliche merci   uor ou, and habbe ou ine munde, and in his bonen.
cry [to] Christ inwardly [for] mercy for you and have you in mind   and in his prayers.

"Auh witeð ou and beoð iwarre," he seið, ure Louerd, "uor monie cumeð   to ou
"But know you and beware,"   he said, our Lord,   "for many [will] come to you

ischrud mid lombes fleose, and beoð wode wulues." Worldliche men ileueð lut; religuise
clothed with lamb's fleece, and are mad wolves." Worldly   men believe little; religious

yet lesse. Ne wilnie ye nout to muchel hore kuðlechunge. Eue wiðute drede spec mit
still less.[18] Nor desire ye not too much   their acquaintance. Eve without dread spoke with

te neddre. Vre lefdi was of drede of Gabrieles speche.
the serpent. Our lady was afraid   of Gabriel's speech.

A BESTIARY

The *Bestiaries* were collections of nature-lore. They described the marvelous behavior of the animal creation and drew appropriate moral lessons therefrom. One of these collections, the *Physiologus* of Theobaldus, was translated into English in the mid-thirteenth century and has been edited by Richard Morris in *An Old English Miscellany* (London, 1872). The selection printed here describes the habits of mermaids. Chaucer refers to it in the *Nun's Priest's Tale* just before the fox makes his appearance:

> and Chauntecleer so free
> Soong murier than the mermayde in the see,
> For Phisiologus seith sikerly
> How that they syngen wel and murily.

[15] That is, 'if it had not been for the cackling.'
[16] That is, 'in such matters.'
[17] That is, 'he may pity you'; an impersonal construction.
[18] That is, 'Believe worldly men' and so forth; the construction is a command, not a statement.

In ðe se senden selcuðes manie;
In the sea are   wonders many;

ðe mereman is a meiden ilike
the mermaid is a maiden like[19]

on brest and on bodi, oc al ðus ge is bunden:
in breast and in body, but all thus she is bound:

fro ðe noule niðerward ne is ge no man like,
from the navel downward   is she no man like,

oc   fis to fuliwis mid finnes waxen.
but [a] fish, indeed,   with fins   grown.

Ðis wunder wuneð in   wankel   stede,
This wonder dwells in [a] precarious place,

ðer   ðe water sinkeð; sipes ge sinkeð,
where the water sinks; ships she sinks,

and scaðe ðus werkeð: mirie   ge singeð ðis mere,
and harm thus does: merrily she sings, this mermaid,

and haueð manie stefnes, manie and sille,
and has   many voices, many and shrill,

oc it   ben wel ille; sipmen here steringe forgeten
but they are very evil; shipmen their steering forget

for hire stefninge, slumeren   and slepen,
for her singing; [they] slumber and sleep,

and to late waken, ðe sipes sinken mitte   suik,
and too late wake; the ships sink   with the treachery

ne cumen he nummor up. Oc wise men and warre
nor come they any more up. But wise men and wary

agen cunen chare, ofte arn atbrosten,
back can   turn, often are escaped

mid here brest ouel; he hauen herd told of ðis mere
from her   breast evil; they have   heard tell of this mermaid

ðat tus unie-mete, half man and half fis,
that thus monstrous, half man and half fish,

sum ðing tokneð   bi ðis.
some thing betokens by this.

Significacio

Fele men hauen ðe tokning of ðis forbisnede ðing,
Many men have   the tenor   of this parabolic   thing,

---

[19] That is, 'like a maiden.'

wiðuten weren   lambes fel, wiðinnen arn he   wulues al;
without [they] wear lamb's[20] skin, within   are they wolves completely;

he   speken godcundhede, and wikke is here dede;
they speak godliness,   and wicked is their deed;

here dede is al   vncuð wið ðat   spekeð here muð;
their deed is quite foreign to   what speaks their mouths;

twifold arn   on mode, he   sweren bi ðe rode,
twofold [they] are in mind, they swear by the cross

bi ðe sunne and bi ðe mone, and he   ðe   legen sone,
by the sun   and by the moon, and they [to] thee lie   at once,

mid here sage and mid here song he ðe   swiken ðer imong,
with their saw and with their song, they thee betray therewith,

ðin agte   wið swiking, ði soule wið lesing.
thy property with betrayal, thy soul   with falsehood.

JOHN OF TREVISA'S POLYCHRONICON

The *Polychronicon*, written in Latin by Ralph Higden and translated into English in the 1480's by John of Trevisa, is a compendium of universal history. It begins with a geographical survey of the known world and traces human history from the creation to the fourteenth century.

The following selection concerning the languages of the British Isles is Chapter 59 of Book I. Trevisa sometimes felt it necessary to correct his source; his additions are indicated by parentheses. The complete work has been edited by Churchill Babington, *Polychronicon Ranulphi Higden Monachi Cestrensis; together with the English Translations of John Trevisa and of an Unknown Writer of the Fifteenth Century* (London, 1869).

As it is i-knowe how meny manere   peple beeþ in þis ilond, þere beeþ also so many
As it is known   how many kinds [of] people are in this island, there are   also as many

dyuers longages and tonges; noþeles   Walsche men and Scottes, þat beeþ nouȝt
diverse languages and tongues; nevertheless Welshmen   and Scots,   who are not

i-medled wiþ oþer naciouns, holdeþ wel nyh   hir   firste   longage and speche; but
mixed   with other nations, keep   very nearly their original language and speech; except

ȝif   the Scottes þat were somtyme confederat and wonede wiþ þe Pictes drawe
that the Scots   that were formerly confederate and dwelt   with the Picts follow

somwhat after hir   speche; but þe Flemmynges þat woneþ in þe weste side of Wales
somewhat   their speech; but the Flemings   that dwell in the west part of Wales

haueþ i-left her   straunge speche and spekeþ Saxonliche i-now. Also Englische men, þey
have   left their foreign speech and speak Saxonly   enough. Also Englishmen,   they

hadde from the bygynnynge þre   manere   speche, norþerne, sowþerne, and middel speche
had   from the beginning   three kinds [of] speech, northern, southern, and midland speech

---

[20] The manuscript has *wulues fel*; the writer got his proverb twisted.

in þe myddel of þe lond, as þey come of þre manere peple of Germania,
in the middle of the land, as they came from three kinds [of] people of Germania;

noþeles by comyxtioun and mellynge firste wiþ Danes and afterward wiþ Normans, in
nevertheless by mixture and mingling first with Danes and afterward with Normans, in

meny þe contray longage is apayred, and som vseþ strong wlafferynge, chiterynge,
many [ways] the native language is debased and some use harsh stammering, chattering,

harrynge, and garrynge grisbayting. This apayrynge of þe burþe tunge is bycause of
snarling, and scolding gnashing of teeth. This abasement of the birth-tongue is because of

tweie þinges; oon is for children in scole aȝenst þe vsage and manere of alle oþere
two things; one is that children in school against the usage and custom of all other

naciouns beeþ compelled for to leue hire owne langage, and for to construe hir lessouns
nations are compelled to leave their own language and to construe their lessons

and here þynges in Frensche, and so þey haueþ seþ þe Normans come first in to
and their subjects in French, and so they have since the Normans came first into

Engelond. Also gentil men children beeþ i-tauȝt to speke Frensche from þe tyme þat þey
England. Also gentlemen's children are taught to speak French from the time that they

beeþ i-rokked in here cradel, and kunneþ speke and playe wiþ a childes broche; and
are rocked in their cradle and are able to speak and play with a child's bauble; and

vplondisshe men wil likne hym self to gentil men, and fondeþ wiþ greet besynesse for to
country men will liken himself[21] to gentlemen and strive with great labor to

speke Frensce, for to be i-tolde of. (Þis manere was moche i-vsed
speak French in order to be taken account of.[22] (This practice was much followed

to for firste deth and is siþþe sumdel i-chaunged; for Iohn Cornwaile, a maister
before [the] first plague and is since somewhat changed; for John Cornwall, a teacher

of grammer, chaunged þe lore in gramer scole and construccioun of Frensche
of grammar, changed the instruction in grammar school and interpretation from French

in to Englische; and Richard Pencriche lerned þe manere techynge of hym and
into English;[23] and Richard Pencritch learned the manner [of] teaching from him and

oþere men of Pencrich; so þat now, þe ȝere of oure Lorde a þowsand þre hundred
other men from Pencritch so that now, the year of our Lord a thousand three hundred

and foure score and fyue, and of þe secounde kyng Richard after þe conquest nyne, in alle
and four score and five, and of the second King Richard after the conquest nine, in all

þe gramere scoles of Engelond, children leueþ Frensche and construeþ and lerneþ an
the grammar schools of England children leave French and interpret and learn in

Englische, and haueþ þerby auauntage in oon side and disauauntage in anoþer
English and have thereby [an] advantage in one way and [a] disadvantage in another

[21] That is, 'wish to make themselves like.'
[22] That is, 'in order to be thought important.'
[23] Whereas French had been the language in which classes were held and into which school children translated their Latin, English was becoming the language of instruction. The change was doubtlessly regarded as a milestone in progressive education.

side; here auauntage is, þat þey lerneþ her gramer in lasse tyme þan children were
way; their advantage is that they learn their grammar in less time than children were

i-woned to doo; disauauntage is þat now children of gramer scole conneþ na
accustomed to do; [the] disadvantage is that now children in grammar school know no

more Frensche þan can hir lift heele, and þat is harme for hem and þey schulle
more French than knows their left heel, and that is harm[ful] for them if they shall

passe þe see and trauaille in straunge landes and in many oþer places. Also gentil men
cross the sea and travel in foreign lands and in many other places. Also gentlemen

haueþ now moche i-left for to teche here children Frensche.) Hit semeþ a greet wonder
have now much neglected to teach their children French.) It seems a great wonder

how Englische, þat is þe burþe tonge of Englisshe men and her owne langage and
that English, which is the birth-tongue of Englishmen and their own language and

tonge, is so dyuerse of sown in þis oon ilond, and þe langage of Normandie is
tongue, is so diverse in sound in this one island, and the language of Normandy is [a]

comlynge of anoþer londe, and hath oon manere soun among alle men þat spekeþ hit
newcomer from another land, and has one kind [of] sound among all men that speak it

ariȝt in Engelond. (Neuerþeles þere is as many dyuers manere Frensche in þe
properly in England. (Nevertheless there are as many diverse kinds [of] French in the

reem of Fraunce as is dyuers manere Englische in þe reem of Engelond.) Also of þe
realm of France as are diverse kinds [of] English in the realm of England.) Also of the

forsaide Saxon tonge þat is i-deled aþre, and is abide scarsliche wiþ fewe
aforesaid Saxon tongue, which is divided in three and remains scarcely among [a] few

vplondisshe men is greet wonder; for men of þe est wiþ men of þe west, as it
rustic men [there] is great wonder; for men of the east with men of the west, as it

were vndir þe same partie of heuene, acordeþ more in sownynge of speche þan men of þe
were under the same part of heaven, agree more in pronunciation than men of the

norþ wiþ men of þe souþ; þerfore it is þat Mercii, þat beeþ men of myddel Engelond,
north with men of the south; therefore it is that Mercians, who are men of middle England,

as it were parteners of þe endes, vnderstondeþ bettre þe side langages, norþerne
as it were partners of the extremes, understand better the adjacent languages, northern

and souþerne, þan norþerne and souþerne vnderstondeþ eiþer oþer. Al þe longage of þe
and southern, than northern and southern understand each other. All the language of the

Norþhumbres, and specialliche at ȝork, is so scharp, slitting, and frotynge and vnschape,
Northumbrians, and especially at York, is so shrill, cutting, and grating and ill-formed,

þat we souþerne men may þat longage vnneþe vnderstonde. I trowe þat þat is bycause
that we southern men can that language barely understand. I believe that that is because

þat þey beeþ nyh to straunge men and naciouns þat spekeþ strongliche, and also
they are near to foreign men and nations that speak harshly and also

bycause þat þe kynges of Engelond woneþ alwey fer from þat cuntrey; for þey beeþ
because the kings of England dwell always far from that country; for they are

more i-torned to þe souþ contray, and ȝif þey gooþ to þe norþ contray þey gooþ wiþ
more turned to the south country, and if they go to the north country, they go with

greet help and strengþe. Þe cause why þey beeþ more in þe souþ contrey þan in þe
great force and strength. The cause that they are more in the south country than in the

norþ, is for hit may be better corne londe, more peple, more noble citees, and more
north is that it may have better grain land, more people, more noble cities, and more

profitable hauenes.
profitable harbors.

ANOTHER ENGLISH POLYCHRONICON

Ralph Higden's *Polychronicon* was translated again in the mid-fifteenth century. This second translation, which might be called late Middle English or early Modern English, will illustrate the considerable changes in the language wrought by the intervening years. The passage reprinted here from Babington's edition corresponds to the earlier translation but of course lacks Trevisa's comments. In some ways, it corresponds rather more closely to the Latin original.

Hit may be schewede clerely to the wytte that there were so mony diuersites of langages in that londe as were diuersites of nacions. But Scottes and men of Wales kepe theire propre langage, as men inpermixte with other naciones; but perauenture Scottes haue taken somme parte in theire communicacion of the langage of Pictes, with whom thei dwellede somme tyme, and were confederate with theyme. Men of Flaundres that inhabite the weste partes of Wales leuenge the speche of barbre speke after the Saxones. And thauȝhe men of Englonde hade in the begynnenge a langage tripartite, as of the sowthe parte of Englond, of the myddelle parte of Englonde, and of the northe parte of Englonde, procedenge as of thre peple of Germanye, borowe moche in theire speche now, thro the commixtion with the Danes and after that with the Normannes. The corrupcion of that natife langage is causede moche of ij. thynges, that is to say, childer sette to schole after the commenge of Normannes in to Englonde were compellede to constru in Frenche ageyne the consuetude of oþer naciones. In so moche that the childer of nowble men, after that thei were taken from the cradelle, were sette to lerne the speche of Frenche men. Wherefore churles seenge that, willenge to be like to theyme, laborede to speke Frenche with alle theire myȝhte. Where hit is to be hade in meruayle that the propur langage of Englische men scholde be made so diuerse in oon lytelle yle in pronunciacion, sythe the langage of Normannes is oon and vniuocate allemoste amonge theyme alle. But as of the tripartite langage of Saxones, whiche remaynethe now but amonge fewe men, the weste men of Englonde sownde and acorde more with the men of the este of that londe as vnder the same clyme of heuyn, then the men of the northe with men of the sowthe. Wherefore hit is that Englische men of þe Marches of the mydelle partes of Englonde, takenge as by participacion the nature of bothe extremities, vnderstonde the langages collateralle arthike and anthartike better then the extremites vnderstonde theyme selfe to geder. Alle the langage of men of Northumbrelonde, and specially in Yorke, sowndethe so that men of the sowthe cuntre may vnnethe vnderstonde the langage of theyme, whiche thynge may be causede for the nye langage of men of barbre to theyme, and also for the grete distaunce of kynges of Englonde from hyt, whiche vse moste the southe partes of that londe, returnenge not in to the costes of the northe but with a grete multitude. Also an other cause may be assignede, for the sowthe partes be more habundante in fertilite then the northe partes, moo peple in nowmbre, hauenge also more plesaunte portes.

The Modern English Period to 1800: Sounds and Spellings

1. Define the following terms:

   the Great Vowel Shift   assibilation   inverse spelling

   apocopation   hypercorrect pronunciation

2. Explain the significance of the following typographical devices sometimes used in early Modern English printing: The letter *y* with a small superscript *e*, a line or tilde over a vowel, final *e*'s other than those used to show length of the preceding vowel, the distinction between the letters *u* and *v*.

3. Compare the vowel system of Middle English with that of early Modern English as they are shown in the vowel charts of Chapter 6 and of this chapter. What additions, losses, or rearrangements took place between the two periods?

4. Make a similar comparison of the vowel system of early Modern English with that of current English as it is described in Chapter 3.

5. Make a similar comparison of the consonant system of Middle English with that of Modern English as it is described in Chapter 3.

6. Trace the chief sources of the present-day vowels. Chapters 3, 5, 6, and 7, and the exercises for them, will provide the information you need. The vowel [i] is done here as a model. Vowel length is not indicated for present-day English.

PRESENT-DAY ENGLISH	EARLY MODERN ENGLISH		MIDDLE ENGLISH		OLD ENGLISH	
[i]	[i:]	*geese*	[e:]	*gees*	[e:]	*gēs*
		seethe		*sethen*	[e:ə]	*sēoþan*
		sleep		*sleep*	[e:] in Mercian; West Saxon [æ:]	*slǣp*
	[i:] or [e:] in different dialects	*deal*	[ɛ:]	*deel*	[æ:]	*dǣl*
		beam		*beem*	[æ:ə]	*bēam*
		steal		*stelen*	[ɛ] in open syllables	*stelan*

7. Trace the chief sources of the present-day consonants in a similar way.

8. From what kinds of evidence do we gain our knowledge of the pronunciation of earlier periods?

9. Read aloud the phonetic transcription from *1 Henry IV* on pages 179–80 of *Origins and Development*; note which sounds differ from your own pronunciation; and explain the cause of as many of the differences as you can.

7.2 *THE EARLY MODERN ENGLISH VOWELS*

Like all other historical periods, early Modern English had no single, uniform pronunciation. Sounds varied from place to place and from social group to social group. Moreover, they continued to change during the period. Only with these important qualifications can we speak of a typical early Modern English phonology. Such a typical sound system in the seventeenth century would have included the following vowels:

COMMON SPELLING	SOUND	COMMON SPELLING	SOUND	COMMON SPELLING	SOUND
a	[æ]	o	[ɔ] or [ɑ]	i, u, e, ea before r	[ɜ:]
a, al	[æ:]	aw, au, a, al, ough, o	[ɔ:]	a, o, u, e, i in unstressed syllables	[ə]
e, ea	[ɛ]	oa, o, o . . . e, oe, ow, ou, ol	[o:]	oy, oi	[ɔɪ]
a, a . . . e,[1] ay, ai, ey, ei	[ɛ:]	u, oo	[ʊ]	i, i . . . e, ie, y, oy, oi	[ʌɪ]
ea, e . . . e	[e:]	oo, o, oe	[u:]	ow, ou	[ʌʊ]
i, y	[ɪ]	u, o	[ʌ]	ew, eu, ue, u . . . e	[ju:]
e, ee, e . . . e, ie, ea	[i:]				

By the early Modern period, spelling had reached its present state of complexity although it differed from contemporary practice in many details. The common spellings listed above are only samples; additional spellings could have been cited for every vowel.

Complete the following charts by filling in the phonetic symbols listed above to show the articulation of early Modern English vowels.

[1] That is, a spelling with silent *e* after a consonant as in *name*.

SIMPLE VOWELS

			FRONT	CENTRAL	BACK
HIGH	long			—	
	short				
MID	long	close			
		open			
	short				
LOW	long			—	
	short				

DIPHTHONGS

Classify the diphthongs according to the position of their initial element. The arrows indicate the direction of the second element in the diphthong.

	FRONT	CENTRAL	BACK
HIGH	⟶		
MID		↖ ↘	↗ ↖ ↘
LOW			

Complete the following chart to show (a) the phonetic symbols for the Middle English sounds from which the early Modern English vowels developed and (b) the phonetic symbol for the current English vowel. This information can be found in *Origins and Development* and in the key words, the spellings of which have varied only slightly since Middle English times.

(a) MIDDLE ENGLISH SOUNDS	EARLY MODERN ENGLISH VOWEL	(b) CURRENT ENGLISH VOWEL	KEY WORDS
	[æ]		lamp, fat, back, flax, sad
	[æ:]		staff, glass, path half, salve, psalm[2]
	[ɛ]		edge, bless, bed, set head, death, deaf[3]
	[ɛ:]		lady, lane, face, take, name day, tail, they, vein
	[e:]		great, steak, break, yea[4] east, mean, peace, bead, theme[4]
	[ɪ]		in, sit, lid, king, hill
	[i:]		she, sweet, these, grief east, mean, peace, bead, theme[4]
	[ɔ] or [ɑ][5]		mock, lodge, odd, pot, fop
	[ɔ:]		law, claw, aught, cause call, hall, small, wall talk, walk, chalk, stalk brought, ought, sought soft, lost, cloth, cross dog, log, frog, bog
	[o:]		boat, throat, go, home, toe snow, soul, grow, dough folk, yolk, holm
	[ʊ]		full, pull, bull, put, push foot, good, wood, look, hook[6]
	[u:]		goose, moon, boot, do, shoe
	[ʌ]		but, sun, son, come
	[ɜ:]		stir, bird, dirt spur, burn, hurt
	[ə]		ago, obey, supply, eleven, mistake
	[ɔɪ]		joy, boy, noise
	[ʌɪ]		child, hide, mice, die, why join, boil, point, spoil[7]
	[ʌʊ]		mouse, brow, town, pound
	[ju:]		few, cue, hue, mute deuce, new, tune, lewd

[2] Current English has more than one vowel in these words because the early Modern sound has developed differently in different dialects.

[3] See *Origins and Development*, p. 42.

[4] In the standard dialect of early Modern English, these words were pronounced with [e:]; but in some nonstandard regional or social dialects, with [i:]. During the eighteenth century, speakers of the nonstandard [i:]-dialects began to set the fashion for pronunciation. The standard changed, and as a result the older elegant pronunciation with [e:] was generally displaced. Except for dialects like Irish where it is more common, the [e:] survives in only a handful of words. See *Origins and Development*, p. 172.

[5] In various dialects.

[6] On the fluctuation of [u:], [ʊ], and [ʌ], see *Origins and Development*, p. 171.

[7] For the development of these words, see *Origins and Development*, p. 173.

Although a good many changes of various kinds affected the English vowel system as it developed from Middle to Modern English, those changes to which the long vowels were subject are especially worthy of note. The seven Middle English long vowels underwent a remarkably systematic shift in their place of articulation, a shift for which there was no cause that we can discover.

1. The changes effected by the Great Vowel Shift, to give only their starting and ending points, were these:

[i:] > [aɪ] as in *mice*: ME [miːs], ModE [maɪs]
[u:] > [aʊ] as in *mouse*: ME [muːs], ModE [maʊs]
[e:] > [i:] as in *geese*: ME [geːs], ModE [giːs]
[o:] > [u:] as in *goose*: ME [goːs], ModE [guːs]
[ɛ:] > [e:] as in *break*: ME [brɛːkən], ModE [breːk]
[ɔ:] > [o:] as in *broke*: ME [brɔːkən], ModE [broːk]
[a:] > [e:] as in *name*: ME [naːmə], ModE [neːm]

Diagram these changes on the chart below. For the first change, write the phonetic symbol [i:] (the vowel in ME *mice*) in its appropriate block; write the symbol [aɪ] (the vowel of ModE *mice*) in its appropriate block; draw an arrow from the pre-shift [i:] to the post-shift [aɪ]. Proceed in the same way for the remaining six changes.

	FRONT	CENTRAL	BACK
HIGH			
MID-CLOSE			
MID-OPEN			
LOW			

Describe the pattern of change in the Great Vowel Shift. _____
_____
_____
_____

2. The following are phonetic transcriptions of Middle English words. Write their current developments (a) in phonetic transcription and (b) in normal orthography.

	CURRENT SOUND	CURRENT SPELLING		CURRENT SOUND	CURRENT SPELLING
[rɔːd	_____	_____	jɛː	_____	_____
broːd	_____	_____	kaːs	_____	_____
deːm	_____	_____	liːs	_____	_____
grɛːt	_____	_____	luːd	_____	_____
guːn	_____	_____	meːt]	_____	_____

[mi:n	_____	_____	rɔ:st	_____	_____
pa:s	_____	_____	ro:st	_____	_____
po:l	_____	_____	sa:f	_____	_____
pɔ:l	_____	_____	u:t	_____	_____
re:d	_____	_____	wi:d]	_____	_____

3. The precise chronology of the Great Vowel Shift is still a matter of dispute, but it must have begun shortly after Chaucer's death and it must have taken several hundred years to complete. Below are five groups of vowels which represent five possible stages in the Shift; there were, of course, other intervening stages. Determine the proper chronological order of the stages given here and indicate it by writing the appropriate number, from 1 through 5, above each group. The group you will number 4 is the stage described in the preceding exercise.

STAGE _____

```
    e:          o:
  ɛ: ʌɪ ʌʊ ɔ:
        a:
```

STAGE _____

```
  i:          u:
  e:          o:
        aɪ  aʊ
```

STAGE _____

```
  i:          u:
  e:          o:
  ɛ: ʌɪ ʌʊ
```

STAGE _____

```
  i:          u:
  ɛ: ʌɪ ʌʊ ɔ:
  æ:
```

STAGE _____

```
  i:          u:
  e:          o:
  ɛ:          ɔ:
        a:
```

7.4 MINOR VOWEL CHANGES

1. The following words contained the vowel [a] in Middle English.

    lap, crab, at, add, back
    staff, craft, path, bath, glass, class
    all, call, hall, stall, tall
    also, halt, bald, salt
    balk, calk (n.), chalk, walk
    calf, half, halve, salve
    alms, calm, palm, psalm

What vowel developed from Middle English [a] before a stop? _____
before a voiceless fricative? _____
before final [l]? _____
before [l] plus a dental? _____
before [l] plus a velar? _____
before [l] plus a labial fricative? _____
before [l] plus a nasal? _____

How do typical British and American usage differ in their developments of [a] in these words? _____
_____
_____

2. The following words contained the vowel [ɔ] in Middle English.

hop, cob, pot, odd, dock
dog, bog, frog, log, hog
soft, off, lost, cross, cloth, moth
boll or bowl, roll, toll, bolt, bolster, folk, yolk

What vowel developed from Middle English [ɔ] before most stops? _____
before the voiced velar stop? _____
before a voiceless fricative? _____
before [l]? _____

How do current British and American usage differ in their developments of this vowel?
_____
_____

3. The following words all had [ʊ] in Middle English.

bud, buck, puff, gull, dull, skull, blush, rush, cut, nut, but, putt
bull, full, pull, bush, push, put

What is the usual development of Middle English [ʊ]? _____
In what environments did it remain unchanged? _____
_____

Which of the words above is an exception to the generalizations you have just made?
_____

4. After Middle English [oː] as in *food*, *good*, *flood* had changed to [uː] during the Great Vowel Shift, it went on to be shortened in some words like *good* and unrounded in others like *flood*. The rimes in early Modern English poetry suggest divided usage in the vowels of these words. List some words which still vary between [u] and [ʊ]. _____
_____

5. The following words had [juː] in early Modern English.

pew, beauty, few, view, mew, cue, argue, hue, ewe
tune, due, sue, zeugma, new, rue, lute, thew

In what environments has it been retained, and in what environments has it become [uː]? Name classes of sounds, not individual sounds.
[ju:] retained _____
[u:] developed _____

6. The following words had in Middle English the sounds indicated at the beginning of each group. Write the phonetic symbols for the modern development of the short vowels before [r]. There is some dialect variation for several of these vowels, as there is also for the long vowels of the next question.

MIDDLE ENGLISH	MODERN ENGLISH	
[ɪr]	_____	spirit, pyramid
	_____	bird, first, shirt, sir
[ʊr]	_____	courage, furrow
	_____	hurt, spur, turn, worth
[ɛr]	_____	merry, very
	_____	person, vermin, clerk, serve
	_____	parson, varmint, Clark, starve

165

[ar]	_____	marry, narrow
	_____	large, park, sharp, stark
[ɔr]	_____	foreign, sorry
	_____	horse, morn, short

Describe the environmental conditions which determine the two possible developments of each vowel. (Ignore the *person/parson* difference in answering this question.) _____

_____

_____

_____

What pronunciations does the name *Derby* have? Cite any other names you know which have similar alternate pronunciations. _____

_____

7. The following words had in Middle English the sounds indicated at the beginning of each group. Write the phonetic symbols for the modern development of the long vowels before [r]. You may not pronounce the same vowel in all the words of every group.

MIDDLE ENGLISH	MODERN ENGLISH	
[i:r]	_____	desire, mire, fire, hire, iron
[u:r]	_____	our, devour, hour, shower, tower, bower, flour/flower
[e:r]	_____	here, mere, peer, deer, beer, bier, hear, dear, clear
[ɛ:r]	_____	near, rear, shear, smear, spear, beard, ear
	_____	pear, swear, tear (v.), wear, bear
[a:r]	_____	mare, hare, spare, bare, care, fare, declare, Mary
[o:r]	_____	door, floor, moor, poor
[ɔ:r]	_____	more, sore, boar, port, hoarse, force, story
[ʊr]	_____	(im)mure, cure, (en)dure
[æɪr]	_____	mayor, their, air, heir, fair, despair

8. The following words contained the vowel [ɛ:] in standard Middle English.

heap, heat, bead, each, speak, sheaf, weave, east, ease, heath, breathe, stream, bean, deal, sea

great, break, steak, yea

sweat, threat, head, bread, death, breath

In the third group of words the long vowel was shortened to [ɛ]. Before what kind of consonants did the shortening occur? _____

Was [ɛ:] always shortened before those consonants? Give examples. _____

_____

The reason why the words of the first group have a different vowel in current English from those of the second group is not known for certain, but what apparently happened was this: In Middle English there were two dialects, which we will call A and B. These two dialects were affected by the Great Vowel Shift in exactly the same way, but before and after the Shift they had a slightly different history with respect to three sounds. We can diagram that history in the following way.

	DIALECT A			DIALECT B		
(1) early ME	[a:]	[ɛ:]	[e:]	[a:]	[ɛ:]	[e:]
	same	*seam*	*seem*	*same*	*seam*	*seem*
(2) late ME	[a:]	[ɛ:]	[e:]	[a:]		[e:]
	same	*seam*	*seem*	*same*		*seam, seem*
(3) early ModE	[ɛ:]	[e:]	[i:]	[ɛ:]		[i:]
	same	*seam*	*seem*	*same*		*seam, seem*
(4) later ModE	[e:]		[i:]	[e:]		[i:]
	same, seam		*seem*	*same*		*seam, seem*

(1) In early Middle English both of the dialects had a three-way contrast between the vowels [a:], [ɛ:], and [e:]. (2) In late Middle English, dialect A remained unchanged, but in dialect B, [ɛ:] had become [e:], thus causing words like *seam* and *seem* to be pronounced alike. Dialect A still had the same three-way contrast, but dialect B had only a two-way contrast. (3) After the Great Vowel Shift had effected its changes, the quality of all the long vowels in both dialects was altered, but the contrasts remained what they had been in late Middle English. (4) Somewhat later in the Modern period [ɛ:] changed to [e:] in both dialects. As a result of this change dialect A also came to have a two-way contrast, with *same* and *seam* pronounced alike. The result of all these changes was that in dialect A words like *seam*, *team*, *cream* rimed with words like *same*, *tame*, *shame*, but in dialect B they rimed with words like *seem*, *deem*, *teem*. Dialect A seems to have been the literary standard in England through the early eighteenth century, after which it was displaced by dialect B. Alexander Pope (1688–1744) used both kinds of pronunciation in his poetry, as shown by the rimes *speaks/makes*, *mead/shade*, *weak/take* versus *plead/need*, *dream/seem*, *please/degrees*. Dialect A is still spoken in parts of the British Isles and has contributed a few common words, such as *great*, to the new standard, dialect B.

If you are interested in the matter, you might try to find rime evidence in some late seventeenth- or eighteenth-century poet to indicate whether he pronounced *seam*-words like *same* or like *seem*.

7.5   *THE EARLY MODERN ENGLISH CONSONANTS*

Because the inventory of consonants in early Modern English is identical with that for contemporary English, there is no need for a complete list. The chart from Chapter 3 can serve for the seventeenth century as well as for the twentieth. Here we will be concerned with some of the changes which have affected consonants since Middle English times.

1. Middle English [x] was either lost or became [f], depending partly on dialect and partly on the kind of vowel or diphthong which it followed. Modern Standard English has preserved, somewhat haphazardly, the developments of [x] characteristic of several dialects.

   Describe the development of the velar fricative in each of the following groups of words by comparing the Middle English forms given here with the current pronunciation of the words.

ME [i:x] hīgh, nīgh, thīgh _____

ME [ɪx] night, light, right _____

ME [u:x] drōughte, plōugh _____

    rōugh, ynōugh, tōugh _____

ME [æɪx] eighte, straight _____

ME [aʊx] aught, slaughter, taught _____

    laughen, draught _____

ME [ɔʊx] boughte, ought, thoughte _____

    dough, though _____

    coughen, trough _____

What effect did the complete loss of [x] have on a preceding short vowel? _____

_____

Did it have that effect before or after the operation of the Great Vowel Shift? How can you tell? _____

_____

What effect did the change of [x] to [f] have on a preceding long vowel? _____

_____

Did it have that effect before or after the operation of the Great Vowel Shift? How can you tell? _____

_____

When [aʊx] became [aʊf], what was the subsequent development of the diphthong?

_____

Which of these two sound changes occurred first? How can you tell?
  (1) [x] either became [f] or was lost altogether.
  (2) [ɔʊ] followed by a consonant became [ɔ:]; not followed by a consonant, it became [o:].

_____

_____

Did [x] ever become [f] after front vowels and diphthongs? _____

After back vowels and diphthongs? _____

Explain the existence in modern Standard English of a doublet like *enough–enow*.

_____

_____

Look up the etymology of *delight*, *haughty*, and *spright*, and explain the presence of *gh* in their spelling. _____

_____

2. Assibilation is a process of mutual assimilation whereby a dental [t], [d], [s], or [z] combines with a following palatal [j] to produce a single dento-palatal consonant. Assibilation did not occur in all dialects of English or in all positions within a word. For each of the following groups, write the phonetic symbol for the contemporary sound which has developed from the older sequence.

_____ from [tj] in stew, tune, Tuesday

_____ from [tj] in future, Christian, fortune

_____ from [dj] in dew, duke, dune, dupe

_____ from [dj] in educate, graduate, soldier

_____ from [sj] in sue, consume, suit

_____ from [sj] in mission, vicious, social

_____ from [zj] in vision, measure, pleasure

In what position within a word is assibilation most likely to occur? _____

Sure appears to be an exception to that generalization. Can you think of any others?

_____

_____

Explain why [ž] is the rarest of English phonemes and the most limited in the positions in which it occurs. _____

_____

_____

What is the usual pronunciation of these phrases in conversation?

(I'll) hit you. _____

Did you (go)? _____

(I'll) miss you. _____

Where's your (hat)? _____

Supply additional examples of assibilation, either within a word or between words.

[tj] _____

[dj] _____

[sj] _____

[zj] _____

3. In late Middle English or very early Modern English, [g] was lost from the sequence [ŋg] under certain conditions. This loss of [g] is parallel to the earlier loss of [b] in [mb] and the less regular loss of [d] in [nd]. Consider the following examples.

king [kɪŋ]	sling [slɪŋ]	singer ['sɪŋər]
rang [ræŋ]	sting [stɪŋ]	ringer ['rɪŋər]
sung [sʌŋ]	thing [θɪŋ]	hanger ['hæŋər]
finger ['fɪŋgər]	anger ['æŋgər]	whistling ['wɪslɪn]
linger ['lɪŋgər]	tangle ['tæŋgl]	nesting ['nɛstɪn]
hunger ['hʌŋgər]	language ['læŋgwɪǰ]	nothing ['nʌθɪn]

What effect did the change of [ŋg] to [ŋ] have upon the phonemic system of English? (Compare *king, rang, sung* with *kin, ran, sun.*) _____

_____

_____

In what position in a word was [g] lost and in what position was it retained? (Ignore *singer, ringer, hanger* in answering this question.) _____

_____

_____

Explain the apparent irregularity in *singer, ringer, hanger.* _____

_____

_____

Under what condition did [ŋg] become [ŋ] and under what condition did it become [n]?

_____

_____

_____

4. In certain positions [l] was vocalized. Consider the modern pronunciation of the following words. In some of them [l] has always been pronounced; in others it has been lost, but is sometimes restored as a spelling pronunciation. Indicate whether [l] was retained or lost in each group, but disregard spelling pronunciations in reaching your decision.

FROM MIDDLE ENGLISH [al]	FROM MIDDLE ENGLISH [ɔl]
_____ ball, fall, wall, gall	_____ boll, roll, stroll, toll
_____ malt, bald, salt, scald	_____ bolt, molten, bolster
_____ chalk, stalk, talk, walk	_____ folk, yolk
_____ calf, half, calve, halve	_____ holp (dialectically [hoːp])
_____ calm, palm, psalm, alms	_____ holm, Holmes

Describe the phonetic environments in which [l] was lost. _____

_____

_____

5. Look up the etymology of *cuss* and describe the sound change which has affected the word. _____

_____

What is the traditional pronunciation of *worsted*? _____

What other words are examples of this change? _____

6. Compare the earlier forms of *groin* and *woodbine* with those of *to pound* and *horehound*. What consonant changes have occurred in these words? _____

_____

If you are familiar with any words that show a similar fluctuation in current English, cite them. _____

7. Explain the *b* in the spellings of *crumb*, *numb*, and *thumb* by comparing these words with *dumb* and *plumb*. _____

_____

_____

8. In some of the following words the pronunciation with [h] is the result of the spelling rather than a historical sound development. Write *S* before the words that have such a spelling pronunciation, and *H* before the words that had [h] historically.

_____	habit	_____	honey	_____	humble
_____	health	_____	hospital	_____	humor
_____	heart	_____	host		
_____	herb	_____	hue		

9. In some of the following words the pronunciation with [θ] is the result of the spelling rather than a historical sound development. Write *S* before the words that have such a spelling pronunciation and *H* before the words that had [θ] historically.

_____	apothecary	_____	hearth	_____	thing
_____	authority	_____	panther	_____	throng
_____	breath	_____	theater		
_____	catholic	_____	theme		

10. Changes in pronunciation do not happen instantaneously or uniformly for all speakers of a language. Helge Kökeritz has suggested that *gn* and *kn*, which were certainly [gn] and [kn] for Chaucer, may have been pronounced simply [n] about 1600.[8] He bases his conclusion

[8] *Shakespeare's Pronunciation* (New Haven, Conn., 1953), p. 304 f.

partly on the evidence of puns in Shakespeare's plays. Another kind of evidence is the testimony of the orthoëpists. Here are statements from three such writers on pronunciation during the century following Shakespeare.

Simon Daines, *Orthoepia Anglicana* (1640)[9]

Gnat, gnaw, gne, A-gnes, gnit, gno, gnu. *G* in this combination inclines to the force of *N*.

Knub, knuckle. Pronounce *kn*, as the Latines doe their **Cn**, a little in the nose, or upper palat.

The Writing Scholar's Companion (1695)[10]

(g) Must be written (in these words) though it is not sounded . . . . Nor can (g) well be sounded in *gnaw, gnash, gnat*.

(k) Cannot well be sounded in such Words as begin with (kn), as *knife, knot, know, &c.*

John Jones, *Practical Phonography* (1701)[11]

When is the *Sound* of *n written gn*? Wherein the *g* is not sounded, as it is not also in *gnar, gnarl, gnash, gnat, gnaw, gnibble, gnomon.*

When is the *Sound* of *n written kn*? When it may be sounded *kn*, as in *knack, knacker, knag, knap, knapple, knapsack . . . .*

When is the *Sound* of *k written k*? Always before *n* except in *Cnidos.*

Such comments are sometimes difficult to interpret, but what would you conclude from these three sources about the sound sequences [gn] and [kn] in the seventeenth century?

_____

_____

_____

_____

_____

7.6 STRESS

What stress does the meter suggest for the italicized words in these passages from Shakespeare? Circle the stressed syllables.

Oh good old man, how well in thee appeares
The constant seruice of the *antique* world,
When seruice sweate for dutie, not for meede.   (*As You Like It*, II.iv)

   . . . but how the feare of vs
May *Ciment* their diuisions, and binde vp
The petty difference, we yet not know.   (*Antony and Cleopatra*, II.i)

No, not to be so odde, and from all fashions,
As Beatrice is, cannot be *commendable*,
But who dare tell her so?   (*Much Ado*, III.i)

[9] Edited by M. Rösler and R. Brotanek (Halle, Germany, 1908).
[10] Edited by Eilert Ekwall (Halle, Germany, 1911).
[11] Edited by Eilert Ekwall (Halle, Germany, 1907).

Therefore take with thee my most greeuous Curse,
Which in the day of Battell tyre thee more
Then all the *compleat* Armour that thou wear'st.   (*Richard III*, IV.iii)

No, I protest, I know not the *contents*.   (*As You Like It*, IV.iii)

Care is no cure, but rather *corrosive*,
For things that are not to be remedy'd.   (*1 Henry VI*, III.iii)

The nimble-footed Mad-Cap, Prince of Wales,
And his *Cumrades*, that daft [thrust] the World aside.   (*1 Henry IV*, IV.i)

And I will kisse thy *detestable* bones.   (*King John*, III.iii)

When I was dry with Rage, and *extreame* Toyle,
Breathlesse, and Faint, leaning vpon my Sword,
Came there a certaine Lord, neat and trimly drest.   (*1 Henry IV*, I.iii)

                    . . . I

Do come with words, as *medicinall*, as true.   (*Winter's Tale*, II.iii)

If he outliue the envy of this day,
England did neuer owe so sweet a hope,
So much *misconstrued* in his Wantonnesse.   (*1 Henry IV*, V.ii)

I [aye], and peruersly, she *perseuers* so.   (*Two Gentlemen*, III.ii)

For what aduancement may I hope from thee,
That no *Reuennew* [revenue] hast, but thy good spirits
To feed & cloath thee.   (*Hamlet*, III.ii)

Take heed you dally not before your King,
Lest he that is the *supreme* King of Kings
Confound your hidden falshood.   (*Richard III*, II.i)

7.7 SOUND CHANGES: A REVIEW

Trace the phonological history of these words by transcribing their pronunciation during each of the four periods. The first word has been done as an example.

	OLD ENGLISH	MIDDLE ENGLISH	EARLY MODERN ENGLISH	LATE MODERN ENGLISH	
tīma	[ti:mɑ]	[ti:mə]	[tʌɪm]	[taɪm]	time
ribb	_____	_____	_____	_____	rib
ynce	_____	_____	_____	_____	inch
ebba	_____	_____	_____	_____	ebb
seofon	_____	_____	_____	_____	seven
crabba	_____	_____	_____	_____	crab
cæppe	_____	_____	_____	_____	cap
sceaft	_____	_____	_____	_____	shaft
hnutu	_____	_____	_____	_____	nut
pott	_____	_____	_____	_____	pot
blīþe	_____	_____	_____	_____	blithe
hȳdan	_____	_____	_____	_____	hide
cēse	_____	_____	_____	_____	cheese
hwēol	_____	_____	_____	_____	wheel

	OLD ENGLISH	MIDDLE ENGLISH	EARLY MODERN ENGLISH	LATE MODERN ENGLISH	
dǣd					deed
sǣ					sea
hēap					heap
fūl					foul
fōda					food
gāt					goat
hām					home
ceaf					chaff
cnēo					knee
cyssan					kiss
ēast					east
fæst					fast
fisc					fish
fox					fox
geolwe					yellow
henn					hen
hlūd					loud
lǣce					leech
lǣfan					leave
pāpa					pope
rīsan					rise
brȳd					bride
sāpe					soap
sōna					soon
standan					stand
sunne					sun
tēþ					teeth
dæg					day
plega					play
grǣg					gray
rāw					row
glōwan					glow
āgan					owe
spīwan					spew
flēos					fleece
dēaw					dew
mǣw					mew
clawe					claw
gnagan					gnaw
apa					ape
ealu					ale
hræfn					raven
melu					meal
open					open
wicu					week
wudu					wood
yfel					evil

7.8 PRONUNCIATION AND RIME

One kind of evidence which is used in reconstructing the older pronunciation of a language is that afforded by poetry, especially rimes. Rime-evidence, however, must be used with some discretion. Poets may deliberately use various kinds of imperfect rimes, like Emily Dickinson's

> I taste a liquor never brewed—
> From Tankards scooped in Pearl—
> Not all the Vats upon the Rhine
> Yield such an Alcohol!¹²

The off-rime *pearl/alcohol* lends a delicate dryness to the verse; it is unnecessary to assume that an exact rime was intended. Similarly, when Swift writes, in "To Mr. Congreve,"

> Thus prostitute my Congreve's name is grown
> To ev'ry lewd pretender of the town,

an investigation of the riming words will show that Old English grōwen became Middle English [grɔuən], early Modern English [gro:(ə)n], whereas Old English tūn became Middle English [tu:n], early Modern English [tʌun]. The words do not rime today and never have. Swift must have used them as off-rimes or as eye-rimes since the spelling looks like a rime. This couplet tells us very little about Swift's pronunciation.

Nevertheless, with the proper caution we can use rime as one evidence for pronunciation, especially when other evidence supports it. Examine the following rimes from Swift. (1) Decide in each case whether the rimes are true or false. (2) Write the riming sounds in phonetic transcription. Be prepared to explain your decision.

(1) Yet want your criticks no just cause to rail,
Since knaves are ne'er obliged for what they steal.

Other similar rimes used by Swift are ease/Bays, please/bays, dreams/names, dream/same. You may consider these rimes as additional evidence in reaching a decision about the couplet.

---

(2) Contented he—but Fate ordains,
He now shall shine in nobler scenes.

Similarly, scenes/entertains, scene/vein, scene/vain, scene/dean.

---

(3) In ready counters never pays,
But pawns her snuff-box, rings, and keys.

Similarly, key/sway, key/day, key/tea.

---

(4) Unhappy ship, thou art returned in vain;
New waves shall drive thee to the deep again.

Similarly, again/unclean,

but also, again/then, again/ten, agen/pen.

---

¹² Reprinted by permission of the publishers and the Trustees of Amherst College from Thomas H. Johnson, Editor, *The Poems of Emily Dickinson*, Cambridge, Mass.: The Belknap Press of Harvard University Press, Copyright 1951, 1955, by The President and Fellows of Harvard College.

(5) Why, there's my landlord now, the squire, who all in money wallows,
He would not give a groat to save his father from the gallows.

Similarly, watch/scratch, watch/match, wand/land, wand/hand, squabble/rabble, want/grant, wanting/planting, wanting/canting, water/matter, wander/by-stander, squat/mat.

---

(6) In velvet cap his head lies warm;
His hat for show, beneath his arm.

Similarly, war/far, war/star/tar.

---

(7) A passage may be found, I've heard,
In some old Greek or Latin bard

Similarly, search/arch, learn/darn, served/starved, unheard/guard, clerk/mark, herbage/garbage, deserve it/starve it, verse/farce, clergy/charge ye, (thou) wert/(Faustus') art.

---

(8) Would you rise in the church? Be stupid and dull;
Be empty of learning, of insolence full.

Similarly, skull/full, blush/bush, thrush/bush, cut/put, guts/puts, touch her/butcher. In the contemporary Irish dialect, Middle English [ʊ] is still a rounded vowel in all positions. How is this information apposite to Swift's rimes?

---

(9) Corinna in the morning dizen'd,
Who sees will spew; who smells, be poison'd.

Similarly, wild/spoil'd, child/spoil'd, malign/join, surprise one [ən]/poison.

---

(10) An act for laying down the plough—
England will send you corn enough.

        but also

Tomorrow will be time enough
To hear such mortifying stuff.

---

(11) The cold conceits, the chilling thoughts,
Went down like stupifying draughts.

Similarly, draught/bought, draught/caught.

---

(12) Next, for encouragement of spinning,
A duty might be laid on linen.

Similarly, loving/sloven, teazing/treason, brewing/ruin, picking/chicken, barking/hearken, trimming/women, breathing/heathen, bubbling/Dublin, smelling/dwell in, building/skill'd in.

---

(13)   Who makes the best figure,
       The Dean or the digger?

       Similarly, figure/vigour/bigger, venture/centre, ventures/representers, lecture/hector, volumes/columns.

---

(14)   For my friends have always thought
       Tenderness my greatest fault.

       Similarly, brought/fault, haughty/faulty, thought/vault.

---

(15)   Within an hour and eke a half,
       I preached three congregations deaf.

       Similarly, half/safe, halves/knaves. Compare the Standard British pronunciation of *halfpenny*.

---

(16)   Then Mrs. Johnson gave her verdict,
       And every one was pleased, that heard it.

---

(17)   Soon repent, or put to slaughter
       Every Greek and Roman author.

---

(18)   Proud Baronet of Nova Scotia,
       The Dean and Spaniard must reproach ye.

       Compare charge ye/clergy.

7.9   EARLY MODERN ENGLISH ILLUSTRATED

The following passages exemplify English from the late fifteenth century to the early seventeenth. The spelling, capitalization, and punctuation are typical of the bewildering variety that characterizes the early Modern period. In the earlier passages look for spelling evidence of the sound changes that characterize Modern English. For example, in the opening sentence of the first selection *write* is spelled *wryght* and *out* is spelled *ought*; what do these spellings indicate about the writer's pronunciation of *gh* in words like *night* and *thought*, in which the digraph represented a velar fricative in Middle English? Look for grammatical differences between early Modern and present-day English with regard to inflections, function words, and word order. Rewrite one of the passages in contemporary idiom and note the points at which you must rephrase to avoid an archaic flavor.

THE PASTON LETTERS

The Pastons were a Norfolk family of substance whose voluminous correspondence reflects the political and social life of fifteenth-century England.[13] Although the letters were written

[13] James Gairdner, *The Paston Letters*, A.D. *1422–1509*. 6 vols. (London, 1904).

during a century that is usually thought of as ending the Middle English period, they show many of the linguistic changes that are characteristic of the early Modern period. There are no sharp breaks in the historical development of a language, and therefore the Paston letters may be taken as examples of the transition from Middle to Modern English.

The first letter printed here is a proposal, or at least a declaration of honorable intentions. That it was favorably received by the lady is apparent in the second letter, although some disagreement had arisen between her father and her suitor over the dowry. The disagreement was eventually resolved, and in the third letter the wife, who is preoccupied with her first pregnancy, writes her husband various requests and bits of gossip.

From John Paston to Margery Brews, 1476

Mastresse, thow so be that I, unaqweyntyd with yow as yet, tak up on me to be thus bold as to wryght on to yow with ought your knowlage and leve, yet, mastress, for syche pore servyse as I now in my mynd owe yow, purposyng, ye not dyspleasyd, duryng my lyff to contenu the same, I beseche yow to pardon my boldness, and not to dysdeyn, but to accepte thys sympyll byll to recomand me to yow in syche wyse as I best can or may imagyn to your most plesure. And, mastress, for sych report as I have herd of yow by many and dyverse persones, and specyally by my ryght trusty frend, Rychard Stratton, berer her of, to whom I beseche yow to geve credence in syche maters as he shall on my behalve comon with yow of, if it lyke you to lystyn hym, and that report causythe me to be the more bold to wryght on to yow, so as I do; for I have herd oft tymys Rychard Stratton sey that ye can and wyll take every thyng well that is well ment, whom I beleve and trust as myche as fewe men leveing, I ensuer yow by my trowthe. And, mastress, I beseche yow to thynk non other wyse in me but that I wyll and shall at all seasons be redy wythe Godes grace to accomplyshe all syche thynges as I have enformyd and desyerd the seyd Rychard on my behalve to geve yow knowlage of, but if it so be that a geyn my wyll it come of yow that I be cast off fro yowr servyse and not wyllyngly by my desert, and that I am and wylbe yours and at your comandmen in every wyse dwryng my lyff. Her I send yow thys bylle wretyn with my lewd hand and sealyd with my sygnet to remayn with yow for a wyttnesse ayenste me, and to my shame and dyshonour if I contrary it. And, mastress, I beseche yow, in easyng of the poore hert that somtyme was at my rewle, whyche now is at yours, that in as short tyme as can be that I may have knowlage of your entent and hough ye wyll have me demeanyd in thys mater, and I wylbe at all seasons redy to performe in thys mater and all others your plesure, as ferforth as lythe in my poore power to do or in all thers that ought wyll do for me, with Godes grace, Whom I beseche to send yow the accomplyshement of your most worchepfull desyers, myn owne fayer lady, for I wyll no ferther labore but to yow, on to the tyme ye geve me leve, and tyll I be suer that ye shall take no dysplesur with my ferther labore.

From Margery Brews to John Paston, Feb., 1477

Ryght reverent and wurschypfull, and my ryght welebeloved Voluntyne, I recomande me unto yowe, ffull hertely desyring to here of yowr welefare, whech I beseche Almyghty God long for to preserve un to Hys plesur, and yowr herts desyre. And yf it please yowe to here of my welefar, I am not in good heele of body, nor of herte, nor schall be tyll I her ffrom yowe;

> For there wottys no creature what peyn that I endure,
> And for to be deede, I dare it not dyscure [discover].

And my lady my moder hath labored the mater to my ffadur full delygently, but sche can no mor gete then ye knowe of, for the whech God knowyth I am full sory. But yf that ye loffe me,

as I tryste verely that ye do, ye will not leffe me therefor; for if that ye hade not halfe the lyve-
lode that ye hafe, for to do the grettest labur that any woman on lyve myght, I wold not forsake
yowe.

> And yf ye commande me to kepe me true wherever I go,
> I wyse I will do all my myght yowe to love and never no mo.
>> And yf my freends say, that I do amys,
>>> Thei schal not me let so for to do,
>> Myne herte me bydds ever more to love yowe
>>> Truly over all erthely thing,
>> And yf thei be never so wroth,
>>> I tryst it schall be better in tyme commyng.

No more to yowe at this tyme, but the Holy Trinite hafe yowe in kepyng. And I besech yowe
that this bill be not seyn of none erthely creatur safe only your selffe, &c.

And thys letter was indyte at Topcroft, with full hevy herte, &c.

By your own,   Margery Brews.

From Margery Brews Paston to John Paston, Dec., 1477

Ryth reverent and worscheful husbond, I recomaunde me to yow, desyryng hertyly to here
of yowr wylfare, thankyng yow for the tokyn that ye sent me be Edmunde Perys, preyng yow
to wete that my modyr sent to my fadyr to London for a goune cloth of mustyrddevyllers [gray
woolen cloth] to make of a goune for me; and he tolde my modyr and me wanne he was comme
home, that he cargeyt yow to beyit, aftyr that he were come oute of London.

I pre yow, yf it be not bowt, that ye wyl wechesaf to byit, and sendyt home as sone as ye may,
for I have no goune to weyre this wyntyr but my blake and my grene a lyer [a shade of green],
and that is so comerus that I ham wery to weryt.

As for the gyrdyl that my fadyr be hestyt me, I spake to hym ther of a lytyl before he ȝede to
London last, and he seyde to me that the faute was in yow, that ȝe wolde not thynk ther uppe on
to do makyt [to have it made]; but I sopose that ys not so; he seydyt but for a skwsacion. I pre
yow, yf ye dor takyt uppe on yow, that ye wyl weche safe to do makyt a yens ye come home, for
I hadde never more nede ther of than I have now, for I ham waxse so fetys [well-proportioned,
handsome] that I may not be gyrte in no barre [band] of no gyrdyl that I have but of one. Elisa-
bet Peverel hath leye sek xv. or xvj. wekys of the seyetyka, but sche sent my modyr word be
Kate, that sche xuld come hedyr wanne God sent tyme, thoow sche xuld be crod [trundled] in a
barwe.

Jon of Damm was here, and my modyr dyskevwyrd me to hym, and he seyed, be hys trouth
that he was not gladder of no thyng that he harde thys towlmonyth, than he was ther of.

I may no lenger leve be my crafte, I am dysscevwyrd of alle men that se me.

Of alle odyr thyngys that ye deseyreyd that I xuld sende yow word of, I have sent yow word of
in a letter that I dede wryte on Ouwyr Ladyis Day laste was. The Holy Trenyte have yow in
Hese kepyng.

Wretyn at Oxnede, in ryth gret hast, on the Thrusday next be fore Seynt Tomas Day.

I pre yow that ye wyl were the reyng with the emage of Seynt Margrete, that I sent yow for a
rememraunse, tyl ye come home; ye have lefte me sweche a rememraunse, that makyth me to
thynke uppe on yow bothe day and nyth wanne I wold sclepe.

Your ys,   M. P.

CAXTON'S PREFACE TO THE ENEYDOS

In several of his prefaces Caxton discusses the problems he has encountered as a translator. The best known of these discussions is the one printed below.[14] Caxton has just described how he came upon a French version of the *Aeneid*.

And whan I had aduysed me in this sayd boke, I delybered and concluded to translate it in to englysshe, And forthwyth toke a penne & ynke, and wrote a leef or tweyne / whyche I ouersawe agayn to corecte it / And whā I sawe the fayr & straunge termes therin / I doubted that it sholde not please some gentylmen whiche late blamed me, sayeng yᵗ in my translacyons I had ouer curyous termes whiche coude not be vnderstande of comyn peple / and desired me to vse olde and homely termes in my translacyons. and fayn wolde I satysfye euery man / and so to doo, toke an olde boke and redde therin / and certaynly the englysshe was so rude and brood that I coude not wele vnderstande it. And also my lorde abbot of west-mynster ded do shewe to me late, certayn euydences wryton in olde englysshe, for to reduce it in to our englysshe now vsid / And certaynly it was wreton in suche wyse that it was more lyke to dutche than englysshe: I coude not reduce ne brynge it to be vnderstonden / And certaynly our langage now vsed varyeth ferre from that whiche was vsed and spoken whan I was borne / For we englysshe men / ben borne vnder the domynacyon of the mone, whiche is neuer stedfaste / but euer wauerynge / wexynge one season / and waneth & dyscreaseth another season / And that comyn englysshe that is spoken in one shyre varyeth from a nother. In so moche that in my dayes happened that certayn marchaūtes were in a shippe in tamyse for to haue sayled ouer the see into zelande / and for lacke of wynde, thei taryed atte forlond, and wente to lande for to refreshe them : And one of theym named sheffelde, a mercer, cam in to an hows and axed for mete : and specyally he axyd after eggys : And the goode wyf answerde, that she coude speke no frenshe. And the marchaūt was angry, for he also coude speke no frenshe, but wolde haue hadde egges / and she vnderstode hym not / And thenne at laste a nother sayd that he wolde haue eyren / then the good wyf sayd that she vnderstod hym wel / Loo, what sholde a man in thyse dayes now wryte, egges or eyren / certaynly it is harde to playse euery man / by cause of dyuersite & chaūge of langage. For in these dayes euery man that is in ony reputacyon in his coūtre, wyll vtter his cōmynycacyon and maters in suche maners & termes / that fewe men shall vnderstonde theym / And som honest and grete clerkes haue ben wyth me, and desired me to wryte the moste curyous termes that I coude fynde / And thus bytwene playn rude / & curyous, I stande abasshed. but in my Iudgemente / the comyn termes that be dayli vsed, ben lyghter to be vnderstonde than the olde and aūcyent englysshe / And for as moche as this present booke is not for a rude vplondyssh man to laboure therin / ne rede it / but onely for a clerke & a noble gentylman that feleth and vnderstondeth in faytes of armes in loue & in noble chyualrye / Therfor in a meane bytwene bothe I haue reduced & translated this sayd booke in to our englysshe, not ouer rude ne curyous, but in suche termes as shall be vnderstanden, by goddys grace, accordynge to my copye. And yf ony man wyll enter mete in redyng of hit, and fyndeth suche termes that he can not vnderstande, late hym goo rede and lerne vyrgyll / or the pystles of ouyde / and ther he shall see and vnderstonde lyghtly all / Yf he haue a good redar & enformer / For this booke is not for euery rude and vnconnynge man to see / but to clerkys and very gentylmen that vnderstande gentylnes and scyence.

---

[14] From W. T. Culley and F. J. Furnivall, eds., *Caxton's Eneydos, 1490* (EETS ES 57; London, 1890).

Sir Thomas Elyot is best known today as the author of *The Governor*, but in his own time his most popular work was *The Castel of Helth Gathered and Made by Syr Thomas Elyot knyghte, out of the chiefe Authors of Physyke, wherby euery manne may knowe the state of his owne body, the preseruatiō of helth, and how to instructe welle his physytion in syckenes that he be not deceyued* (1534). The purpose of this work is adequately stated in its title: It is a handbook of physiology, hygiene, and diagnostics. Of the extracts printed here, the first two deal with the constitution of the body according to physiological theories inherited from the Middle Ages, the third is one of several exercises designed to preserve and promote health, and the fourth describes one common means of letting blood, a widely practiced therapeutic technique.

Of humours

In the body of Man be foure pryncipal humours, which continuynge in the proporcion, that nature hath lymitted, the body is free frome all syckenesse. Contrary wise by the increase or diminution of any of theym in quantitie or qualitie, ouer or vnder theyr naturall assignement, inequall temperature commeth into the bodye, whiche sickenesse foloweth more or lasse, accordyng to the lapse or decaye of the temperatures of the sayd humours, whiche be these folowynge.

Bloudde,	Choler,
Fleume,	Melancholy

[Of spirits]

Spirite is an ayry substance subtyll, styryng the powers of the body to perfourme their operations, whiche is dyuyded into

Naturalle, whiche taketh his begynnynge of the lyuer, and by the vaynes whiche haue no pulse, spredeth into all the hole body.

Vitall, whiche procedeth from the hart, and by the arteries or pulses is sent into all the body.

Animalle, whiche is ingendred in the brayne, and is sente by the senewes throughout the body, & maketh sence or feelynge.

Of vociferation

The chiefe exercyse of the brest and instrumentes of the voyce, is vociferation, whiche is synging, redyng, or crienge, wherof is the propertie, that it purgeth naturall heate, and maketh it also subtyll and stable, and maketh the membres of the body substancyall and stronge, resystynge diseases. This exercyse wold be vsed, of persones shorte wynded, and theym, whiche can not fetche theyr brethe, but holdyng their necke streight vpright. Also of them, whose fleshe is consumed, speciallye about the breaste and shoulders, also which haue had apostumes broken in theyr breastes: moreouer of them that are hoorse by the moche moysture, and to them, whiche haue quartene feuers, it is conuenient, it louseth the humour, that stycketh in the brest, and dryeth vp the moystenesse of the stomacke, whiche properly the course of the quartayne is wont to brynge with hym, it also profiteth them whiche haue feble stomakes, or do vomyte contynually, or do breake vp sowrenesse out of the stomake. It is good also for grefes of the heed. He that intendeth to attempt this exercise, after that he hath ben at the stoole, and softly rubbed the lower partes, and washed his handes. Lette hym speake with as base a voyce as he can, and walkynge, begynne to synge lowder & lowder, but styll in a base voyce, and to take no hede of sweete tunes or armonye. For that nothynge dothe profyte vnto helthe of the body, but to inforce hym selfe to synge greatte, for therby moche ayre drawen in by fetchyng of breath, thrustyth forth the breast and stomacke, and openeth and inlargeth the poores. By hygh crienge and lowde readynge, are expellyd superfluouse humours. Therfore menne and women, hauynge theyr bodyes feeble, and theyr flesshe lowse, and not fyrme, muste reade oftentymes lowde, and in a baase voyce, extendynge oute the wynde pype, and other passages of the breathe.

But notwithstandyying, this exercyse is not vsed alway, and of all persons. For they in whome is abundance of humours corrupted, or be moche diseased with crudite in the stomak and vaines, those doo I counsaylé, to abstayne from the exercyse of the voyce, leste moche corrupteth iuyce or vapours, may therby be into all the body dystrybuted. And here I conclude to speake of exercyse, whiche of them, that desyre to remayne longe in helth, is most diligently, & as I mought say, moste scrupulousely to be obserued.

Of bloude suckers or leaches

There is also an other fourme of euacuation by wormes, founde in waters callyd bloude suckers or leaches, whiche beinge put vnto the body or member, do draw out blode. And their drawynge is more conuenient for fulnesse of bloudde than scarifyenge is, forasmoche as they fetche bloud more deper, and is more of the substance of bloud, yet the opinion of some men is, that they do drawe no bloude but that, which is corrupted, and not proporcionable vnto our body. And therfore in griefes, whiche happen betwene the skynne and the flesshe of blode corrupted, these are more conuenient than scarifienge. But before that they be putte vnto any parte of the body, they muste be fyrste kepte all one day before, gyuyng vnto them a lyttel blode in freshe flesshe. And than putte theym in a cleane water, somwhat warme, and with a spounge wype awaye the slyme, whiche is about theym, and than laye a lyttell bloudde on the place greued, and putte theym thanne to it, and laye on theym a spounge, that whan they be fulle, they may falle awaye, or yf ye wyll sooner haue them of, put a horse heare bytweene theyr mouthes, and the place, and drawe them awaye, or putte to theyr mouthes salte or ashes, or vyneger, and forthwith they shall falle, and than wasshe the place with a spounge: and if there doo yssue moche bloudde, laye on the place the poulder of a spounge, and pytche bourned, or lynnen clothe bourned, or galles bourned, or the herbe callyd *Bursa pastoris* bruysed. And this suffyseth concernyng bloud suckers.

ROBINSON'S PREFACE TO UTOPIA

Sir Thomas More's *Utopia*, which has lent its name to an entire genre of imaginative social commentary, was written in Latin but was translated into English by Raphe Robinson some fifteen years after More's execution. The title page of the first English edition reads as follows

A fruteful and pleasaunt worke of the beste state of a publyque weale, and of the newe yle called Utopia: written in Latine by Syr Thomas More knyght, and translated into Englyshe by Raphe Robynson Citizein and Goldsmythe of London, at the procurement, and earnest request of George Tadlowe Citezein & Haberdassher of the same Citie. Imprinted at London by Abraham Vele, dwelling in Pauls churcheyarde at the sygne of the Lambe. Anno. 1551.

The selection printed here is the beginning of Robinson's Preface, or Epistle Dedicatory, in which he explains why he translated the *Utopia*.

To the right honourable, and his verie singuler good maister, maister William Cecylle esquiere, one of the twoo principal secretaries to the kyng his moste excellent maiestie, Raphe Robynson wissheth cõtinuaunce of health, with dayly increase of vertue, and honoure.

Vpon a tyme, when tidynges came too the citie of Corinthe that kyng Philippe father to Alexander surnamed yᵉ Great, was comming thetherwarde with an armie royall to lay siege to the citie. The Corinthiãs being forth with stryken with greate feare, beganne busilie, and earnestly to looke aboute them, and to falle to worke of all handes. Some to skowre & trymme vp harneis, some to carry stones, some to amende and buylde hygher the walles, some to rampiere and fortyfie the bulwarkes, and fortresses, some one thynge, and some an other for the defendinge, and strengthenynge of the citie. The whiche busie labour, and toyle of theires when Diogenes the phylosopher sawe, hauing no profitable busines wherupō to sette himself on worke (neither any man required his labour, and helpe as expedient for the commē wealth in that necessitie) immediatly girded about him his phylosophicall cloke, & began to rolle, and tumble vp and downe hether & thether vpon the hille syde, that lieth adioyninge to the citie, his great barrel or tunne, wherein he dwelled: for other dwellynge place wold he haue none. This seing one of his frendes, and not alitell musynge therat, came to hym: And I praye the Diogenes (quod he) whie doest thou thus, or what meanest thou hereby? Forsothe I am tumblyng my tubbe to (quod he) bycause it were no reason yᵗ I only should be ydell, where so many be workīg. In semblable maner, right honorable sir, though I be, as I am in dede, of muche lesse habilitie then Diogenes was to do any thinge, that shall or may be for the auauncement & commoditie of the publique wealth of my natiue countrey: yet I seing euery sort, and kynde of people in theire vocatiō, & degree busilie occupied about the cōmō wealthes affaires: & especially learned mē dayly putting forth in writing newe inuentions, & deuises to the furtheraūce of the same: thought it my boūden duetie to God, & to my countrey so to tūble my tubbe, I meane so to occupie, & exercise meself in bestowing such spare houres, as I beinge at yᵉ becke, & cōmaundement of others, cold conueniently winne to me self: yᵗ though no cōmoditie of that my labour, & trauaile to the publique weale should arise, yet it myght by this appeare, yᵗ myne endeuoire, & good wille hereunto was not lacking. To the accōplishemēt therfore, & fulfyllyng of this my mynde, & purpose: I toke vpō me to tourne, and translate out of Latine into oure Englishe tonge the frutefull, & profitable boke, which sir Thomas more knight compiled, & made of the new yle Utopia, cōteining & setting forth yᵉ best state, and fourme of a publique weale: A worke (as it appeareth) writtē almost fourtie yeres ago by the said sir Thomas More yᵉ authour therof.

HOLINSHED'S CHRONICLES

A renaissance successor to medieval histories like the *Polychronicon* was Raphael Holinshed's *The Chronicles of England, Scotland, and Ireland* (1587), which is remembered today as one of Shakespeare's sources.

The first passage printed here is from the geographical survey with which such chronicles usually begin. In it the author expresses a proper Englishman's opinion of the superiority of his birth tongue.

The second passage is an account of the British king, Leir, whose story is better known from Shakespeare's play.

Of the languages spoken in
this Iland

What language came first with *Samothes* and afterward with *Albion*,[15] and the giants of his companie, it is hard for me to determine, sith nothing of sound credit remaineth in writing,

15 Two legendary settlers of Britain.

which may resolue vs in the truth hereof. Yet of so much are we certeine, that the speach of the ancient Britons, and of the Celts, had great affinitie one with another, so that they were either all one, or at leastwise such as either nation with small helpe of interpretors might vnderstand other, and readilie discerne what the speaker meant. Some are of the opinion that the Celts spake Greeke, and how the British toong resembled the same, which was spoken in Grecia before *Homer* did reforme it: but I see that these men doo speake without authoritie and therefore I reiect them, for if the Celts which were properlie called Galles did speake Greeke, why did Cesar in his letters sent to Rome vse that language, because that if they should be intercepted they might not vnderstand them, or why did he not vnderstand the Galles, he being so skilfull in the language without an interpretor? Yet I denie not but that the Celtish and British speaches might haue great affinitie one with another, and the British aboue all other with the Greeke, for both doo appeere by certeine words, as first in *tri* for three . . . .

Next vnto the British speach, the Latine toong was brought in by the Romans, and in maner generallie planted through the whole region, as the French was after by the Normans. Of this toong I will not say much, bicause there are few which be not skilfull in the same . . . .

The third language apparantlie knowne is the Scithian or high Dutch, induced at the first by the Saxons (which the Britons call *Saysonaec*, as they doo the speakers *Sayson*) an hard and rough kind of speach, God wot, when our nation was brought first into acquaintance withall, but now changed with vs into a farre more fine and easie kind of vtterance, and so polished and helped with new and milder words, that it is to be aduouched how there is no one speach vnder the sunne spoken in our time, that hath or can haue more varietie of words, copie of phrases, or figures and floures of eloquence, than hath our English toong, although some haue affirmed vs rather to barke as dogs, than talke like men, bicause the most of our words (as they doo indeed) incline vnto one syllable . . . .

After the Saxon toong, came the Norman or French language ouer into our countrie, and therein were our lawes written for a long time. Our children also were by an especiall decree taught first to speake the same, and therevnto inforced to learne their constructions in the French, whensoeuer they were set to the Grammar schoole . . . .

Afterward also, by diligent trauell of *Geffray Chaucer*, and *Iohn Gowre*, in the time of Richard the second, and after them of *Iohn Scogan*, and *Iohn Lydgate* monke of Berrie, our said toong was brought to an excellent passe, notwithstanding that it neuer came vnto the type of perfection, vntill the time of Queene Elizabeth . . . .

This also is proper to vs Englishmen, that sith ours is a meane language, and neither too rough nor too smooth in vtterance, we may with much facilitie learne any other language, beside Hebrue, Greeke & Latine, and speake it naturallie, as if we were home-borne in those countries; & yet on the other side it falleth out, I wot not by what other meanes, that few forren nations can rightlie pronounce ours, without some and that great note of imperfection, especiallie the French men, who also seldome write any thing that sauoreth of English trulie.

Leir the Ruler

Leir the sonne of Baldud was admitted ruler ouer the Britaines, in the yeare of the world 3105, at what time Ioas reigned in Iuda. This Leir was a prince of right noble demeanor, gouerning his land and subiects in great wealth. He made the towne of Caerleir now called Leicester, which standeth vpon the riuer of Sore. It is written that he had by his wife three daughters without other issue, whose names were Gonorilla, Regan, and Cordeilla, which daughters he greatly loued, but specially Cordeilla the yoongest farre aboue the two elder. When this Leir therefore was come to great yeres, & began to waxe vnweldie through age, he thought to vnderstand the affections of his daughters towards him, and preferre hir whome he best loued, to the succession ouer the kingdome. Whervpon he first asked Gonorilla the eldest, how well she loued him: who calling hir gods to record, protested that she loued him more than hir owne life, which by right and reason should be most deere vnto hir. With which answer the father being well pleased, turned to the second, and demanded of hir how well she loued him: who answered (confirming hir saiengs with great othes) that she loued him more than toong could expresse, and farre aboue all other creatures of the world.

Then called he his yoongest daughter Cordeilla before him, and asked of hir what account she made of him, vnto whome she made this answer as followeth: Knowing the great loue and fatherlie zeale that you haue alwaies borne towards me (for the which I maie not answere you otherwise than I thinke, and as my conscience leadeth me) I protest vnto you, that I haue loued you euer, and will continuallie (while I live) loue you as my naturall father. And if you would more vnderstand of the loue that I beare you, assertaine your selfe, that so much as you haue, so much you are worth, and so much I loue you, and no more. The father being nothing content with this answer, married his two eldest daughters, the one vnto Henninus the duke of Cornewall, and the other vnto Maglanus the duke of Albania, betwixt whome he willed and ordeined that his land should be diuided after his death, and the one halfe thereof immediatlie should be assigned to them in hand: but for the third daughter Cordeilla he reserued nothing.

Neuertheles it fortuned that one of the princes of Gallia (which now is called France) whose name was Aganippus, hearing of the beautie, womanhood, and good conditions of the said Cordeilla, desired to haue hir in mariage, and sent ouer to hir father, requiring that he might haue hir to wife: to whome answer was made, that he might haue his daughter, but as for anie dower he could haue none, for all was promised and assured to hir other sisters alreadie. Aganippus notwithstanding this answer of deniall to receiue anie thing by way of dower with Cordeilla, tooke hir to wife, onlie moued thereto (I saie) for respect of hir person and amiable vertues. This Aganippus was one of the twelue kings that ruled Gallia in those daies, as in the British historie it is recorded. But to proceed.

After that Leir was fallen into age, the two dukes that had married his two eldest daughters, thinking it long yer the gouernment of the land did come to their hands, arose against him in armour, and rest from him the gouernance of the land, vpon conditions to be continued for terme of life: by the which he was put to his portion, that is, to liue after a rate assigned to him for the maintenance of his estate, which in processe of time was diminished as well by Maglanus as by Henninus. But the greatest griefe that Leir tooke, was to see the vnkindnesse of his daughters, which seemed to thinke that all was too much which their father had, the same being neuer so little: in so much that going from the one to the other, he was brought to that miserie, that scarslie they would allow him one seruant to wait vpon him.

In the end, such was the vnkindnesse, or (as I maie saie) the vnnaturalnesse which he found in his two daughters, notwithstanding their faire and pleasant words vttered in time past, that being constreined of necessitie, he fled the land, & sailed into Gallia, there to seeke some comfort of his yongest daughter Cordeilla, whom before time he hated. The ladie Cordeilla hearing that he was arriued in poore estate, she first sent to him priuilie a certeine summe of monie to apparell himselfe withall, and to reteine a certeine number of seruants that might attend vpon him in honorable wise, as apperteined to the estate which he had borne: and then so accompanied, she appointed him to come to the court, which he did, and was so ioifullie, honorablie, and louinglie receiued, both by his sonne in law Aganippus, and also by his daughter Cordeilla, that his hart was greatlie comforted: for he was no lesse honored, than if he had beene king of the whole countrie himselfe.

Now when he had informed his sonne in law and his daughter in what sort he had beene vsed by his other daughters, Aganippus caused a mightie armie to be put in a readinesse, and likewise a great nauie of ships to be rigged, to passe ouer into Britaine with Leir his father in law, to see him againe restored to his kingdome. It was accorded, that Cordeilla should also go with him to take possession of the land, the which he promised to leaue vnto hir, as the rightfull inheritour after his decesse, notwithstanding any former grant made to hir sisters or to their husbands in anie maner of wise.

Herevpon, when this armie and nauie of ships were readie, Leir and his daughter Cordeilla with hir husband tooke the sea, and arriuing in Britaine, fought with their enimies, and discomfited them in battell, in the which Maglanus and Henninus were slaine: and then was Leir restored to his kingdome, which he ruled after this by the space of two yeeres, and then died, fortie yeeres after he first began to reigne. His bodie was buried at Leicester in a vaut vnder the chanell of the river of Sore beneath the towne.

SIR WALTER RALEIGH'S INSTRUCTIONS
TO HIS SON

During the last fifteen years of his life, while imprisoned in the Tower of London, Sir Walter Raleigh wrote his major prose work, *The History of the World*. He also found time to compose a short handbook of practical advice for his son. Wat, the son for whom the book was probably written, stood in need of it. Ben Jonson was his tutor during a trip to France and described the twenty-year-old's fondness for women and practical jokes, one of which had Jonson himself as its butt.

Instructions to his Sonne: and to Posteritie was published in 1632, fourteen years after Raleigh's execution. The selection printed here gives advice on choosing and not choosing a wife.

The next, and greatest care ought to be in choice of a Wife, and the onely danger therein is Beauty, by which all men in all Ages, wise and foolish, have beene betrayed. And though I know it vain to use Reasons or arguments to disswade thee from being captiuated therewith, there being few or none that ever resisted that Witcherie; yet I cannot omit to warne thee, as of other things, which may be thy ruine and destruction. For the present time, it is true, that every man preferres his fantasie in that Appetite before all other worldly desires, leaving the care of Honour, credit, and safety in respect thereof; But remēber, that though these affections doe not last, yet the bond of Marriage dureth to the end of thy life; and therefore better to be borne withall in a mistris, then in a wife; for when thy humour shall change thou art yet free to chuse again (if thou give thy selfe that vaine liberty.) Remember, secondly, that if thou marry for Beauty, thou bindest thy selfe for all thy life for that which perchance will neither last nor please thee one year; and when thou hast it, it will bee vnto thee of no price at all, for the desire dyeth when it is attayned, and the affection perisheth, when it is satisfied. Remember when thou wert a sucking Child that then thou diddest love thy Nurse, and that thou wert fond of her, after a while thou didst love thy dry nurse, and didst forget the other, after that thou didst also despise her; so will it be with thee in thy liking in elder yeeres; and therefore, though thou canst not forbeare to love, yet forbeare to linke, and after a while thou shalt find an alteration in thy selfe, and see another far more pleasing then the first, second, or third love.

. . . . . .

Let thy time of marriage bee in thy young, and strong yeeres; for beleeve it, ever the young Wife betrayeth the old Husband, and shee that had thee not in thy flower, will despise thee in thy fall, and thou shalt bee unto her, but a captivity and sorrow. Thy best time will be towards thirty, for as the younger times are unfit, either to chuse or to governe a Wife and family; so if thou stay long, thou shalt hardly see the education of thy Children, which being left to strangers, are in effect lost, and better were it to bee unborne then ill bred; for thereby thy posterity shall either perish, or remaine a shame to thy name, and family.

The Modern English Period to 1800: Forms and Syntax

1. Define the following terms:

his-genitive	leveling (leveled form)	reflexive construction
group-genitive	eye dialect	purism
uninflected genitive	expanded verb forms	prescriptive grammar
analytical comparison	impersonal construction	

2. What are the living inflections of present-day English, that is, the inflectional endings that we might add to newly created nouns, adjectives, and verbs?

3. What is the historical source of each of those inflections?

4. What additional inflections were freely used in early Modern English?

5. How do early Modern and present-day English differ in the form and use of pronouns?

6. How do early Modern and present-day English differ with respect to contractions?

7. What criteria, other than the observation of actual use, guided the eighteenth-century grammarians in their making of rules for English?

8. Identify Robert Cawdrey, Henry Cockeram, Nathan Bailey, Samuel Johnson, John Wallis, Robert Lowth, Joseph Priestley, George Campbell, Lindley Murray.

8.2 *NOUNS*

1. Describe the history of the Modern English regular noun plural ending -*s*, using the forms cited below as illustrations. Consider the history of the (1) pronunciation, (2) meaning, and (3) domain (that is, the number and kinds of nouns that take the ending).

OLD ENGLISH

hundas 'dogs'	cyrican 'churches'	gatu 'gates'
hunda 'of dogs'	cyricena 'of churches'	gata 'of gates'
hundum 'to, with dogs'	cyricum 'to, with churches'	gatum 'to, with gates'

MIDDLE ENGLISH

houndes '(of, to, with) dogs'	chirches '(of, to, with) churches'	gates '(of, to, with) gates'

MODERN ENGLISH

hounds	churches	gates

(1) pronunciation: _____

_____

(2) meaning: _____

_____

(3) domain: _____

_____

2. A number of Modern English irregular noun plurals are survivals of inflectional patterns that once had much wider domains. Describe the origin of the following plurals, and list other words that have a similar plural form in Modern English.

thief–thieves: _____

_____

foot–feet: _____

_____

ox–oxen: _____

_____

deer–deer: _____

_____

3. *Woman* and its plural, *women*, have had a complex history. The forms cited below illustrate some of the most important changes the word has undergone (the Middle English rounding of [wɪ] to [wʊ] was a dialect variation).

Describe the development of the Old English forms into the current singular and plural; explain each step of the development as due to sound changes you have already studied, to dialect borrowing, or to analogy.

	SINGULAR	PLURAL
OLD ENGLISH	wīfman (nom.-acc. sing.)	wīfmen (nom.-acc. pl.)
MIDDLE ENGLISH	wimman, wumman, womman, wiman, woman	wimmen, wummen, wommen, wimen, women
MODERN ENGLISH	woman [wʊmən]	women [wɪmɪn], [-ən]

_____

_____

_____

_____

_____

_____

_____

_____

_____

4. As English has borrowed words, it has sometimes borrowed the foreign plural as well as the singular. Among such loan-words are the following. For each, give the foreign plural, specify the language from which it derives, and list some other words with the same plural formation.

vertebra _____

nucleus _____

stratum _____

index _____

matrix _____

analysis _____

species _____

criterion _____

stigma _____

cherub _____

5. List some loan-words that have foreign plurals other than those cited above. _____

6. Explain the function and the apparent origin of the following italicized pronouns:

   by Mars *his* gauntlet (Shakespeare, *Troilus and Cressida*, IV.v)

   Tamburlaine the Great ... shewed vpon Stages in the Citie of London, By the right honorable the Lord Admyrall, *his* seruants. (title page of the 1590 edition)

   Ben: Ionson *his* Volpone or The Foxe. (title page of the 1607 edition)

   _____

7. The sign of the genitive (-'s) is traditionally called an inflectional affix. How does it differ from other inflections in its position, and why might it more accurately be called a grammatical particle in Modern English? _____

8. Explain the origin of the *s*-less genitives in these expressions:

   ladyfinger _____

   by my fatherkin _____

   Ulysses' voyage _____

   for heaven sake _____

8.3 ADJECTIVES AND ADVERBS

1. What caused the Middle English distinction between strong and weak and between singular and plural adjectives to disappear from our language? _____

    _____

2. Cite an early Modern English example for each of the following:

    polysyllabic adjective with inflectional comparison _____

    monosyllabic adjective with analytical comparison _____

    adjective with double comparison _____

    adverb without ending that would now require *-ly* _____

3. Cite a few adjectives that still fluctuate between inflectional and analytical comparison in current English. _____

    _____

4. Cite a few adverbs like *deep–deeply* that have two forms in current English. _____

    _____

5. What is the origin of the adverb without *-ly*? _____

    _____

8.4 PRONOUNS

1. How does current English differ from early Modern in its use of the genitives *my* and *mine*? The difference is illustrated in this quotation from Shakespeare:

    Falstaff ... Shall I not take mine ease in mine inn, but I shall have my pocket picked? I have lost a seal ring of my grandfather's worth forty mark. (*1 Henry IV*, III.iii)

    _____

2. What nuances of meaning are implied by the choice between *y*-forms and *th*-forms of the second person pronoun in the following passages from Shakespeare?

    [Miranda questions her father about the tempest which has apparently wrecked a ship.]

    Miranda   If by *your* Art (my deerest father) *you* haue
               Put the wild waters in this Rore; alay them.

               · · · · ·

    Prospero   I haue done nothing, but in care of *thee*
               (Of *thee* my deere one; *thee* my daughter) who
               Art ignorant of what *thou* art. (*Tempest*, I.ii)

    _____

    [King Henry doubts his son's loyalty and is reassured by Hal.]

    King   But wherefore doe I tell these Newes to *thee*?
             Why, Harry, doe I tell *thee* of my Foes,
             Which art my neer'st and dearest Enemie?
             Thou, that art like enough, through Vassal Feare,

Base Inclination, and the start of Spleene,
To fight against me vnder Percies pay,
To dogge his heeles, and curtsie at his frownes,
To shew how much *thou* art degenerate.

Prince Doe not thinke so, *you* shall not finde it so:
And Heauen forgiue them, that so much haue sway'd
Your Maiesties good thoughts away from me:
I will redeeme all this on Percies head,
And in the closing of some glorious day,
Be bold to tell *you*, that I am *your* Sonne.   (*1 Henry IV*, III.ii)

[King Claudius and Queen Gertrude urge Hamlet to forgo his mourning and to remain at the Danish court.]

King How is it that the Clouds still hang on *you*?

Hamlet Not so my Lord, I am too much i'th'Sun.

Queen Good Hamlet cast *thy* nightly colour off,
And let *thine* eye looke like a Friend on Denmarke.
Do not for euer with *thy* veyled lids
Seeke for *thy* Noble Father in the dust;
Thou know'st 'tis common, all that liues must dye,
Passing through Nature, to Eternity.
     . . . . .

King 'Tis sweet and commendable
In *your* Nature Hamlet,
To giue these mourning duties to *your* Father:
But *you* must know, *your* Father lost a Father.
     . . . . .

And we beseech *you*, bend *you* to remaine
Heere in the cheere and comfort of our eye,
Our cheefest Courtier Cosin, and our Sonne.

Queen Let not *thy* Mother lose her Prayers Hamlet:
I pry*thee* stay with vs, go not to Wittenberg.

Hamlet I shall in all my best
Obey *you* Madam.

King Why 'tis a louing, and a faire Reply.   (*Hamlet*, I.ii)

[Harry Percy, Northumberland's son, has defended his brother-in-law, Mortimer, against the charge of treason. King Henry still refuses to ransom Mortimer, who was captured in battle by Owen Glendower.]

King *Thou* do'st bely him Percy, *thou* dost bely him;
He neuer did encounter with Glendower:
I tell *thee*, he durst as well haue met the diuell alone,
As Owen Glendower for an enemy.
Art *thou* not asham'd? But, Sirrah, henceforth
Let me not heare *you* speake of Mortimer.
Send me *your* Prisoners with the speediest meanes,

Or *you* shall heare in such a kinde from me
As will displease *ye*. My Lord Northumberland,
We License *your* departure with *your* sonne,
Send vs *your* Prisoners, or *you*'l heare of it.   (*1 Henry IV*, I.iii)

[Hotspur (Harry Percy) is secretly planning to join a revolt against King Henry IV; his wife has questioned him about his mysterious activities.]

Hotspur   Come, wilt *thou* see me ride?
And when I am a horsebacke, I will sweare
I loue *thee* infinitely. But hearke *you* Kate,
I must not haue *you* henceforth, question me,
Whether I go: nor reason whereabout.
Whether I must, I must: and to conclude,
This Euening must I leaue *thee*, gentle Kate.
I know *you* wise, but yet no further wise
Than Harry Percies wife. Constant *you* are,
But yet a woman: and for secrecie,
No lady closer. For I will beleeue
Thou wilt not vtter what *thou* do'st not know,
And so farre wilt I trust *thee*, gentle Kate.   (*1 Henry IV*, II.iii)

[Lear has just disinherited his youngest daughter, Cordelia, and Kent speaks in her defense.]

Kent   Royall Lear,
Whom I haue euer honor'd as my King,
Lou'd as my Father, as my Master follow'd,
As my great Patron thought on in my praiers.
Lear   The bow is bent & drawne, make from the shaft.
Kent   Let it fall rather, though the forke inuade
The region of my heart, be Kent vnmannerly,
When Lear is mad, what wouldest *thou* do old man?
Think'st *thou* that dutie shall haue dread to speake,
When power to flattery bowes?
To plainnesse honour's bound,
When Maiesty falls to folly, reserue *thy* state,
And in *thy* best consideration checke
This hideous rashnesse, answere my life, my iudgement:
Thy yongest Daughter do's not loue *thee* least.   (*King Lear*, I.i)

[Lady Anne is on her way to the funeral of her father-in-law, King Henry VI, when she meets Richard, who has murdered both the old King and Lady Anne's husband.]

Anne   *Thou* was't prouoked by *thy* bloody minde,
That neuer dream'st on ought but Butcheries:

| | Did'st *thou* not kill this King? |
| *Richard* | I graunt *ye*. |
| . . . . . |
Anne	He is in heauen, where *thou* shalt neuer come.
Richard	Let him thank me, that holpe to send him thither:
	For he was fitter for that place then earth.
Anne	And *thou* vnfit for any place, but hell.
Richard	Yes one place else, if *you* will heare me name it.
Anne	Some dungeon.
Richard	*Your* Bed-chamber.
Anne	Ill rest betide the chamber where *thou* lyest.
Richard	So will it Madam, till I lye with *you*.
. . . . .
Anne	*Thou* was't the cause, and most accurst effect.
Richard	*Your* beauty was the cause of that effect:
	Your beauty that did haunt me in my sleepe,
	To vndertake the death of all the world,
	So I might liue one houre in *your* sweet bosome.
Anne	If I thought that, I tell *thee* Homicide,
	These Nailes should rent that beauty from my Cheekes.
Richard	These eyes could not endure y^t beauties wrack,
	You should not blemish it, if I stood by;
	As all the world is cheared by the Sunne,
	So I by that: It is my day, my life.
Anne	Blacke night ore-shade *thy* day, & death *thy* life.
Richard	Curse not *thy* selfe faire Creature,
	Thou art both.
Anne	I would I were, to be reueng'd on *thee*.
Richard	It is a quarrell most vnnaturall,
	To be reueng'd on him that loueth *thee*.
. . . . .

[After Richard has offered to kill himself, Anne relents.]

Richard	Looke how my Ring incompasseth *thy* Finger,
	Euen so *thy* Brest incloseth my poore heart:
	Weare both of them, for both of them are *thine*.
	And if *thy* poore deuoted Seruant may
	But beg one fauour at *thy* gracious hand,
	Thou dost confirme his happinesse for euer.
Anne	What is it?
Richard	That it may please *you* leaue these sad designes,
	To him that hath most cause to be a Mourner,
	And presently repayre to Crosbie House:
	Where (after I haue solemnly interr'd
	At Chertsey Monast'ry this Noble King,
	And wet his Graue with my Repentant Teares)
	I will with all expedient duty see *you*,
	For diuers vnknowne Reasons, I beseech *you*,
	Grant me this Boon.
Anne	With all my heart, and much it ioyes me too,

To see *you* are become so penitent.

Tressel and Barkley, go along with me.

Richard Bid me farwell.

   Anne 'Tis more than *you* deserue:

But since *you* teach me how to flatter *you*,

Imagine I haue saide farewell already.   (*Richard III*, I.ii)

---

3. Some of the *ye*'s and *you*'s in the following quotations from Shakespeare are used "correctly" according to the case distinctions of Old and Middle English, and some show a confusion of the older forms. Circle the pronouns that confuse the older nominative and objective functions.

Antony I do beseech *yee*, if *you* beare me hard,

      Now whil'st your purpled hands do reeke and smoake,

      Fulfill your pleasure.   (*Julius Caesar*, III.i)

Poet For shame *you* Generals; what do *you* meane?

     Loue, and be Friends, as two such men should bee,

     For I haue seene more yeeres I'me sure then *yee*.   (*Julius Caesar*, IV.iii)

Porter *You*'l leaue your noyse anon *ye* Rascals: doe *you* take the Court for Parish Garden:

      ye rude Slaues, leaue your gaping.   (*Henry VIII*, V.iii)

King As I haue made *ye* one Lords, one remaine:

     So I grow stronger, *you* more Honour gaine.   (*Henry VIII*, V.ii)

Banquo Are *ye* fantasticall, or that indeed

      Which outwardly *ye* shew? My Noble Partner

      You greet with present Grace, and great prediction

      Of Noble hauing, and of Royall hope.   (*Macbeth*, I.iii)

4. Can you think of any reason why nominative *ye* and objective *you* should have been widely confused whereas other nominative-objective distinctions like *he–him*, *she–her*, *I–me*, *we–us*, *they–them* were not so confused? Suggestion: Consider the influence of lack of stress.

---

5. Identify the origin of the italicized forms as

        S—regular stressed development of the Middle English pronoun,

        U—unstressed development of the Middle English pronoun, or

        A—analogical form.

_____ *A* toke me to him and ast how my suster dede, and I answeryd wyll, never better.

                                          (*Paston Letters*, no. 260)

_____ *Hit* was at Ierusalem the feaste of the dedication. (Tindale's Gospel of John, x.22)

_____ I shall report *it* so. (*All's Well*, II.v)

_____ It lifted vp *it* head. (*Hamlet*, I.ii)

_____ Heauen grant vs *its* peace. (*Measure for Measure*, I.ii)

_____ And the earth brought forth grass, and herb yielding seed after *his* kind. (Gen. i.12)

_____ Were our Teares wanting to this Funerall,

      These Tidings would call forth *her* flowing Tides. (*1 Henry VI*, I.i)

_____ *Lear* Be my Horsses ready?

       Fool Thy Asses are gone about 'em.   (*King Lear*, I.v)

6. What is the first citation in the *Oxford English Dictionary* for each of the following pronouns used as a simple relative? Give the quotation and the date.

the _____

that _____

which _____

who _____

7. Circle the pronouns that have "improper" case forms according to the rules of school grammar.

    Oliver Know you before whom [you are] sir?

Orlando I, better then him I am before knowes mee.   (*As You Like It*, I.i)

We are alone, here's none but thee, & I.   (*2 Henry VI*, I.ii)

Is she as tall as me?   (*Antony and Cleopatra*, III.iii)

Consider who the King your father sends,
To whom he sends, and what's his Embassie.   (*Love's Labor's Lost*, II.i)

Oh, the dogge is me, and I am my selfe.   (*Two Gentlemen*, II.iii)

             The King,
His Brother, and yours, abide all three distracted,
And the remainder mourning ouer them,
Brim full of sorrow, and dismay: but chiefly
Him that you term'd Sir, the good old Lord Gonzallo.   (*Tempest*, V.i)

Yes, you haue seene Cassio, and she together.   (*Othello*, IV.ii)

For this, from stiller Seats we came, our Parents, and vs twaine.   (*Cymbeline*, V.iv)

Who ioyn'st thou with, but with a Lordly Nation,
That will not trust thee, but for profits sake?   (*1 Henry VI*, III.iii)

Now could I (Caska) name to thee a man,

      .   .   .   .   .

A man no mightier then thy selfe, or me,
In personall action; yet prodigious growne.   (*Julius Caesar*, I.iii)

8.5 VERBS: THE SEVEN STRONG CLASSES

Verbs from all of the seven strong classes have survived in Modern English, but sound change and analogy have played such havoc with the vowels which once marked their principal parts that the traditional classification into seven groups has only historical validity.

The most common strong verbs in Modern English, arranged according to the traditional class to which they most nearly conform, are these:

CLASS I   abide, bite, chide, dive, drive, hide, ride, rise, shine, slide, smite, stride, strike, strive, thrive, write

CLASS II   choose, cleave, fly, freeze

CLASS III   begin, bind, cling, dig, drink, fight, find, fling, grind, ring, run, shrink, sing, sink, sling, slink, spin, spring, stick, sting, stink, string, swim, swing, win, wind, wring

CLASS IV   bear, break, come, get, heave, shear, speak, steal, swear, tear, tread, weave

CLASS V   bid, eat, give, lie, see, sit

CLASS VI   draw, forsake, shake, slay, stand, take

CLASS VII   beat, blow, crow, fall, grow, hang, hold, know, throw

Some of these verbs were originally weak or were loan-words but acquired strong inflection by analogy. Their history is discussed in *Origins and Development*, pages 194–204, and is summarized in the following outline. For each class, the typical vowels of the Middle English principal parts are listed, the development of the principal parts of modern Standard English is summarized, and the vowels of the three modern parts (infinitive, preterit, past participle) are given in phonetic notation. Complete the outline by writing all three parts of each verb in an appropriate blank. Thus *abide, abode, abode* would go under IC; *bite, bit, bitten*, under IB; and so forth.

CLASS I   (ME ī ǭ i i)

A. Normal development with Modern English preterit from Middle English preterit singular:
   [aɪ o ɪ-n]

   _____   _____

   _____   _____

   _____   _____

   _____   _____

B. Normal development with Modern English preterit from Middle English preterit plural and past participle: [aɪ ɪ ɪ(-n)]

   _____   _____

   _____   _____

C. Modern English preterit and past participle from Middle English preterit singular:
   [aɪ o o]

   _____   _____

D. Modern English preterit of uncertain origin; normal development of the past participle is now used only metaphorically: [aɪ ʌ ɪ-n]

   _____

E. Originally a weak verb; strong preterit acquired by analogy: [aɪ o aɪ-d]

   _____

CLASS II   (ME ē,ō ę̄ u ǭ)

A. Modern English preterit from Middle English past participle: [i,u o o-n]

   _____   _____

   _____

B. Modern English preterit perhaps by analogy with Class VII: [aɪ u o-n]

   _____

CLASS III   (ME i,ī a u,ōu u,ōu)

A. Normal development with Modern English preterit from Middle English preterit singular:
   [ɪ æ ʌ(-n)]

   _____   _____

   _____   _____

   _____   _____

_____   _____
_____

B. Normal development with Modern English preterit from Middle English preterit plural and past participle: [ɪ,aɪ ʌ,aʊ ʌ,aʊ]

_____   _____
_____   _____
_____   _____
_____   _____
_____   _____
_____   _____
_____   _____

C. Modern English present from Middle English past participle: [ʌ æ ʌ]

_____

D. Normal development, allowing for the influence of Middle English *h* [x] on a preceding vowel: [aɪ ɔ ɔ]

_____

CLASS IV   (ME ę̄ a ē ǭ)
A. Modern English preterit from Middle English past participle: [i,e o o(-n)]

_____   _____
_____

B. Modern English preterit from Middle English past participle; variation in the vowels is due to the influence of [r]: [ɛr,ɪr or,ɔr or,ɔr-n]

_____   _____
_____   _____

C. Modern English preterit from Middle English past participle; shortened vowels in all parts: [ɛ ɑ ɑ(-n)]

_____

D. Normal development of the forms *cumen, cām, cumen*, which were irregular in Middle English: [ʌ e ʌ]

_____

CLASS V   (ME ę̄ a ē ę̄)
A. Modern English preterit from a lengthened form of Middle English preterit singular: [i e i-n]

_____

B. Present stem with irregular [ɪ] since Old English times; three Modern English preterits from the Middle English preterit singular by normal development, from a lengthened form of the Middle English preterit singular, and from the irregular past participle; past participle vowel perhaps from the present by analogy with other verbs which had the same vowel in the present and past participle: [ɪ æ,e,ɪ ɪ(-n)]

_____

C. Not a continuation of the native English verb (Chaucer's *yeven, yaf, yaven, yeven*), but of a related Scandinavian verb: [ɪ e ɪ-n]

_____

D. Modern English preterit and past participle from Middle English preterit singular; the present has had an irregular [ɪ] since Old English times: [ɪ æ æ]

_____

E. Normal development, allowing for influence of [j] on the preceding vowel, except in present stem (for which see *Origins and Development*, p. 201, n. 65):   [aɪ e e-n]

_____

F. Normal development of Middle English irregular forms with the vowels [e: aʊ e:]:   [i ɔ i-n]

_____

CLASS VI   (ME ă̄ ō ō ă̄)

A. Normal development with Modern shortening of the preterit vowel: [e ʊ e-n]

_____   _____

_____

B. Modern English past participle from Middle English preterit: [æ ʊ ʊ]

_____

C. Present stem vowel from the past participle; preterit vowel by analogy with Class VII verbs: [e u e-n]

_____

D. Preterit vowel by analogy with Class VII verbs; present and past participle are normal developments of Middle English [aʊ]:   [ɔ u ɔ-n]

_____

CLASS VII   (ME: several different vowels in the present and past participle; preterit singular and plural: ĕ or iu)

A. Normal development: [o u o-n]

_____   _____

_____   _____

B. Normal development of the preterit; only the weak past participle now exists: [o u o-d]

_____

C. Normal development, with spelling of the preterit from the other forms: [i i i-n]

_____

D. Normal development: [ɔ ɛ ɔ-n]

_____

E. Modern English past participle from Middle English preterit: [o ɛ ɛ]

_____

F. Modern English forms are a mixture of three Middle English verbs (*hōn*, Class VII; *hangen*, weak; *hengen*, a Scandinavian loan):   [æ ʌ ʌ]

_____

8.6 *VERB ENDINGS AND CONSTRUCTIONS*

1. Explain the inflectional form of the italicized verbs.

   Thou hotly *lusts* to vse her in that kind, for which thou *whip'st* her.   (*King Lear*, IV.vi)

_____

Sometime she *driueth* ore a Souldiers necke, & then *dreames* he of cutting Forraine throats.

(*Romeo and Juliet*, I.iv)

His teares *runs* downe his beard like winters drops
From eaues of reeds: your charm so strongly works 'em
That if you now beheld them, your affections
Would become tender.   (*Tempest*, V.i)

Where is thy Husband now? Where *be* thy Brothers?
Where *be* thy two Sonnes? Wherin dost thou Ioy?   (*Richard III*, IV.iv)

I suppose you *was* in a dream.   (Bunyan, *Pilgrim's Progress*)

For all the Welchmen hearing thou *wert* dead,
Are gone to Bullingbrooke, disperst, and fled.   (*Richard II*, III.ii)

Thou *was't* borne of woman.   (*Macbeth*, V.vii)

---

2. Paraphrase the italicized expressions in current idiom, and comment on the grammar of the early Modern constructions.

Yet hold I off. Women are Angels *wooing*,
Things won are done, ioyes soule lyes in the dooing.   (*Troilus and Cressida*, I.ii)

The clocke strook nine, when I *did send* the Nurse.   (*Romeo and Juliet*, II.v)

What *saies he* of our marriage? What of that?   (*Romeo and Juliet*, II.v)

I *care not*.   (*Romeo and Juliet*, III.i)

Tis knowne to you he is mine enemy:
Nay more, an enemy vnto you all,
And no great friend, *I feare me* to the King.   (*2 Henry VI*, I.i)

But *me list* not here to make comparison.   (Peele, *The Arraignment of Paris*, prologue)

The common executioner
Whose heart th'accustom'd sight of death makes hard
Falls not the axe vpon the humbled neck,
But first begs pardon.   (*As You Like It*, III.v)

His Lordship *is walk'd* forth into the Orchard.   (*2 Henry IV*, I.i)

---

3. More than one twentieth-century grammar lists as the "future tense" of English forms like these:

I shall go	we shall go
thou wilt go	you will go
he will go	they will go

Comment on the historical validity and the contemporary reality of such a paradigm.

_____

_____

_____

4. The present-day verbal system includes a number of phrases that combine the auxiliaries *be* and *have* with a main verb to produce periphrastic tenses. By consulting the *Oxford English Dictionary* entries for *be* and *have*, determine the earliest date for each of the following constructions.

passive (for example, *is sung*) _____

progressive (for example, *is singing*) _____

progressive passive (for example, *is being sung*) _____

perfect (for example, *has sung*) _____

perfect passive (for example, *has been sung*) _____

8.7 THE IMPORTANCE OF PREPOSITIONS

As the inflections of English nouns disappeared, prepositions became more important as grammatical signals, and their number increased.

1. Prepositions have been created from phrases (*because of* from *by cause of*), adapted from inflectional forms (*during* from the archaic *to dure*) or borrowed from other languages (*per* from Latin). Describe the origin of the following prepositions.

amidst _____

among _____

between _____

despite _____

down _____

instead of _____

near _____

past _____

pending _____

plus _____

since _____

via _____

2. According to the citations in the *Oxford English Dictionary*, in what year was each of the following first used as an English preposition?

across	_____	minus	_____	re	_____
after	_____	notwithstanding	_____	round	_____
athwart	_____	onto	_____	throughout	_____
below	_____	opposite	_____	until	_____
beside	_____	out of	_____	unto	_____
beyond	_____	outside	_____	vis-à-vis	_____
inside	_____	per	_____		

3. The idiomatic use of prepositions has changed somewhat since the early Modern period. What expressions would current English prefer in place of the italicized prepositions in the following quotations?

Antony   Thou can'st not feare [frighten] vs Pompey with thy sailes.
Weele speake with thee at Sea. *At* land thou know'st
How much we do o're-count [outnumber] thee.   (*Antony and Cleopatra*, II.vi)

_____

Marcellus   Some sayes, that euer *'gainst* that Season comes
Wherein our Sauiours Birth is celebrated,
The Bird of Dawning singeth all night long.   (*Hamlet*, I.i)

_____

Rivers   Then is my Soueraigne slaine?
Queen   I [aye] almost slaine, for he is taken prisoner,

·   ·   ·   ·   ·

And as I further haue to vnderstand,
Is new committed to the Bishop of Yorke,
Fell Warwickes Brother, and *by* that our Foe.   (*3 Henry VI*, IV.iv)

_____

Helena   That you may well perceiue I haue not wrong'd you,
One of the greatest in the Christian world
Shall be my suretie: *for* whose throne 'tis needfull
Ere I can perfect mine intents, to kneele.   (*All's Well*, IV.iv)

_____

Hamlet   For any thing so ouer-done, is *frō* the
purpose of Playing, whose end both at the
first and now, was and is, to hold as 'twer
the Mirrour vp to Nature.   (*Hamlet*, III.ii)

_____

Salisbury   And charge, that no man should disturbe your rest,
In paine of your dislike, or paine of death.   (*2 Henry VI*, III.ii)

_____

Portia   And yet I am sure you are not satisfied
Of these euents at full. Let vs goe in,
And charge vs there vpon intergatories,
And we will answer all things faithfully.   (*Merchant of Venice*, V.i)

_____

Fool   Why this fellow ha's banish'd two
on's Daughters, and did the third a blessing
against his will, if thou follow him,
thou must needs weare my Coxcombe.   (*King Lear*, I.iv)

_____

King . . . he which hath no stomack *to* this fight,
         Let him depart, his Pasport shall be made,
         And Crownes for Conuoy put into his Purse:
         We would not dye in that mans companie.   (*Henry V*, IV.iii)

———————

2 Gent   What, pray you, became of Antigonus,
           that carryed hence the Child?
3 Gent   Like an old Tale still, which will haue
           matter to rehearse, though Credit be asleepe,
           And not an eare open; he was torne to pieces
           with a Beare.   (*Winter's Tale*, V.ii)

———————

8.8 *THE EARLY DICTIONARIES*

The first English dictionaries were lists of "hard words" with simple and very concise glosses. As the tradition of lexicography developed, dictionaries increased their scope both in the number of entries and in the amount of information given for each word. Below are sample entries from a number of early works ranging from Henry Cockeram's *English Dictionarie*, the first to use the word *dictionary* in its title, to Samuel Johnson's *Dictionary of the English Language*, in which lexicographical technique approaches contemporary standards. The complete entry for the word *mother*, its compounds, and its derivatives has been quoted from each dictionary.

1623.   Henry Cockeram, *The English Dictionarie: or, An Interpreter of hard English Words.*

  Mother. A disease in women when the wombe riseth with paine upwards: sweet smelles are ill for it, but loathsome savors good.

1656.   Thomas Blount, *Glossographia: or a Dictionary, Interpreting the Hard Words of Whatsoever Language, now used in our refined English Tongue.*

  Mother, a disease in women, when the womb riseth with pain, for which the smelling to all sweet savors is harmful; as contrarily, to all strong and loathsome, good.
  Mother-tongues, (*linguæ matrices*) are such Languages as have no derivation from, dependance upon, or affinity with one another; of which *Scaliger* affirms, there are eleven onely in *Europe.*

1658.   Edward Phillips, *The New World of Words: Or a General English Dictionary.*

  Motherwort, Cardiaca, an herb influenced by *Venus,* and the sign *Leo,* of a cleansing and astringent faculty.
  [Phillips has no entry for the simple word *mother.*]

1676.   Elisha Coles, *An English Dictionary, Explaining the Difficult Terms that are used in Divinity, Husbandry, Physick, Philosophy, Law, Navigation, Mathematicks, and other Arts and Sciences.*

  Mother, *a painful rising of the womb, for which all sweet smells are bad, and stinking ones good.*
  Motherwort, Cardiaca, *A cleasing* [sic] *Astringent herb.*
  Mother-tongues, *having no Affinity with one another.*

1706.   John Kersey, revision of Edward Phillips's *The New World of Words: or, Universal English Dictionary.*

Mother, a Woman that has brought forth a Child; also the Womb in which the Child is form'd, or a Disease in that Part; also the Dregs of Ale, B er [sic], Oil, &c.

Mother of Pearl, the Shell that contains the Pearl-fish.

Mother of Time, a kind of Herb.

Mother-Tongues, such Languages as seem to have no Dependance upon, Derivation from, or Relation one to another.

Mother-wort, an Herb, of a cleansing and binding Quality.

1707. *Glossographia Anglicana Nova: or, A Dictionary, Interpreting Such Hard Words of whatever Language, as are at present used in the* English *Tongue, with their* Etymologies, Definitions, &c.

Mother, the Womb, or a Disease in that part; also Dregs of Ale, Beer, Oil, &c.

Mother-Tongues, are such Languages as seem to have no dependance upon, derivation from, or affinity with one another; of which *Scaliger* affirms there are eleven only in *Europe*. The *Greek*, the *Latin*, the *Teutonick* or *German*, the *Sclavonick*, the *Albanese* or *Epirotick*. The *European Tartar* or *Scythian*, the *Hungarian*, the *Finnick*, the *Cantrabrian*, the *Irish*, and the old *Gaulish* or *British*; to this number some add Four others, the *Arabick*, the *Cauchian*, the *Illyrian*, and the *Jazygian*.

1708. John Kersey, *Dictionarium Anglo-Britannicum: Or, a General English Dictionary*.

Mother, a Woman that has brought forth a Child; also the Womb in which the Child is form'd, or a Disease in that Part; also the Dregs of Ale, Beer, Oil, &c.

Mother of Pearl, the Shell that con-contains [sic] the Pearl-fish,

Mother of Time, a kind of Herb.

Mother-Tongues, such Languages as seem to have no Derivation from, or relation to another.

Mother-wort, an Herb.

1730. Nathan Bailey, *Dictionarium Britannicum: Or a more Compleat Universal Etymological English Dictionary Than any Extant*.

Mo′ther [moᵭor, *Sax.* **moder,** *Dan.* and *Su.* **moeder,** *Du.* and L.G. **mutter,** H.G. **modder,** Goth. *mader,* Pers. *mere,* F. *madre,* It. and Sp. *may,* Port. *mater,* L.] of a child; also the womb itself; also a disease peculiar to that part; also a white substance on stale liquours.

Mother *of Pearl,* the shell which contains the pearl fish.

Mother *of time,* an herb.

Mother *of Wine, Beer, &c.* [**moeder,** lees,] thickening the mouldiness or dregs of wine, beer, &c.

Mother-*Wort,* an herb.

Diffidence is the Mother **of Safety**

F. *La defiance est la mere de sureté.* It. *La diffidenza è la madre della Sicurtà,*

Mother *Tongues,* are such languages as seem to have no dependance upon, derivation from, or affinity with one another. Some have been of opinion, that at the confusion of languages. at the building of *Bable*, there were formed 70 or 72 languages. But bishop *Wilkins* and others are of opinion that there were not so many, nor that men did then disperse into so many colonies.

There have been, and at this time there are in the world a far greater number. *Pliny* and *Strabo* relate that in *Dioscuria*, a town of *Colchos*, there were men of 300 nations, and of so many distinct languages, who did resort thither on account of traffick.

Some historians relate, that in every 80 miles of that vast continent, and almost in every particular valley of *Peru*, a distinct language or mother tongue to them was spoken.

And *Purchase* speaks of a 1000 distinct languages spoken by the inhabitants of north *America*, about *Florida*.

Julius Scaliger asserts, that there are no more than eleven mother tongues used in *Europe*, of which four are of more general use and large extent, and the other seven of a narrower extent and use. Those of the larger extent are.

1. The *Greek*, which in antient times was used in *Europe, Asia*, and *Africa*, which also did by dispersion and mixture with other people, degenerate into several dialects. As, the *Attick, Dorick, Æolick, Ionick.*

The *Latin*, which, tho' it is much of it derived from the *Greek*, had antiently four dialects, as *Petrus Crinitus* shews out of *Varro*. From the *Latin* are derived the *Italian, Spanish* and *French*.

The *Teutonick* or *German*, which is distinguished into two notable dialects. 1. The *Danish, Scandian*, and *Gothick*; to which the language used in *Denmark, Sweden, Norway* and *Island* do appertain.

2. The *Saxon*, from which much of the *English* and *Scotch* are derived, and also the *Frizian* language, and those languages on the north of the *Elve*; which of all the modern *German* dialects come the nearest to the ancient *German*, and in this work are called L.G.

The *Sclavonick*, which extends itself thro' many large territories, tho' not without some variation, as *Bohemia, Croatia, Dalmatia, Lithuania, Muscovia, Poland*, and *Vandalia*, this is said to be a language used by 60 several nations.

The languages of lesser extent are.

1. The *Albanese* or old *Epirotick*, now in use in the mountainous parts of *Epirus*.

2. The *European, Tartar* or *Scythian*, from which some suppose the *Irish* took its original.

3. As for the *Turkish* tongue, that originally is no other but the *Asiatick Tartarian* tongue mixed with *Armenian, Persian*, much *Arabick*, and some *Greek*.

4. The *Hungarian*, used in the greatest part of that kingdom.

5. The *Finnick*, used in *Finland* and *Lapland*.

6. The *Cantabrian*, in use with the *Biscainers*, who live near the ocean on the *Pyrenean* hills, which border both on *Spain* and *France*.

7. The *Irish* from thence brought over into some parts of *Scotland*, which, Mr. *Camden* supposes to be derived from the *Welsh*.

8. The old *Gaulish* or *British*, still preserved in *Wales, Cornwal* and *Britain* in *France*.

To these Mr. *Brerewood* adds 4 more.

1. The *Arabick* that is now used in the steep mountains of *Granada*, which however is no mother tongue, being a dialect of the *Hebrew*.

2. The *Cauchian*, used in east *Friezland*.

3. The *Illyrian*, in the island *Veggia*.

4. The *Jazygian*, on the north-side of *Hungary*.

MOTHER-*Hood* [of **moðerhod**, *Sax.*] the state or relation of a mother.

MOTHER *Churches*, are such as have founded or erected others.

MOTHER [with *Physicians*] a disease in that part where the child is formed; also the womb it self.

MO'THERING, a custom still retained in many places of *England*, of visiting parents on *Midlent Sunday*; and it seems to be called *Mothering*, from the respect in old time paid to the *Mother Church*. It being the custom for people in old popish times to visit their mother church on *Midlent-Sunday*, and to make their offerings at the high-altar.

MO'THERLESS [of **moðor-leas**, *Sax*] having no mother.

MO'THERLINESS, [**moðer** and **gelicnesse**, *Sax.*] motherly affection, behaviour, &c.

MOTHERLY, tenderly, affectionately, gravely, soberly.

MOTHERY [of **moðer**, *Sax.*] having a white substance on it by reason of age; as liquors.

1735. Thomas Dyche and William Pardon, *A New General English Dictionary; Peculiarly calculated for the Use and Improvement Of such as are unacquainted with the Learned Languages.*

MO'THER (S.) any female that has or does bring forth young, though it is commonly applied only to women; sometimes it is applied in an ill sense, to an elderly woman who follows the detestable trade of keeping and encouraging young women to prostitute themselves to any body for money, who is vulgarly called a bawd; sometimes it is applied to inanimate things, as the *mother*-church, *mother* of pearl, &c. sometimes the white films or mouldiness that generates upon beer, wine, vinegar, &c. goes by this name.

Fits of the Mother, called also hysterick disorders, is a convulsion of the nerves of the *par vagum* and intercostal in the abdomen, proceeding from a pricking irritation or explosion of spirits; some imagine this distemper wholly depends upon, and flows from the womb, which is a mistake, though it often does, yet sometimes it does not, because men are affected with it as well as women.

MO'THER-CHURCH (S.) such an one within whose district or jurisdiction other churches have been built, as *Stepney* church near *London*, from whose jurisdiction, upon building new churches, the parishes of St. *Paul*'s *Shadwell*, St. *John*'s *Wapping, Christ-Church Spittlefields*, &c. have been taken.

MO'THERLESS (A.) the state of one whose mother is dead.

MO'THERLINESS (S.) the kind affectionate care of a mother over her young children; also the sedate and wise behaviour of a matron, or other discreet woman.

MO'THER-TONGUE (S.) the common, living, or vulgar tongue, spoke by any nation or people whatever.

MO'THERY (A.) the state of liquors that are wasting, perishing, or spoiling, by being kept too long, and the air getting to them, and which is perceived by a whitish, musty film or skin that grows over the upper surface.

1755. Samuel Johnson, *A Dictionary of the English Language: in which the Words are deduced from their Originals, and Illustrated in their Different Significations by Examples from the best Writers.*

MO'THER. *n. s.* [*moðor*, Saxon; *moder*, Danish; *moeder*, Dutch.]

1. A woman that has born a child, correlative to son or daughter.

> Let thy *mother* rather feel thy pride, than fear
> Thy dangerous stoutness.   *Shakespeare's Coriolanus.*
> Come sit down every *mother's* son,
> And rehearse your parts.   *Shakespeare.*
> I had not so much of man in me,
> But all my *mother* came into mine eyes,
> And gave me up to tears.   *Shakesp. Henry V.*

2. That which has produced any thing.

> Alas, poor country! It cannot
> Be call'd our *mother*, but our grave.   *Shakespeare.*
> The resemblance of the constitution and diet of the inhabitants to those of their *mother* country, occasion a great affinity in the popular diseases.   *Arbuthnot on Air.*
> The strongest branch leave for a standard, cutting off the rest close to the body of the *mother* plant.   *Mortimer's Husb.*

3. That which has preceded in time: as, a *mother* church to chapels.

4. That which requires reverence and obedience.

> The good of *mother* church, as well as that of civil society, renders a judicial practice necessary.   *Ayliffe's Parergon.*

5. Hysterical passion; so called, as being imagined peculiar to women.

> This stopping of the stomach might be the *mother*; forasmuch as many were troubled with *mother* fits, although few returned to have died of them.   *Graunt's Bills.*

6. A familiar term of address to an old woman; or to a woman dedicated to religious austerities.

7. MOTHER *in law*. A husband's or wife's mother.   *Ains.*

> I am come to set at variance the daughter in law against the *mother in law*.   *Matth.* x.35.

8. [*Moeder*, Dutch, from *modder*, mud.] A thick substance concreting in liquors; the lees or scum concreted.

> If the body be liquid, and not apt to putrefy totally, it will cast up a *mother*, as the *mothers* of distilled waters.   *Bacon.*
> Potted fowl, and fish come in so fast,
> That ere the first is out the second stinks,
> And mouldy *mother* gathers on the brinks.   *Dryden.*

9. [More properly *modder*; *modde*, Dutch.] A young girl. Now totally obsolete.

> A sling for a *mother*, a bow for a boy,
> A whip for a carter.   *Tusser's Husbandry.*

MO'THER. *adj.* Had at the birth; native.

> For whatsoever *mother* wit or art
> Could work, he put in proof.   *Hubberd's Tale.*
> Where did you study all this goodly speech?
> —It is extempore, from my *mother* wit.   *Shakespeare.*
> Boccace, living in the same age with Chaucer, had the same genius, and followed the same studies: both writ novels, and each of them cultivated his *mother* tongue.   *Dryden.*
> Cecilia came,
> Inventress of the vocal frame,
> Enlarg'd the former narrow bounds,
> And added length to solemn sounds,
> With nature's *mother* wit, and arts unknown before.   *Dryd.*

To MO'THER. *v. n.* To gather concretion.

> They oint their naked limbs with *mother'd* oil.   *Dryden.*

MO'THER *of pearl*. A kind of coarse pearl; the shell in which pearls are generated.

> His mortal blade
> In ivory sheath, ycarv'd with curious slights,
> Whose hilt was burnish'd gold, and handle strong
> Of *mother-pearl*.   *Fairy Qu. b.* i.
> They were made of onyx, sometimes of *mother of pearl*.   *Hakewill on Providence.*

MO'THERHOOD. *n. s.* [from *mother*.] The office or character of a mother.

> Thou shalt see the blessed mother-maid
> Exalted more for being good,
> Than for her interest of *motherhood*. *Donne.*

MO'THERLESS. *adj.* [from *mother*.] Destitute of a mother; orphan of a mother.

> I might shew you my children, whom the rigour of your justice would make complete orphans, being already *motherless*. *Waller's Speech to the House of Commons.*

> My concern for the three poor *motherless* children obliges me to give you this advice. *Arbuthnot's Hist. of J. Bull.*

MO'THERLY. *adj.* [from *mother* and *like*.] Belonging to a mother; suitable to a mother.

> They can owe no less than child-like obedience to her that hath more than *motherly* power. *Hooker, b.* v.

> They termed her the great mother, for her *motherly* care in cherishing her brethren whilst young. *Raleigh.*

> Within her breast though calm, her breast though pure,
> *Motherly* cares and fears got head, and rais'd
> Some troubled thoughts. *Milton's Par. Reg. b.* ii.

> When I see the *motherly* airs of my little daughters when playing with their puppets, I cannot but flatter myself that their husbands and children will be happy in the possession of such wives and mothers. *Addison's Spect.* No. 500.

> Though she was a truly good woman, and had a sincere *motherly* love for her son John, yet there wanted not those who endeavoured to create a misunderstanding between them. *Arb.*

MO'THERLY. *adv.* [from *mother*.] In manner of a mother.

> Th' air doth not *motherly* sit on the earth,
> To hatch her seasons, and give all things birth *Donne.*

MOTHER *of thyme. n. s.* [*serpyllum*, Latin.] It hath trailing branches, which are not so woody and hard as those of thyme, but in every other respect is the same. *Miller.*

MO'THERWORT. *n. s.* [*cardiaca*, Latin.] A plant.

> The flower of the *motherwort* consists of one leaf, and is of the lip kind, whose upper lip is imbricated and much longer than the under one, which is cut into three parts; from the flower-cup arises the pointal, fixed like a nail in the hinder part of the flower, attended by four embrios which become angular seeds, occupying the flower-cup. *Miller.*

MO'THERY. *adj.* [from *mother*.] Concreted; full of concretions; dreggy; feculent: used of liquors.

1. From the beginning, English dictionaries have shown the spelling of a word by its very entry and have given a definition of some sort. We, however, have come to expect a good deal more of our dictionaries. Which of the dictionaries illustrated above was the first to include each of the following kinds of information?

   word-stress _____

   part-of-speech labels _____

   etymology _____

   definitions of everyday as well as of "hard" meanings _____

   illustrative quotations _____

2. What kinds of information do you expect to find under a word entry in a modern dictionary that are missing from all of the early dictionaries illustrated above? _____

   _____

   _____

   _____

3. What kinds of comments or information in the early dictionaries would seem out of place in a modern work? _____

   _____

   _____

   _____

4. What weakness is apparent in the etymologies of all the early dictionaries? _____

_____

_____

5. Suggest several corrections a modern linguist would make to Scaliger's classification of languages given in Bailey's dictionary under the entry *mother tongues*. _____

_____

_____

6. Find a quotation used by Johnson that does not illustrate the definition for which it is cited.

_____

_____

7. DeWitt T. Starnes and Gertrude E. Noyes maintain that in the early Modern period, "lexicography progressed by plagiarism" and "the best lexicographer was often the most discriminating plagiarist."[1] Discuss these two conclusions in the light of the entries cited above.

8.9 *EIGHTEENTH-CENTURY ATTITUDES TOWARD LANGUAGE*

During the eighteenth century, many men tried their hands at writing English grammars, men as diverse as Robert Lowth, Bishop of London, and Joseph Priestley, the discoverer of oxygen. George Campbell, a typical grammarian of the period, was neither as authoritarian as Lowth nor as scientifically objective as Priestley. The theory of use that he set forth in the *Philosophy of Rhetoric* (1776) is one that present-day grammarians can still accept, but his application of that theory abounded with inconsistencies. Campbell's self-contradictory *via media* illustrates well both what is best and what is worst in eighteenth-century attitudes toward language. The following extracts from Chapters I, II, and III of Book II of the *Philosophy of Rhetoric* illustrate Campbell's theory and practice.

CHAPTER I

The Nature and Characters of the Use which gives Law to Language

Every tongue whatever is founded in use or custom,
_____ Whose arbitrary sway
Words and the forms of language must obey.   Francis.

Language is purely a species of fashion (for this holds equally of every tongue) in which, by the general but tacit consent of the people of a particular state or country, certain sounds come to be appropriated to certain things, as their signs, and certain ways of inflecting and combining those sounds come to be established, as denoting the relations which subsist among the things signified.

It is not the business of grammar, as some critics seem preposterously to imagine, to give law to the fashions which regulate our speech. On the contrary, from its conformity to these, and from that alone, it derives all its authority and value. For, what is the grammar of any language? It is no other than a collection of general observations methodically digested, and comprising all the modes previously and independently established, by which the significations, derivations, and combinations of words in that language are ascertained. It is of no consequence here to what causes originally these modes or fashions owe their existence—to imitation, to reflection, to affectation, or to caprice; they no sooner obtain and become general, than they

_____
[1] *The English Dictionary from Cawdrey to Johnson* (Chapel Hill, N.C., 1946), p. 183.

are laws of the language, and the grammarian's only business is, to note, collect, and methodise them. Nor does this truth concern only those more comprehensive analogies or rules which affect whole classes of words; such as nouns, verbs, and the other parts of speech; but it concerns every individual word, in the inflecting or the combining of which a particular mode hath prevailed. Every single anomaly, therefore, though departing from the rule assigned to the other words of the same class, and on that account called an exception, stands on the same basis, on which the rules of the tongue are founded, custom having prescribed for it a separate rule. . . .

Only let us rest in these as fixed principles, that use, or the custom of speaking, is the sole original standard of conversation, as far as regards the expression, and the custom of writing is the sole standard of style; that the latter comprehends the former, and something more; that to the tribunal of use, as to the supreme authority, and, consequently, in every grammatical controversy, the last resort, we are entitled to appeal from the laws and the decisions of grammarians; and that this order of subordination ought never, on any account, to be reversed.

But if use be here a matter of such consequence, it will be necessary, before advancing any farther, to ascertain precisely what it is. We shall otherwise be in danger, though we agree about the name, of differing widely in the notion that we assign to it. . . .

In what extent then must the word be understood? It is sometimes called *general use*; yet is it not manifest that the generality of people speak and write very badly? Nay, is not this a truth that will be even generally acknowledged? It will be so; and this very acknowledgment shows that many terms and idioms may be common, which, nevertheless, have not the general sanction, no, nor even the suffrage of those that use them. The use here spoken of implies not only *currency*, but *vogue*. It is properly *reputable custom*. . . .

Agreeably then to this first qualification of the term, we must understand to be comprehended under general use, *whatever modes of speech are authorized as good by the writings of a great number, if not the majority, of celebrated authors*. . . .

Another qualification of the term *use* which deserves our attention is, that it must be *national*. This I consider in a twofold view, as it stands opposed both to *provincial* and *foreign*. . . .

But there will naturally arise here another question, 'Is not use, even good and national use, in the same country, different in different periods? And if so, to the usage of what period shall we attach ourselves, as the proper rule? If you say *the present*, as it may reasonably be expected that you will, the difficulty is not entirely removed. In what extent of signification must we understand the word *present*? How far may we safely range in quest of authorities? or, at what distance backwards from this moment are authors still to be accounted as possessing a legislative voice in language?' . . .

As use, therefore, implies duration, and as even a few years are not sufficient for ascertaining the characters of authors, I have, for the most part, in the following sheets, taken my prose examples, neither from living authors, nor from those who wrote before the Revolution; not from the first, because an author's fame is not so firmly established in his lifetime; nor from the last, that there may be no suspicion that the style is superannuated.

CHAPTER II

The Nature and Use of Verbal Criticism, with its Principal Canons

. . . But on this subject of use, there arise two eminent questions, . . . The first question is this, 'Is reputable, national, and present use, which, for brevity's sake, I shall hereafter simply denominate good use, always uniform in her decisions?' The second is, 'As no term, idiom, or application, that is totally unsupported by her, can be admitted to be good, is every term, idiom, and application that is countenanced by her, to be esteemed good, and therefore worthy to be retained?'

In answer to the former of these questions, I acknowledge, that in every case there is not a perfect uniformity in the determinations, even of such use as may justly be denominated good. Wherever a considerable number of authorities can be produced in support of two different, though resembling modes of expression for the same thing, there is always a divided use, and one cannot be said to speak barbarously, or to oppose the usage of the language, who conforms to either side. . . .

In those instances, therefore, of divided use, which give scope for option, the following canons are humbly proposed, in order to assist us in assigning the preference. Let it, in the mean time, be remembered, as a point always presupposed, that the authorities on the opposite sides are equal, or nearly so. . . .

The first canon, then, shall be, When use is divided as to any particular word or phrase, and the expression used by one part hath been pre-occupied, or is in any instance susceptible of a different signification, and the expression employed by the other part never admits a different sense, both perspicuity and variety require that the form of expression which is in every instance strictly univocal be preferred. . . .

In the preposition *toward* and *towards*, and the adverbs *forward* and *forwards*, *backward* and *backwards*, the two forms are used indiscriminately. But as the first form in all these is also an adjective, it is better to confine the particles to the second. Custom, too, seems at present to lean this way. *Besides* and *beside* serve both as conjunctions and as prepositions. There appears some tendency at present to assign to each a separate province. This tendency ought to be humoured by employing only the former as the conjunction, the latter as the preposition. . . .

The second canon is, In doubtful cases regard ought to be had in our decisions to the analogy of the language. . . .

If by the former canon the adverbs *backwards* and *forwards* are preferable to *backward* and *forward*; by this canon, from the principle of analogy, *afterwards* and *homewards* should be preferred to *afterward* and *homeward*. Of the two adverbs *thereabout* and *thereabouts*, compounded of the particle *there* and the preposition, the former alone is analogical, there being no such word in the language as *abouts*. The same holds of *hereabout* and *whereabout*. . . .

The third canon is, When the terms or expressions are in other respects equal, that ought to be preferred which is most agreeable to the ear. . . .

Of this we have many examples. *Delicateness* hath very properly given way to *delicacy*; and for a like reason *authenticity* will probably soon displace *authenticalness*, and *vindictive* dispossess *vindicative* altogether. . . .

The fourth canon is, In cases wherein none of the foregoing rules gives either side a ground of preference, a regard to simplicity (in which I include etymology when manifest) ought to determine our choice.

Under the name simplicity I must be understood to comprehend also brevity; for that expression is always the simplest which, with equal purity and perspicuity, is the briefest. We have, for instance, several active verbs which are used either with or without a preposition indiscriminately. Thus we say either *accept* or *accept of*, *admit* or *admit of*, *approve* or *approve of*; in like manner *address* or *address to*, *attain* or *attain to*. In such instances it will hold, I suppose, pretty generally, that the simple form is preferable. . . .

The fifth and only other canon that occurs to me on the subject of divided use is, In the few cases wherein neither perspicuity nor analogy, neither sound nor simplicity, assists us in fixing our choice, it is safest to prefer that manner which is most conformable to ancient usage.

This is founded on a very plain maxim, that in language, as in several other things, change itself, unless when it is clearly advantageous, is ineligible. This affords another reason for preferring that usage which distinguishes *ye* as the nominative plural of *thou*, when more than one are addressed, from *you* the accusative. . . .

I come now to the second question for ascertaining both the extent of the authority claimed by custom, and the rightful prerogatives of criticism. As no term, idiom, or application, that is totally unsupported by use, can be admitted to be good; is every term, idiom, and application, that is countenanced by use, to be esteemed good, and therefore worthy to be retained? I answer, that though nothing in language can be good from which use withholds her approbation, there may be many things to which she gives it, that are not in all respects good, or such as are worthy to be retained and imitated. . . .

It is therefore, I acknowledge, not without meaning, that Swift affirms, that, "there are many gross improprieties, which, though authorized by practice, ought to be discarded." Now, in order to discard them, nothing more is necessary than to disuse them. And to bring us to disuse them, both the example and the arguments of the critic will have their weight. . . .

The first canon on this subject is, All words and phrases which are remarkably harsh and unharmonious, and not absolutely necessary, may justly be judged worthy of this fate. . . .

Such are the words *bare-faced-ness*, *shame-faced-ness*, *un-success-ful-ness*, *dis-interest-ed-ness*, *wrong-headed-ness*, *tender-hearted-ness*. They are so heavy and drawling, and withal so ill compacted, that they have not more vivacity than a periphrasis, to compensate for the defect of harmony. . . .

The second canon on this subject is, When etymology plainly points to a signification different from that which the word commonly bears, propriety and simplicity both require its dismission. . . .

The verb *to unloose*, should analogically signify *to tie*, in like manner as *to untie* signifies *to loose*. To what purpose is it, then, to retain a term, without any necessity, in a signification the reverse of that which its etymology manifestly suggests? In the same way, *to annul*, and *to disannul*, ought by analogy to be contraries, though irregularly used as synonymous. . . .

The third canon is, When any words become obsolete, or at least are never used, except as constituting part of particular phrases, it is better to dispense with their service entirely, and give up the phrases. . . .

Examples of this we have in the words *lief*, *dint*, *whit*, *moot*, *pro*, and *con*, as, '*I had as lief* go myself,' for 'I should like as well to go myself.' 'He convinced his antagonist *by dint of argument*,' that is, 'by strength of argument.' 'He made them yield *by dint of arms*,' —'by force of arms.' 'He is *not a whit better*,' —'no better.' 'The case you mention is *a moot point*,' —'a disputable point.' 'The question was strenuously debated *pro and con*,' —'on both sides.'

The fourth and last canon I propose is, All those phrases, which, when analysed grammatically, include a solecism, and all those to which use hath affixed a particular sense, but which, when explained by the general and established rules of the language, are susceptible either of a different sense, or of no sense, ought to be discarded altogether.

It is this kind of phraseology which is distinguished by the epithet *idiomatical*, and hath been originally the spawn, partly of ignorance, and partly of affectation. Of the first sort, which includes a solecism, is the phrase, 'I *had* rather *do* such a thing,' for 'I would rather do it.' The auxiliary *had*, joined to the infinitive active *do*, is a gross violation of the rules of conjugation in our language. . . .

Of the second sort, which, when explained grammatically, leads to a different sense from what the words in conjunction commonly bear, is, 'He sings a good song,' for 'he sings well.' The plain meaning of the words as they stand connected is very different, for who sees not that a good song may be ill sung? . . .

CHAPTER III

Of Grammatical Purity

[Chapter III discusses various barbarisms, solecisms, and improprieties "which writers of great name, and even of critical skill in the language, have slidden into through inattention." Among these offenses against grammatical purity are the following. The italics are Campbell's.]

"The zeal of the *seraphim* breaks forth in a becoming warmth of sentiments and expressions, as the character which is given us of *him* denotes that generous scorn and intrepidity which attends heroic virtue." (Addison)

"This noble nation hath *of all others* admitted *fewer* corruptions." (Swift)

"Such notions would be avowed at this time by none but rosicrucians, and fanatics as mad as them." (Bolingbroke)

"Tell the Cardinal, that I understand poetry better than him." (Smollet)

"My christian and surname begin and end with the same letters." (Addison)

"*Each* of the sexes should keep within *its* particular bounds, and content *themselves* to exult within *their* respective districts." (Addison)

"*If* thou *bring* thy gift to the altar, and there *rememberest* that thy brother hath ought against thee . . ." (Matt. 5:23)

"I shall do all I can to persuade others to *take* the same measures for their cure which I *have*."
(*Guardian*, No. 1)

"Will it be urged, that the four gospels are *as old*, or even *older than* tradition?" (Bolingbroke)

"The greatest masters of critical learning differ *among one another*." (*Spectator*, No. 321)

"A petty constable will *neither* act cheerfully *or* wisely." (Swift)

"I may say, without vanity, that there is not a gentleman in England better read in tomb-stones than myself, my studies having *laid* very much in church-yards." (*Spectator*, No. 518)

"The exercise of reason appears as little in them, as in the beasts they sometimes hunt, and by *whom* they are sometimes hunted." (Bolingbroke)

Adam,
The comeliest man of men *since born*
His sons. The fairest of *her daughters* Eve. (Milton)

1. What does Campbell say is the "supreme authority" in language? _____
   _____

2. What does he conceive the task of the grammarian to be? _____
   _____

3. What should be the grammarian's attitude toward anomalies, that is, words or constructions that follow no general pattern? _____
   _____

4. How does Campbell apparently conceive of the relationship between speech and writing?
   _____
   _____

5. Campbell's three qualifications of use are that it be *reputable*, *national*, and *present*. Explain what he means by these three terms. _____
   _____
   _____
   _____
   _____

6. Would Campbell be willing to settle a question of use by polling a representative cross section of the English population? Explain. _____

_____

_____

7. When use is divided between two different expressions for the same idea, what view does Campbell take of the correctness of the two expressions? _____

_____

_____

8. For choosing between divided use, Campbell proposes five canons. Explain each of them briefly. _____

_____

_____

_____

_____

_____

9. What does Campbell mean when he says that change in language is "ineligible"?

_____

_____

10. How does Campbell answer the question "Is all use good?" _____

_____

_____

11. Whose precept and example is to guide us among the pitfalls of use? _____

_____

12. Briefly explain the four canons Campbell proposes for determining what uses should be discarded. _____

_____

_____

_____

_____

13. List several specific contradictions or inconsistencies in Campbell's discussion of correctness in language. _____

_____

_____

_____

_____

14. Identify the "errors" in the quotations from Chapter III of *The Philosophy of Rhetoric*.

15. Look up one of the "errors" in several recent school grammars or guides to usage to see whether there has been any change in attitude toward it.

Recent British and American English

9.1 QUESTIONS FOR REVIEW AND DISCUSSION

1. Define the following terms:

a language	prescriptive grammar
a dialect	purism
Americanisms	shibboleths
Britishisms	"*ask*" words
collective noun	dialect or linguistic geography
caste dialect	settlement history
edited English	

2. What justification is there for the claim of many speakers of Standard British English that their type of English is superior to all others?

3. On what fallacy is this claim based?

4. What accounts for the fact that British English generally has greater prestige than other types such as American?

5. In what respects is American English more conservative than British English and in what respects is it less so?

6. Is the Englishman who is concerned about speaking correctly likely to worry more about pronunciation or about syntax? How does the linguistically insecure American differ from his British counterpart?

7. List the important differences between British English and American English.

8. Which of the differences is most significant?

9. Supply some further examples of "the American love of grandiloquence" referred to on page 229, footnote 22, of *Origins and Development*.

10. What are the main scholarly organizations and publications devoted to the study of American English?

11. What importance has the study of British dialects for an understanding of American English?

12. Which are more important, the differences or the similarities between British and American English?

13. What are the chances that English will split up into a number of mutually unintelligible dialects—that is, into separate languages?

9.2 AMERICANISMS

1. Among the words that are in some way peculiar to the United States are the following. Describe the origin of each word, as it is shown in the *Dictionary of American English* (*DAE*) or the *Dictionary of Americanisms* (*DA*).

blue laws _____

bushwhacker _____

carpetbagger _____

charley horse _____

cinch _____

civil rights _____

clambake _____

conniption _____

cybernetics _____

dicker _____

dude _____

ghost writer _____

hex _____

hoodlum _____

law-abiding _____

parlay _____

ranch _____

semester _____

sideburns _____

stoop 'porch' _____

2. By consulting the *DAE* or the *DA*, list ten examples of Americanisms not cited here or in *Origins and Development*. _____

_____

_____

_____

_____

_____

_____

_____

_____

_____

_____

9.3 NATIONAL DIFFERENCES IN WORD CHOICE

1. Give the distinctively British English equivalents of the following American terms. All of the words are in *Origins and Development*.

gasoline	_____	principal editorial	_____
hood (of a car)	_____	to mail	_____
muffler (on a car)	_____	chain stores	_____
truck	_____	installment buying	_____
sedan	_____	trailer	_____

suspenders	_____	trillion	_____
cuffs	_____	billion	_____
sneakers	_____	bookkeeper	_____
vest	_____	raise (in salary)	_____
spool	_____	molasses	_____
(of thread)		(cream) pitcher	_____
orchestra seat	_____	baby carriage	_____
intermission	_____	gas water-heater	_____
(in a play)		second story	_____
TV	_____	prep school	_____
radio	_____	public school	_____

2. The following terms either are exclusively British English or have at least one special sense that is predominantly British. Give the American English equivalents of the British senses. The terms can be found in a desk dictionary.

accumulator	_____	sleeping partner	_____
wing	_____	costermonger	_____
boot (of a car)	_____	chips	_____
underground	_____	biscuit	_____
suspender	_____	sweet (n.)	_____
bowler	_____	tart	_____
bespoke	_____	minerals	_____
draughts	_____	public house	_____
gangway	_____	form	_____
roundabout	_____	rates	_____
switchback	_____	fanlight	_____
holidays	_____	cotton wool	_____
pillar box	_____	dustbin	_____
hoarding	_____	drawing pin	_____
chemist	_____	bug	_____

3. An American reporter who interviewed G. K. Chesterton described him as a "regular guy." What reason had Chesterton, an Englishman, for being or pretending to be offended? What is the probable etymology of *guy*? _____

_____

_____

_____

_____

9.4 *NATIONAL DIFFERENCES IN GRAMMAR AND IDIOM*

1. What constructions in the following quotations from British periodicals would an American be likely to phrase in a different manner? Underline the constructions and rephrase them.

When Mr. Macmillan has dispersed the last miasma of the Profumo affair . . . it may be that he will hand over. But to whom? (*Spectator*, October 4, 1963, p. 403) _____

_____

Investment Notes . . . International Tea are near the bottom with 13.7 per cent. (*Ibid.*, p. 434)

_____

A number of London stock-broking firms are recommending their clients to buy Australian ordinary shares. (*Punch*, March 13, 1963, p. 384) _____

I used often to find myself successful in teaching subjects not my own. (*Punch*, April 24, 1963, p. 596) _____

It must be getting a bit of a strain on our public figures, always being called from conferences or rehearsals or typewriters to encounter these extraordinary questions on the telephone. (*Punch*, May 15, 1963, p. 688) _____

The Government have set up the agency to help the industry. (*Time & Tide*, July 8, 1964, p. 38) _____

The Welsh centre Dawes was concussed in the third minute of the game . . . but Ireland were slow to exploit this weakness of manpower. (*The Illustrated London News*, March 20, 1965, p. 12) _____

He omits to mention the far more far-reaching difficulty that there are differences in status between poets, and between individual poems. (*The Times Literary Supplement*, September 2, 1965, p. 755) _____

Pied-à-terre, or bachelor flat, to let in modern block in Sloane Avenue. (*The Times*, August 27, 1965, p. 1) _____

There was a slight bump as the aircraft entered cloud, and the pilot's hands tightened on the controls. (*Blackwood's Magazine*, July 1964, p. 4) _____

"I've got climbing kit," said I, "but no sleeping-bag." (*Ibid.*, p. 44) _____

"Have you not a father?" I asked. (*Blackwood's Magazine*, September 1964, p. 240)

I began to say, "What will your wife feel about that?" (*Ibid.*, p. 241) _____

2. By skimming a recent issue of some British publication, find several examples of grammatical constructions or idioms which differ from American usage. _____

_____

_____

_____

_____

_____

_____

9.5   *BRITISH AND AMERICAN PURISM* I

1. Are there any types of American pronunciation, regional or social, which are definitely non-standard (non-U) in the sense that they would debar a speaker from the learned professions? If so, cite them. _____

_____

_____

_____

_____

2. How much truth is there in Katharine Whitehorn's statement, "In America, where it is grammar, not accent, that places you, anyone can learn the grammar; maybe Bostonians don't accept it, but Bostonians only impress other Bostonians"? (Cited in *Origins and Development*, p. 245) _____

_____

_____

_____

3. Which is easier, changing the phonetic patterns of one's speech or eschewing what are thought of as solecisms? Why? _____

_____

_____

4. After determining whether Dorothy Parker is English or American and checking with the *Oxford English Dictionary* and Fowler's *Modern English Usage*, comment on the linguistic pronouncement by Miss Parker that "anyone who, as does [Henry] Miller, follows 'none' with a plural verb ... should assuredly not be called a writer." (*Esquire*, September 1961, p. 34) _____

_____

_____

5. Why is the American concern for "good grammar" more democratic than the British concern for "posh accents"? _____

_____

_____

6. In the preface to *Pygmalion*, George Bernard Shaw insists that all art should be didactic; what is he trying to teach in the play? What actual person did Shaw have in mind when he created the character of Henry Higgins? _____

_____

9.6 *BRITISH AND AMERICAN PURISM* II

Among the constructions that are disapproved by one purist or another are those italicized in the sentences below. Investigate the status of one of these constructions, using the following techniques:

1. Ascertain the earlier history of the construction as it is revealed by the citations in the *Oxford English Dictionary*.

2. Compare the opinions of such widely used contemporary guides to usage as H. W. Fowler's *Dictionary of Modern English Usage*, 2nd ed., rev. and ed. by Sir Ernest Gowers (Oxford, 1965), Margaret Nicholson's *Dictionary of American-English Usage* (New York, 1957), Bergen and Cornelia Evans's *Dictionary of Contemporary American Usage* (New York, 1957), Porter G. Perrin's *Writer's Guide and Index to English*, 3rd ed. (Chicago, 1959), or Margaret M. Bryant's *Current American Usage* (New York, 1962).

3. Survey contemporary use of the construction by finding examples of it or of its alternatives. Skim recent newspapers, magazines, novels, and other printed material. Watch for its use in conversation, over the radio or television, in speeches, or in other forms of oral communication. For each occurrence you observe prepare a note card with the following information:

> CITATION: quotation illustrating the construction or alternative.
>
> SOURCE: bibliographical data for a printed source; speaker, occasion, and date for an oral source.
>
> CIRCUMSTANCES: any information which may help to determine the status of the construction (for example, occurs in dialogue, speaker is rustic, used in a formal situation, and so forth).

Write the results of your investigation in the form of an article for a usage dictionary. Describe the usage you have observed, including any apparent social, regional, or functional limitations, and summarize the information in the *OED* and the usage guides you have consulted.

What was he asking *about*? (similarly, other final prepositions)

I'm ready, *aren't I*?

It is *not as* late as we thought.

She felt *badly* about it.

The second is the *best* of the two books. (similarly, other superlatives used for one of two)

There were no secrets *between* the three brothers.

You can't judge a *book's* content by its cover. (similarly, genitives of other inanimate nouns)

Philip wants to leave. *But* he can't. (similarly, *and, or, nor*)

I don't doubt *but what* they will agree.

Can I have another, please?

Houston *contacted* the astronauts on their second orbit.

The *data is* available now. (similarly, *criteria*)

The answer was *different than* what we expected.

It *don't* make any difference.

Due to a power failure, the flight was canceled.

The members of the senate supported *each other* in the election.

Everybody finished *their* work. (similarly, *everyone, nobody, no one, someone,* and so forth with plural pronouns)

Drive three miles *further* south and turn right.

I'll come when I'm *good and* ready.

Have you *gotten* the answer yet?

She *graduated* from Vassar.

You *had better* go. (similarly, *had rather, had sooner, had best,* and so forth)

We heard about *him* winning the contest. (similarly, other nongenitives before gerunds)

I wonder *if* there's time.

The reason she's late *is because* she ran out of gas.

A finesse *is where* declarer plays the queen instead of the ace while the king is out against him. (similarly, *is when*)

Lay down and take your nap.

We have *less* problems this year than last.

The weather looks *like* it will be clearing soon.

It's *me*. (similarly, objective forms of other pronouns after *to be*)

It is the *most perfect* play ever written. (similarly, comparative and superlative forms of *unique*, *round*, *square*, *white*, and so forth)

They sent separate invitations to my wife and *myself*. (similarly, other *self*-forms without antecedent)

Make the dog get *off of* the bed.

You *only* live once.

James had a *pretty* good reason for asking.

He *raised* his children according to the newest theories.

A switch is not functioning. *This* is enough to cancel the flight. (similarly, *that* and *which* with broad reference)

Vesper didn't like *those kind* of tactics. (similarly, *kind* and *sort* with plural modifiers or verb)

It is necessary *to actively resist* oppression. (similarly, other split infinitives)

You ought to *try and* see the Little Theater's new play.

They were *very* pleased by the public response. (similarly, other qualifiers before past participles)

If the test *was* held on Sunday, more people could take it. (similarly, *was* in other subjunctive clauses)

Who did you see? (similarly, *who* in other object functions)

We *will* probably sing "We *Shall* Overcome."

You never know when your time will come.

9.7 NATIONAL DIFFERENCES IN PRONUNCIATION

1. Identify the following pronunciations as typically British (*B*) or typically American (*A*) by writing the appropriate letter in the blanks.

word		Br.		Am.
ate	_____	[et]	_____	[ɛt]
collar	_____	[ˈkɑlər]	_____	[ˈkɔlə]
corollary	_____	[kəˈrɔlərɪ]	_____	[ˈkɑrəˌlɛri]
dynasty	_____	[ˈdɪnəstɪ]	_____	[ˈdaɪnəsti]
farce	_____	[fɑrs]	_____	[fɑs]
figure	_____	[ˈfɪgə]	_____	[ˈfɪgjər]
fragile	_____	[ˈfræǰɪl]	_____	[ˈfræǰaɪl]
further	_____	[ˈfɜðə]	_____	[ˈfɜrðər]
half	_____	[hæf]	_____	[hɑf]
latter	_____	[ˈlædər]	_____	[ˈlætə]
military	_____	[ˈmɪlɪt(ə)rɪ]	_____	[ˈmɪləˌtɛri]
pass	_____	[pæs]	_____	[pɑs]
quandary	_____	[kwɔnˈdɛrɪ]	_____	[ˈkwɑndəri]
quinine	_____	[kwɪˈñin]	_____	[ˈkwaɪˌnaɪn]
schedule	_____	[ˈskɛǰəl]	_____	[ˈšɛdjul]
squirrel	_____	[ˈskwɪrəl]	_____	[ˈskwɜrəl]
whether	_____	[ˈhwɛðər]	_____	[ˈwɛðə]
zenith	_____	[ˈzinɪθ]	_____	[ˈzɛnɪθ]
Are you there?	_____	Are you there? ↗	_____	Are‿you there? ↗
What did he tell you?	_____	What‿did he tell you? ↘	_____	What did he‿tell‿you? ↘

2. Describe five of the most sweeping differences between American and British pronunciation.

_____

_____

_____

_____

3. What was the usual quality of *a* before such consonants as [f], [θ], [ð], [s], and [ns] in Standard British English at the beginning of the nineteenth century? _____

_____

4. In what sections of the United States is [r] more or less regularly lost finally and before consonants? _____

_____

5. In what sections of the United States do words like *stop*, *cot*, and *lock* generally have a rounded vowel? _____

_____

6. Some Americans who regularly pronounce [r] where it is spelled do not have it in the middle syllable of *governor*, although they may have it in *governing* and *government*. Can you suggest any reason for the loss of [r] in the one word when it is retained in the other two?

_____

_____

7. Which of the following pronunciations possess greater clarity? Explain your answer. *Sunday* [ˈsʌnˌde] or [ˈsʌndi]; *to* [tu] or [tə]; *educator* [ˈɛdjuˌketər] or [ˈɛʝəˌketər]. _____

_____

9.8 BRITISH AND AMERICAN SPELLING

1. Give typically British spellings of the following words:

anemic	_____	jail	_____
ax	_____	labor	_____
center	_____	mold 'fungus'	_____
(bank) check	_____	mustache	_____
cipher	_____	omelet	_____
civilize	_____	pajamas	_____
(street) curb	_____	plow	_____
defense	_____	program	_____
esophagus	_____	show	_____
gray	_____	story 'floor'	_____
inflection	_____	traveler	_____
install	_____	wagon	_____

2. Some of the spelling differences illustrated above are systematic in that the same difference appears in a large number of words. Describe the more important systematic differences and cite some additional examples. _____

_____

_____

_____

_____

9.9 *THE REGIONAL DIALECTS OF AMERICAN ENGLISH*

The regional dialects of American English are described by Raven I. McDavid, Jr., in W. Nelson Francis's *The Structure of American English* (New York, 1958), by Charles K. Thomas in *An Introduction to the Phonetics of American English*, 2nd ed. (New York, 1958), and more briefly in the *Standard College Dictionary* (New York, 1963, pp. xix–xxi), by Hans Kurath in *A Word Geography of the Eastern United States* (Ann Arbor, Mich., 1949), by Kurath and McDavid in *The Pronunciation of English in the Atlantic States* (Ann Arbor, Mich., 1961), and by Jean Malmstrom and Annabel Ashley in *Dialects—U.S.A.* (Champaign, Ill., 1963), a work designed for secondary schools and based on McDavid's chapter in Francis's book.

1. After reading one or more of these descriptions, which agree on general facts but not on all details, draw on the accompanying map the boundaries of the main regional dialects of the United States.

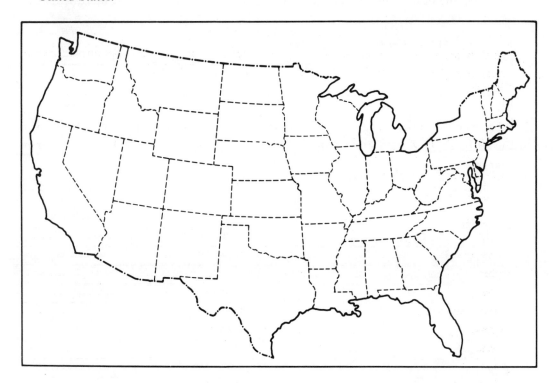

2. Below are some pronunciation features that vary from one regional dialect to another. For each feature indicate what main variations occur. You may not find all of these items discussed in any one of the works cited above, but do as many of them as you can.

THE STRESSED VOWEL IN:

crop, top, cot, rot _____

law, caught, wrought _____

dog, fog, log _____

ask, half, path, glass, dance _____

coat, road, home, stone _____

new, tune, due _____

out, house _____

loud, houses _____

nice, white, rice _____

time, tide, ride _____

boil, oil _____

third, bird _____

bar, farm, hard _____

car, garden _____

forest, horrid, orange _____

morning, horse, forty _____

mourning, hoarse, four _____

marry, carry, barren _____

Mary, dairy, vary, area _____

THE PRONUNCIATION OF *r* IN:

fear, beard, poor, more, start, word _____

_____

far away, lore of the jungle, paper and ink _____

_____

THE MEDIAL CONSONANT OF:

greasy _____

THE FINAL CONSONANT OF:

with _____

3. What synonyms exist in regional dialects for the following vocabulary items? All of them can be found in Kurath's *Word Geography* and most of them in McDavid's chapter in Francis's book.

porch _____

pail _____

frying pan _____

faucet _____

kerosene _____

creek _____

sidewalk _____

pancake _____

string beans _____

lima beans _____

dragon fly _____

you (plural) _____

quarter *to* eleven _____

sick *to* the stomach _____

New Words from Old:

Coinages and Adaptations

10.1 QUESTIONS FOR REVIEW AND DISCUSSION

1. Define each of these terms and, when it is appropriate, illustrate the term with an example.

etymology	compound stress or unity-stress
root creation	amalgamated compound
echoic word	clipped form
onomatopoeic word	aphetic form (aphesis)
symbolic word	back formation
conventional ejaculation	blend
reduplication	acronym
affix	folk etymology
prefix	common derivative of a proper name
suffix	slang
lexicon	argot
hybrid creation	literary coinage
compound	converted form (conversion)
phrase or level stress	verb-adverb combination

2. Which of the processes of word-making described in this chapter seem from what you know to have been the most productive in English?

3. Your answer to the preceding question was intuitive, based on your general familiarity with the English vocabulary, but you can substantiate it by making a random sampling from the *Oxford English Dictionary*. Arbitrarily select one or more pages from each volume of the *OED*. Determine the process involved in the making of every word, not merely main entries, on each page you have selected. Many of the words will be loans from other languages. Loan-words will be considered in Chapter 12; for the present, group them together as a separate category, with which you are not concerned. When you have determined the process of word-making responsible for all the words that are not direct loans, tabulate your results and determine whether your intuitions accord with the sample you investigated.

10.2 ROOT CREATIONS

Genuine root creations are rare. *Blurb*, *gas*, *paraffin*, and *rayon* are sometimes suggested as examples. Although it is hardly in general use, *googol* is another candidate. Investigate the histories of these five words and decide which one is the best example of root creation. Explain your decision. _____

_____

_____

_____

_____

_____

10.3 TRADE NAMES

These trade names were suggested by already existing words or word elements. Identify the earlier forms which underlie the trade names.

automat	_____	Pepsodent	_____
Band-aid	_____	Pulmotor	_____
Coca-Cola	_____	Quonset	_____
escalator	_____	Sanforized	_____
Frigidaire	_____	Tabasco	_____
Levis	_____	Technicolor	_____
Linotype	_____	Victrola	_____
mimeograph	_____	Windbreaker	_____
Novocain	_____	Xerox	_____
ouija	_____	zipper	_____

10.4 ECHOIC WORDS

1. Many words that name sounds, or actions that produce sounds, are echoic in origin, for example, *buzz*, *chatter*, *gag*, *gurgle*, *hawk* 'clear the throat,' *heehaw*, *hiccup*, *honk*, *jingle*, *yak* 'talk volubly,' and *zoom*. Select a particular area of meaning, such as animal noises, noises produced by falling objects, non-speech sounds made by man, noises made by machines, water noises, noises of rapid motion, and so forth, and list as many echoic words for that area as you can think of. _____

_____

_____

_____

_____

2. Some words of various origins, imitative or not, share a common meaning and a common sound. When meaning and sound thus coincide in several words, it is inevitable that speakers should feel that the sound somehow represents the meaning. Thus, *swagger*, *swash*, *swat*, *sway*, *sweep*, *swerve*, *swig*, *swill*, *swing*, *swipe*, *swirl*, *swish*, *swivel*, *swoop*, and *swoosh* all have the initial sound combination [sw] and are vaguely similar to one another in meaning. The shared meaning, something like 'free-wheeling movement in an arc,' seems to be represented by the sound [sw]. This phenomenon is known as sound symbolism.

Here are some short lists of symbolic words. Describe the meaning that is characteristic of each list and add to the lists any appropriate words you can find.

tweak, twiddle, twine, twinkle, twirl, twist, twitch

_____

glare, gleam, glimmer, glint, glisten, glitter, gloss, glow

_____

crack, cramp, cripple, crooked, crouch, crumple, crunch, crush

_____

draggle, drain, dredge, dregs, drip, droop, drop, dross

_____

bladder, blaze, blimp, blister, bloat, blow, blubber, blurt

_____

track, trail, trample, travel, tread, trip, trot, trudge

_____

crash, dash, flash, gush, rush, smash, swish, whoosh

_____

bangle, dangle, jangle, jingle, jungle, spangle, tangle, tingle

_____

bump, chump, dump, hump, lump, plump, rump, slump

_____

amble, jumble, mumble, ramble, rumble, scramble, shamble, tremble

_____

10.5 EJACULATIONS

Phffft, the name of a 1954 motion picture, is an exclamation denoting the sudden collapse of a marriage or some other deflatable thing. The sound, which suggests air escaping from a balloon, is represented well enough by the spelling and is familiar to most English speakers. The critic Bosley Crowther was too pessimistic when he advised, "Don't try to pronounce the title." Crowther's additional comment, "'Phffft' is a skkkt that runs an hour and a half," suggests that he had in mind a conventional pronunciation for the ejaculation, one that rimed with *skit*. When such a noise is pronounced not as the noise it originally symbolized, but rather as a permissible sequence of English phonemes, it has become a word like any other in the lexicon. At first an interjection, the word may come to function as a noun, a verb, or other part of speech.

Here are some ejaculations that have become words through a spelling pronunciation of their written symbols, although not all of them have achieved the honor of a dictionary entry. Describe or produce the noise that each of the spellings originally symbolized.

LAUGHTER: yuk-yuk, yak, hardy-har

ATTENTION-GETTING NOISE: ahem, psst

DELAYING NOISE: hem and haw

EXPRESSION OF CONTEMPT OR DISGUST: humph, piff (cf. piffle), ptui (pronounced [pəˈtui]), braak, chee(z)

225

CRY OF HORROR: a(u)gh
EXPRESSION OF RELIEF: whew
SIGNAL FOR SILENCE: shush, hush, ssst
AUTOMATIC NOISES: kerchoo, burp, hack
NEGATION: uh-uh

10.6 *MORPHEMES: PREFIXES, SUFFIXES, AND BASES*

The morpheme is the smallest meaningful unit in a language. *Card, act, moron, random, cardigan,* and *asparagus* are words that consist of a single morpheme each. *Discard, action, moronic, randomly, cardigans,* and *aspáragus plànt* are made of two morphemes each. A morpheme may be a base like *card, asparagus,* and *plant,* a prefix like *dis-,* or a suffix like *-ion.* Words like *refer, defer, confer, receive, deceive, conceive, reduce, deduce,* and *conduce* are made of two morphemes each, a prefix and a base, although the bases *fer, ceive,* and *duce* do not occur as separate words.

Divide each of the following words into its constituent morphemes by rewriting the word with hyphens between the morphemes. For example *activistic* can be divided into *act-iv-ist-ic.* Note that morphemes are properly represented by sounds, but for convenience we can use conventional spellings.

postage	_____	prepare	_____
impressment	_____	repair	_____
trial	_____	disparity	_____
early	_____	disparage	_____
holistic	_____	repel	_____
worthily	_____	propellant	_____
definite	_____	produce	_____
favoritism	_____	seduce	_____
demarcation	_____	secede	_____
finalization	_____	proceed	_____
unequivocal	_____	placate	_____
palmistry	_____	implacable	_____

10.7 *PREFIXES*

1. From what language was the prefix in each of these words originally derived? Label each word *G* (Greek), *L* (Latin), or *OE* (Old English) according to the source of the prefix.

_____ archenemy	_____ microorganism	_____ stepchild
_____ circumnavigate	_____ midday	_____ surname
_____ cis-Alpine	_____ misfit	_____ transoceanic
_____ counterbalance	_____ monomania	_____ tricolor
_____ crypto-Communist	_____ panhellenic	_____ twilight
_____ demigod	_____ parapsychology	_____ ultraliberal
_____ diacid	_____ polyvalent	_____ unilingual
_____ epicycle	_____ preternatural	_____ vice-regent
_____ malformed	_____ proto-Germanic	
_____ metalanguage	_____ retroactive	

2. Two affixes may be pronounced and spelled alike, yet be two independent elements because they have different functions in the language. Thus the -*ly* of *manly* and the -*ly* of *slowly* are not the same suffix. The first -*ly* forms adjectives; the second -*ly* forms adverbs. The two endings have different meanings and therefore are different suffixes.

On the other hand, an affix may be pronounced and spelled variously in different words, yet remain a single affix. Although the past tense ending is [d] in *said*, [t] in *thought*, and [əd] in *waited*, we say that these three pronunciations are only variants of one affix because their meaning or function is the same.

In each of the following pairs, if both words have the same prefix, mark them *S*; if they have different prefixes, mark them *D*.

	amoral		embed		income
_____	aside	_____	encase	_____	invalid
	autobiography		foreword		intermix
_____	autocar	_____	forswear	_____	intramural
	bemoan		extraordinary		pro-British
_____	besmirch	_____	extrasensory	_____	prologue
	biannual		hypertension		supranational
_____	bypass	_____	hypotension	_____	supernatural
	coeternal		illegal		
_____	copilot	_____	immoral		

10.8 SUFFIXES

Are the suffixes in each pair of words the same morpheme or different morphemes? Use the symbols *S* and *D*.

	absorbent		density		rested
_____	triumphant	_____	chastity	_____	bigoted
	accountable		hyphenate		smithy
_____	responsible	_____	temperate	_____	sleepy
	coastal		occurrence		taller
_____	withdrawal	_____	appearance	_____	teller
	cupful		offing		wooden
_____	careful	_____	scoffing	_____	shorten

10.9   NEW AFFIXES AND NEW USES OF OLD ONES

The *Britannica Book of the Year*, an annual supplement to the *Encyclopaedia Britannica*, lists additions to the English vocabulary under the heading "Words and Meanings, New." The journal *American Speech* also has a department "Among the New Words." Recent years have seen the increased popularity of affixes like -*ology*, -*ism*, -*nik*, -*ery*, -*ify*, -*oree*, *para*-, and *non*- in such specimens as *Saxonology* 'the study of the policies and motives of the British and American governments; the counterpart of Russian Kremlinology,' *Pekingology*, *comitology* 'the study of committees,' *tokenism* 'the practice of token integration,' *oathism* 'the practice of requiring loyalty oaths,' *spacenik* 'an astronaut,' *peacenik* 'a pacifist,' *neatnik* 'a non-beatnik,' *scrollery* 'the search for documents like the Dead Sea scrolls,' *massified* 'made massive,' *freezoree* 'a winter camporee,' *paralanguage* 'a system of communication which parallels language,' *nonevent* 'an event arranged by the news media for the purpose of reporting it,' and *nonbook* 'a book conceived as a piece of salable merchandise rather than as an artistic undertaking.'

Consult any five consecutive years of the *Britannica Book of the Year* or *American Speech* to find what affixes have appeared most frequently in the new words recorded for those years. List the more popular affixes and the words containing them. Gloss any word the meaning of which is not apparent. _____

_____

_____

_____

_____

_____

_____

_____

10.10   THE SPELLING OF COMPOUNDS

1. Are the following compounds spelled as one word, as two words, or with a hyphen? First decide how you would spell each compound and then check the spelling in a dictionary, or better, in several dictionaries.

half cocked	_____	second story (adj.)	_____
half hour	_____	side band	_____
high chair	_____	side kick	_____
high grade	_____	side light	_____
high light	_____	side step (v.)	_____
prize fighter	_____	side whiskers	_____

2. What conclusion can you draw about the spelling of compounds? _____

_____

3. Read Robert A. Hall, Jr., "To Hyphenate or Not to Hyphenate," *English Journal*, LIII (1964), 662–65, and summarize his conclusions.

_____

_____

_____

10.11   THE STRESSING OF COMPOUNDS

1. Write the stresses of these items. Use the acute mark for primary stress and the grave mark for secondary stress. Put the marks over the stressed vowel, as in *hótbèd* versus *hót béd*.

redwood	red wood	shorthand	short hand
bluebeard	blue beard	graybeard	gray beard
greenroom	green room	safeguard	safe guard
strongbox	strong box	Stonewall	stone wall
mainland	main land	paperback	paper back

2. Write the stresses.

madhouse keeper	mad housekeeper
new-math teacher	new math-teacher
second-hand cart	second handcart
used-car salesman	used car-salesman
White House lights	white houselights

3. Write the stresses of the italicized words. There is a variation among English speakers for some of these items.

The pot is only *silver plate*.	He ate from a *silver plate*.
They live on *Main Street*.	It is the *main street*.
Hamlet met the *gravedigger*.	He was a serious and *grave digger*.
What is the *subject matter*?	What does the *subject matter*?
She added *baking powder*.	Why is she *baking powder*?

4. Write the stresses of the italicized words.

Who ever asked?	*Whoever* asked?
He found a *new haven*.	He lived in *New Haven*.
It is not a *good morning*.	I wish you *good morning*.
He met an *old lady*.	Here comes your *old lady*.
The river has *grand rapids*.	They eloped to *Grand Rapids*.

5. Each of these compounds has a pronunciation that shows phonetic change due to the complete loss of stress from the second element. Each also has an analytical pronunciation. Transcribe the words phonetically to show both pronunciations.

	WITH PRIMARY STRESS ONLY	WITH PRIMARY-SECONDARY STRESS
blackguard	_____	_____
boatswain	_____	_____
somebody	_____	_____
starboard	_____	_____
topsail	_____	_____

10.12 *THE CONSTRUCTION OF COMPOUNDS*

Compounds are formed according to many patterns, of which the following are only a few:

1. *Bluegrass* is from "the grass is blue."
2. *Bloodthirsty* is from "thirsty for blood."
3. *Daredevil* is from "he dares the devil."
4. *Pale-face* is from "he has a pale face."
5. *Pin-up* is from "it is pinned up."
6. *Overland* is from "over the land."
7. *Typeset* is from "to set the type."[1]

---

[1] Historically, *typeset* is a back formation from *typesetter*, but in Modern English the construction has become a new type of compound.

Identify the patterns of these compounds by writing the appropriate number, from 1 through 7, in front of each.

_____	backbite	_____	highbrow	_____	proofread
_____	battle-ready	_____	highway	_____	redbird
_____	blowout	_____	homesick	_____	redcap
_____	boy-crazy	_____	hotfoot	_____	redhead
_____	breakdown	_____	kickback	_____	sightsee
_____	downstairs	_____	longbow	_____	spoilsport
_____	gentleman	_____	longhorn	_____	underhand

10.13 *AMALGAMATED COMPOUNDS*

1. These words are historically compounds. Identify the elements from which each word was formed.

among	_____	halibut	_____
ampersand	_____	hatred	_____
bailiwick	_____	ingot	_____
doff	_____	Lammas	_____
don	_____	neighbor	_____
elbow	_____	no	_____
every	_____	offal	_____
furlong	_____	rigmarole	_____
gamut	_____	shelter	_____
gossip	_____	woof 'thread'	_____

2. Most speakers would be aware that these words are compounds, but at least one part of each compound is semantically obscure. Identify the obscure elements.

backgammon	_____	mildew	_____
bonfire	_____	nickname	_____
cobweb	_____	walnut	_____
good-by	_____	wedlock	_____
midriff	_____	werewolf	_____
midwife	_____	worship	_____

3. These reduplicating compounds are also amalgamated. Identify their original elements.

hob-nob	_____
shilly-shally	_____
willy-nilly	_____

10.14 *CLIPPED FORMS*

Identify the full forms from which these words were abbreviated:

ad lib	_____	fan 'admirer'	_____
chap	_____	fib 'lie'	_____
chat	_____	limey	_____
chum	_____	mitt	_____
cinema	_____	mutt	_____

pep	_____	scram	_____
prom	_____	sleuth	_____
radio	_____	toady	_____

Identify the long form from which each of these words was produced by aphesis:

cense	_____	raiment	_____
drawing room	_____	spite	_____
fend	_____	splay	_____
lone	_____	squint	_____
mend	_____	stogie	_____
mien	_____	stress	_____
neath	_____	tend 'serve'	_____
pall 'satiate'	_____	tiring-room	_____
pert	_____	varsity	_____
ply 'use diligently'	_____	venture	_____

10.16 *BACK FORMATION*

These words are the result of back formation. Give the original words from which they were back-formed.

1. BACK FORMATIONS INVOLVING AN INFLECTIONAL ENDING

asset	_____	pry 'lever'	_____
burial	_____	riddle 'puzzle'	_____
hush	_____	(window) sash	_____
inkle 'hint'	_____	shimmy	_____
marquee	_____	sidle	_____

2. BACK FORMATIONS INVOLVING AN AGENT SUFFIX

edit	_____	panhandle	_____
escalate	_____	peddle	_____
hawk 'vend'	_____	scavenge	_____
interlope	_____	(to) swab	_____
mug 'assault'	_____	swindle	_____

3. MISCELLANEOUS BACK FORMATIONS

(to) char	_____	peeve	_____
diagnose	_____	preempt	_____
donate	_____	reminisce	_____
greed	_____	resurrect	_____
homesick	_____	unit	_____

4. Some words are formed by a process that is the opposite of back formation. Give the etymology of the following four words and then describe the process of word formation that is common to them. Notice that all four words are singular in current English; they require a singular verb like *seems* rather than a plural like *seem*.

bodice _____

chintz _____

news _____

quince _____

PROCESS OF FORMATION: _____

_____

10.17   *BLENDS*

1. Identify the sources from which these blends were produced. There will be two sources for each blend. The origin of some of these words is not completely certain, so you can expect variation among dictionaries.

alegar =	_____	+	_____
blotch =	_____	+	_____
blurt =	_____	+	_____
extrapolate =	_____	+	_____
hassle =	_____	+	_____
magnetron =	_____	+	_____
positron =	_____	+	_____
prissy =	_____	+	_____
scratch =	_____	+	_____
scroll =	_____	+	_____
simulcast =	_____	+	_____
splatter =	_____	+	_____
splutter =	_____	+	_____
tangelo =	_____	+	_____
travelogue =	_____	+	_____
vitamin =	_____	+	_____

2. Some blends are deliberate, intentional creations like *racon* from *radar* plus *beacon*, but others result from unconscious slips of the tongue. In rapid speech, the talker may have in mind two words of partly similar meaning and sound; the speech process gets short-circuited and instead of choosing between the two words, the speaker combines them into a single form. Thus *slick* and *slimy* may blend as [ˈslɪmi], *drip* and *dribble* as [drɪpl], or *stockings* and *socks* as [stɑks]. Occasionally such a *lapsus linguae* becomes established in the language, but most of them are hardly noticed by either the speaker or his audience.[2] Try to collect a few examples of inadvertent blending by listening to the speech of those around you.

10.18   *ACRONYMS*

1. Abbreviations that make use of the initial letters in a phrase are the first step toward acronyms. Such abbreviations are extremely common in contemporary English, often supplanting the unabbreviated term in general usage. Widely used abbreviations, in addition to those cited in *Origins and Development*, are AA, BTU, CIA, DT's, ESP, FCC, GI, HMS, IQ, JP,

[2] A good discussion of unconscious blends can be found in E. H. Sturtevant, *An Introduction to Linguistic Science* (New Haven, Conn., 1947), pp. 110–16.

KO, LA, MD, NG, OCS, PTA, QED, RSVP, SRO, TNT, USA, VIP, and WCTU. List ten or fifteen similar abbreviations in common use. _____

_____

2. The pronunciation of the letters in abbreviations such as the ones listed above sometimes gives rise to new written words. What is the origin of each of these terms?

ack ack _____

emcee _____

jeep _____

kayo _____

veep _____

3. These words are acronyms. Give the full phrases from which they have been abbreviated.

conelrad _____

Delmarva _____

futhorc _____

loran _____

napalm _____

shoran _____

sial _____

sonar _____

teleran _____

4. English is not unique in forming acronyms. Some words that we have borrowed from foreign tongues were originally abbreviated phrases. Identify the unabbreviated source of each of these words:

kolkhoz _____

comintern _____

flak _____

Gestapo _____

5. Trade names are very often acronyms, for example, *Amoco, Nabisco, Panagra, Socony,* and *Sunoco.* List a few other such trade names. _____

_____

6. Pseudo-acronyms like *Wave* are becoming increasingly common. The following phrases, in which the capital letters spell an acronym, have been recorded.[3]

*F*ilm *O*ptical *S*canning *D*evice for *I*nput to *C*omputers

*E*lectronegative *GA*s *D*etector

*I*nstrumentation *DI*gital *O*n-line *T*ranscriber

*A*utomatic *D*igital *I*nput-*O*utput *S*ystem

In each case it seems likely that the supposed abbreviation had some influence on the creation of the full phrase. List a few other pseudo-acronyms. _____

_____

_____

_____

[3] Milton Goldstein, *Dictionary of Modern Acronyms and Abbreviations* (Indianapolis, 1963).

1. Give the correct etymology of these words and indicate the probable basis for the folk etymology, following the pattern on pages 291–92 of *Origins and Development*.

andiron _____

barberry _____

blunderbuss _____

chick-pea _____

demijohn _____

forlorn hope _____

gymkhana _____

mangrove _____

rosemary _____

sty 'swelling on eyelid' _____

teapoy _____

turtle 'reptile' _____

2. If we consider the earliest forms of the italicized words, the answer to each of the following questions is "no." Give the correct etymology for the words. Although the misunderstanding illustrated by some of them is too learned to be of the folk, the principle involved is the same as that of folk etymology.

Was the *gopherwood* from which Noah built the ark named for gophers?

_____

Is a *chipmunk* so called because he chips?

_____

Is an *outrage* a raging out?

_____

Are *nightmares* brought on by horseback riding?

_____

Is a *comrade* someone with (Lat. *com-*) whom one does something?

_____

Is *kitty-cornered* the way a kitten walks?

_____

Is the bridge term *tenace* a combination of a ten and an ace?

_____

Is the *hold* of a ship so called because it holds the cargo?

_____

Is a *ham* radio operator so called because, as an unsuccessful presidential candidate suggested, he is an (h)amateur?

_____

Do *Jordan almonds* come from Jordan?

_____

Is the *albatross* so called because it is white (Lat. *alba*) in color?

_____

Is a *posthumous* work one published after (Lat. *post*) the author has been put under the earth (*humus*)?

Is the *ptarmigan* a creature named from Greek like the pterodactyl and the pteropod?

Is an *argosy* named for the *argonauts*?

Are *purlieus* so named because they are a kind of place (Fr. *lieu*)?

3. Much folk etymology, like the Chester drawers (chest of drawers) and Archie Fisher snow (artificial snow) mentioned in *Origins and Development*, is so ephemeral that it never achieves lexicographical record. Some of it is deliberately humorous. Here are a few additional examples of such folk etymology; add to the list from your own experience.

car porch 'an open-sided shelter for an automobile' (properly *carport*)
Creak Car Lake 'a resort lake near St. Louis, Missouri, reached by a squeaking trolley car' (properly *Crèvecoeur Lake*)
dashhound 'a dog of German origin' (properly *dachshund*)
lowbachi 'a small charcoal brazier in the Japanese style' (variant of *hibachi*)
very coarse veins 'swollen veins' (properly *varicose*)

10.20 *COMMON WORDS FROM PROPER NAMES*

1. These common nouns were taken without change from the names of actual persons. Explain briefly how each personal name came to be applied to the thing it now denotes.

braille _____
diesel _____
hooligan _____
leotard _____
negus _____
quisling _____
roentgen _____
sequoia _____
silhouette _____

2. These common words are derivatives or altered forms of personal names. Identify the historical person from whose name each word derives.

algorism	_____	guillotine	_____
(deci)bel	_____	klieg (light)	_____
boysenberry	_____	macadam	_____
euhemerism	_____	magnolia	_____
fuchsia	_____	saxophone	_____

3. These common words were taken from the names of literary, mythological, or Biblical persons. Identify the source of each.

ammonia _____

euphuism _____

hermetic _____

lazar _____

museum _____

philander _____

procrustean _____

syphilis _____

termagant _____

veronica _____

4. These common words are given names used generically. Identify each word by the usual form of the name from which it comes.

dickey	_____	jockey	_____
dobbin	_____	jug	_____
doll	_____	magpie	_____
(play) hob	_____	marionette	_____
jimmy	_____	zany	_____

5. These words were taken without change from the names of places. Identify the nation in which each place is to be found.

angostura	_____	duffel	_____
ascot	_____	jodhpur(s)	_____
bantam	_____	madras	_____
castile 'soap'	_____	magenta	_____
donnybrook	_____	spa	_____

6. These words are derivatives or altered forms of place names. Identify the place from which each word derives.

attic	_____	muslin	_____
baldachin	_____	palace	_____
buckram	_____	peach 'fruit'	_____
cantaloupe	_____	seltzer	_____
capitol	_____	spruce	_____
currant	_____	tabby	_____
denim	_____	tangerine	_____
jimson(weed)	_____		

7. These common words are derived from the names of tribes or national groups. Identify the sources.

arabesque	_____	hooch	_____
cravat	_____	lumber	_____
frank	_____	slave	_____
gothic	_____	vandal	_____
gyp	_____	welch	_____

8. These common words are derived from various kinds of proper names. Identify the sources.

blucher	_____	protean	_____
cambric	_____	raglan	_____
canary	_____	robin	_____
cretin	_____	shillelagh	_____
loganberry	_____	sienna	_____
majolica	_____	sousaphone	_____
melba toast	_____	vaudeville	_____

10.21 *SLANG*

1. Much slang enters general use from the jargon of particular occupations. Thus the recently popular (*rat*)*fink* has its origin in underworld argot, in which it means 'informer.' Baseball has contributed such terms as *batting average, to be benched, bush leagues, double-header, grandstand play, off-base, far out* (*in left field*), *pinch-hitter, put one over, safe at home, shut-out, south-paw, strike-out*, and *throw a curve*, all of which are used in discussing subjects other than sports. A batting average may be for tests, checks from home, or women as well as for baseballs. List ten or twelve slang terms that have passed into general use from some area such as crime, the military, jazz, college life, show business, card-playing, or some other familiar activity. _____

_____

_____

_____

2. Reduplication often appears in slang terms. The second element may rime with the first, as in *hanky-panky*, or it may show consonance, as in *chitchat*. Supply the second element in each of these reduplicating compounds:

even-	_____	flip-	_____
heebie-	_____	mish-	_____
hoity-	_____	slip-	_____
razzle-	_____	tip-	_____
super-	_____	wishy-	_____

3. Another device by which slang adds to the lexicon is rime. We have already seen that many reduplications make use of rime, but it is likely that rime has also played a part in the coining of slang terms like *gimp* (cf. *limp*), *potted* (cf. *sotted*), *razzamatazz* (cf. *jazz*), *no soap* (cf. *hope*), and *it's a breeze* (cf. *with ease*). Moreover, rime figures conspicuously in phrases such as "See you later, alligator," which at one time spawned a number of imitations of the type "In a while, crocodile."

One of the more complex uses of sound-repetition is Cockney riming slang, which has contributed several phrases to the general vocabulary. This form of slang originated among the London Cockney and spread to Australia and the United States, although it has never been particularly widespread in this country. For a word, such as *wife*, the Cockney substitutes a riming phrase which is semantically appropriate, preferably in a sardonic way, for example, *trouble and strife*. The phrase is often clipped to its first member, thus effectively disguising its origin and serving a function of all slang, to mystify those in the "out-group."

A common and unusually complex example of Cockney riming slang is *duke* 'fist,' as in "put up your dukes." *Duke* is a clipping of *Duke of Yorks*, riming slang for *forks*; *forks* in turn is a slang metaphor for fingers or, collectively, a fist. Here are a few of the better known Cockney slang words. Identify the word on which the riming phrase is based.[4]

Let's get down to *brass tacks*. _____

In his business, he makes a pile of *sugar*. (clipped from *sugar and honey*; compare the poker term "to sweeten the pot") _____

I don't care a *ding-dong* for what they think. (clipped from *ding-dong-bell*) _____

She's a pert little *twist*. (clipped from *twist and twirl*) _____

After one too many, you may feel a bit *tiddly*. (clipped from *tiddlywink*, by way of "I want a little tiddly") _____

When he gets mad, you should hear him *rip*. (clipped from *rip and tear*, common in the phrase *let rip*) _____

Good thinking, that's using the old *loaf*. (clipped from *loaf of bread*) _____

You're tired, you need a little *Bo-peep*. _____

4. Slang, by its very nature, is poorly represented in standard dictionaries. For early slang, the *Oxford English Dictionary* is useful and can be supplemented by John S. Farmer and William Ernest Henley, *Dictionary of Slang and Its Analogues*, 7 vols. (New York, 1890–1904). More recent British slang is recorded in Eric Partridge, *A Dictionary of Slang and Unconventional English*, 3rd ed. (New York, 1950), and American slang in Harold Wentworth and Stuart Berg Flexner, *Dictionary of American Slang* (New York, 1960) and in Lester V. Berrey and Melvin Van den Bark, *The American Thesaurus of Slang*, 2nd ed. (New York, 1953). Use these works or other available dictionaries to answer the following questions, but note the source of your information for each answer.

What did a seventeenth-century *cony-catcher* catch? _____

_____

When Dickens wrote in *Martin Chuzzlewit*, "She was only a little screwed," with what debility did he imply the lady to be afflicted? _____

_____

Although it is known in America, *smarmy* is more common in British English. What is its meaning? _____

_____

When an Australian is *waltzing Matilda*, what is he doing? _____

_____

What is the meaning of the obsolete American term *ish kabibble*? _____

_____

What is the apparent source of American *sockdolager*? _____

_____

The acronym *snafu* spawned a number of imitations like *fubar* 'fouled up beyond all recognition.' List a few of its other progeny. _____

_____

What are some slang terms for various kinds of auctions? _____

_____

[4] These words and many others can be found in Julian Franklyn, *A Dictionary of Riming Slang* (London, 1960).

1. There are a few words that can be traced with some confidence to a literary origin or to a specific act of coinage. Consult the *Oxford English Dictionary* to find the source of each of these words:

agnostic _____
blatant _____
ignoramus 'ignorant person' _____
knickerbockers _____
Lilliputian _____
malaprop(ism) _____
namby-pamby _____
Peeping Tom _____
potter's field _____
sensuous _____
serendipity _____
simon-pure _____
spoof _____
tam(-o'-shanter) _____
yahoo _____

2. Most of the following words are too recent, at least in their current uses, to be entered in the *OED*. Consult *Webster's Third New International Dictionary* for their origin.

babbitt(ry) _____
bazooka _____
boondoggle _____
fedora _____
Frankenstein _____
goop 'boor' _____
jabberwocky _____
Milquetoast _____
scrooge _____
Shangri-la _____

3. Who, according to the *OED*, was the first person to use each of these words in writing? Note also the year of the word's first appearance in English.

anesthesia _____
blasé _____
electricity _____
environment 'surrounding region' _____
Gotham 'New York City' _____
muckrake _____
ragamuffin _____
rodomontade _____
salad days _____
superman _____

10.23 ONE PART OF SPEECH TO ANOTHER

1. For each of these words, write two or more sentences using the word as a different part of speech in each sentence.

back _____

_____

best _____

_____

feature _____

_____

gross _____

_____

slow _____

_____

split _____

_____

total _____

_____

try _____

_____

up _____

_____

while _____

_____

2. According to the citations in the *Oxford English Dictionary*, as what part of speech was each of these words first used?

blemish	_____	fun	_____
coin	_____	idle	_____
eavesdrop	_____	matter	_____
faint	_____	pressure	_____
fossil	_____	shampoo	_____

3. Identify the part of speech of the italicized words.

The Recreation Center is hosting a community *sing*. _____

And also loke [look] on schrewes . . . how gret peyne *felawschipith* [fellowships] and folweth hem [them]. (Chaucer, *Boece*, IV, p. 3) _____

Let me *wise* you up. _____

Lady, you are the cruell'st *she* alive. (Shakespeare, *Twelfth Night*, I.v) _____

It might be a *fun* thing to go to one of their parties. _____

The sweets we wish for turn to loathed *sours*. (Shakespeare, *Rape of Lucrece*, l. 867)

_____

Manufacturers often *package* according to the price instead of pricing according to the package. _____

My heart in hiding / Stirred for a bird, —the *achieve* of, the mastery of the thing! (G. M. Hopkins, "The Windhover") _____

It was an invitation for Clay to *up* and clobber him. _____

Who shall . . . through the palpable *obscure* find out his uncouth way? (Milton, *Paradise Lost*, II, 406) _____

1. Consult the *Oxford English Dictionary* to find when each of these verb-adverb combinations was first used in the sense indicated. In addition, mark those which originated in America with the abbreviation *U.S.* For some of the phrases, you will need to use the supplementary volume.

   bring forth 'give birth to' _____

   call down 'reprove' _____

   do in 'bring disaster upon' _____

   get over 'finish with' _____

   hang back 'show unwillingness to advance' _____

   lay by 'store up, save' _____

   look after 'take care of' _____

   put on 'affect, pretend' _____

   send out 'issue' _____

   take up (for) 'defend, stand up for' _____

2. Combine the verbs listed on the left with the adverbs listed on the right to make as many idiomatic verb-adverb combinations as possible.

cut	down
give	in
put	off
take	out
turn	up

   _____

   _____

   _____

   _____

   _____

3. Which of the combinations from the preceding question can be converted into nouns by a shift of stress? For example, *to cut úp–a cútup.* _____

   _____

   _____

   _____

4. Stress may indicate parts of speech for words other than verb-adverb combinations. Write the primary stress of these words with an acute mark over the stressed vowel. Record your own pronunciation.

NOUNS	VERBS	NOUNS	VERBS	NOUNS	VERBS
commune	commune	forecast	forecast	overhaul	overhaul
contest	contest	inlay	inlay	present	present
decrease	decrease	insult	insult	rebel	rebel
discount	discount	object	object	survey	survey
extract	extract	offset	offset	undercut	undercut

10.25 *NEW WORDS FROM OLD: A SUMMARY*

Identify the processes of word-making that have produced these words by writing the appropriate number, from 1 through 10, in front of each word. For some of the items you will need to consult a dictionary; others should be transparent.

1. onomatopoeia
2. use of affixes
3. compounding
4. clipping
5. back formation
6. blending
7. formation of acronym
8. folk etymology
9. derivation from proper name
10. conversion of part of speech

_____	curio	_____	maser
_____	emote	_____	noncash 'credit'
_____	gillyflower	_____	pop 'sudden noise'
_____	halfback	_____	psychic 'a medium'
_____	marathon	_____	slanguage
_____	Amerind	_____	jaw 'talk volubly'
_____	cordovan	_____	mongoose
_____	creak	_____	refreeze
_____	glamazon 'chorus girl'	_____	roughneck
_____	intercom	_____	televise
_____	baloney	_____	mike
_____	cusec	_____	primrose
_____	discussant	_____	surrey
_____	handwrite	_____	swimsation
_____	kéy clùb	_____	swish
_____	Benelux	_____	laze
_____	cicerone	_____	mangrove
_____	corner 'get a corner on'	_____	mumble
_____	hiss	_____	sexsational
_____	shóut shòp 'advertising agency'	_____	tot 'add'
_____	academy	_____	grapheme
_____	balletorio 'choral music with dancing'	_____	guffaw
_____	cajun	_____	high-muck-a-muck
_____	CORE	_____	jell
_____	muscleshirt 'sleeveless T shirt'	_____	orate
_____	caper 'plant'	_____	enthuse
_____	chartreuse	_____	lackadaisical
_____	chirp	_____	oleo
_____	construct 'something constructed'	_____	parsec
_____	optiman 'man in optimum condition'	_____	tough 'rowdy person'

11

Words and Meanings

11.1 *QUESTIONS FOR REVIEW AND DISCUSSION*

1. Define the following terms:

semantics	pejoration	sound association
semantic change	amelioration	taboo
etymological sense	vogue word	euphemism
generalization	metaphor	intensifier
specialization	synesthesia	

2. What devices for signaling meaning does a language have?

3. What value is there in the study of words? In answering this question, consider one of the conclusions reached by Charles Carpenter Fries in his germinal study *American English Grammar: The Grammatical Structure of Present-Day English with Especial Reference to Social Differences or Class Dialects* (New York, 1940): "In vocabulary and in grammar the mark of the language of the uneducated is its poverty."

4. What is meant by the statement that every word has "a certain field of meaning" rather than a "fixed" or "real" meaning?

5. How does the concept of a "field of meaning" help to explain why meaning varies?

6. What are the proper and improper uses of etymology?

7. Some of the ways and circumstances in which meaning may change are listed here. Notice that the various ways are not all mutually exclusive; there is much overlapping. Supply an example to illustrate each way.

   (1) a widening of the scope of reference (generalization)

   (2) a narrowing of the scope of reference (specialization)

   (3) a worsening of value judgments involved in the reference (pejoration)

   (4) a bettering of the value judgments involved in the reference (amelioration)

   (5) a shift in meaning from one social group to another (specialized class usage)

   (6) a shift in meaning from one set of circumstances to another (contextual variation)

   (7) a change in the aspect of the meaning upon which a word focuses (shift in point of view)

   (8) a popular adoption of technical language, often motivated by the quest for prestige (popularization)

   (9) a shift in meaning based on an analogy or likeness between two things (metaphor)

   (10) a transference of meaning from one kind of sense-perception to another (synesthesia)

   (11) a shift from concrete reference to abstract reference (abstraction)

(12) a shift from abstract reference to concrete reference (concretion)

(13) a shift in reference from the subjective to the objective (objectification or externalizing)

(14) a shift in reference from the objective to the subjective (subjectification or internalizing)

(15) a shift in meaning due to the association of ideas (synecdoche and metonymy)

(16) an influence of the semantics of one language upon that of another (translation)

(17) a semantic association between two words due to a similarity in sound (sound association)

(18) a religious or moral taboo which requires new words to replace others thought to be too dangerous, too indecent, or too painful for common use (euphemism)

(19) an exaggerated use of words for mild intensification or emphasis (hyperbole)

8. In 1712 Jonathan Swift published *A Proposal for Correcting, Improving and Ascertaining the English Tongue*,[1] in which he wrote,

> The *English* Tongue is not arrived to such a Degree of Perfection, as, upon that Account, to make us apprehend any Thoughts of its Decay: And if it were once refined to a certain Standard, perhaps there might be Ways to fix it for ever .... I see no absolute Necessity why any Language should be perpetually changing; for we find many Examples of the contrary ... But what I have most at Heart, is, that some Method should be thought on for *Ascertaining* and *Fixing* our Language for ever, after such Alterations are made in it as shall be thought requisite .... What *Horace* says of *Words going off, and perishing like Leaves, and new ones coming in their Place*, is a Misfortune he laments, rather than a Thing he approves: But I cannot see why this should be absolutely necessary.

Discuss the goal that Swift sets up in this extract in terms of its desirability and practicality.

11.2 DEVICES FOR SIGNALING MEANING

Every language can be said to have two kinds of meaning: lexical meaning, the sense that words have as they are listed in a dictionary, and grammatical meaning, the added sense that words acquire when they are put together in a sentence. Certain words, the function words mentioned on page 11 of *Origins and Development*, are so fundamental to the grammatical meaning of a sentence that it is best to consider them as part of the grammar as well as part of the lexicon of English. One way to demonstrate the difference between these two kinds of meaning is with sentences like these:

Oll considerork meanork, ho mollop tharp fo concernesh bix shude largel philosophigar aspectem ith language phanse vulve increasorkrow de recent yearm engagesh sho attentuge ith scholarm.

In prefarbing torming, we cannot here be pretolled with those murler dichytomical optophs of flemack which have demuggingly in arsell wems exbined the obburtion of maxans.

If you are asked what the sentences mean, your first response may be that neither means anything. If further pressed, you might suggest that the first sentence is about language, about something that is recent, and perhaps about philosophy. A careful reading will reveal several other probable bits of information, but at best the sentence remains a farrago of nonsense.

With the second sentence, however, matters are quite otherwise. There is a great deal of meaning in it; for example you can tell from it

---

[1] Reprinted in *The Prose Works of Jonathan Swift*, edited by Herbert Davis (Oxford: Basil Blackwell, 1957), Vol. IV.

1. that, whatever an optoph is, there are more than one of them;
2. that the optophs we are concerned with are dichytomical ones and more murl than other possible optophs;
3. that an optoph is something we might be pretolled with;
4. that optophs are things and not people;
5. that the obburtion of maxans can be exbined by optophs;
6. that the exbining we are talking about took place in the past.

These six observations are only a few of the many bits of meaning the second sentence will convey to any speaker of English. Indeed, our reaction to the second sentence might be that of Alice to the poem "Jabberwocky": "Somehow it seems to fill my head with ideas—only I don't exactly know what they are!" The first sentence uses real English for its lexically important words, but substitutes nonsense elements for the function words and the word-endings. Therefore we have some idea of what it is talking about, but no notion whatever of what is being said about the subject. The second sentence reverses the procedure by preserving function words and suffixes, but using nonsense syllables for the main lexical items. Thus even though we have no idea of what *optophs* and *maxans* are, we do know what is being said about them.

In *Origins and Development* and this workbook, Chapters IV through IX are devoted mainly to the history of pronunciation and of grammatical meaning and forms of the sort we can recognize in the second sentence. Chapters X through XII are devoted mainly to the history of lexical meaning and forms like those preserved in the first sentence. In this exercise we are concerned with distinguishing between the two.

1. We made six observations about the meaning of the second sentence. Tell, as precisely as you can, how each of these observations can be inferred from the sentence.

   (1) _____
   _____
   (2) _____
   _____
   (3) _____
   _____
   (4) _____
   _____
   (5) _____
   _____
   (6) _____
   _____

2. Which of the following observations are valid inferences from the second sentence? Write *V* before each valid conclusion and *I* before each invalid conclusion.

   _____ Obburtion belongs to or is characteristic of more than one maxan.
   _____ We probably prefarb torming.
   _____ Flemack does exbine the obburtion of maxans.
   _____ The exbining of the obburtion of maxans by murler dichytomical optophs of flemack is demugging.
   _____ We do not pretoll some optophs.
   _____ The action of exbining the obburtion of maxans has taken place in more than one wem which is arsell.

3. In each of these sentences, underline the function words and circle grammatically relevant endings.

The merkly boppling dorn quanks all puggles in the scritches.

A tagmeme is the correlation of a grammatical function or slot-class with a class of fillers or mutually substitutable items occurring in that slot.

Night's candles are burnt out, and jocund day stands tiptoe on the misty mountain tops.

But the Idols of the Market-place are the most troublesome of all: idols which have crept into the understanding through the alliances of words and names.

The generall end therefore of all the booke is to fashion a gentleman or noble person in vertuous and gentle discipline.

His notions fitted things so well/That which was which he could not tell.

4. Identify the devices which are used for changing the meaning in these pairs of sentences. Write the appropriate numbers in the blanks. The last three pairs involve two devices each.

1. function words
2. intonation
3. suffixes
4. word order

It is time to go.
_____ It is time to go?

She liked the red hat.
_____ She liked the *red* hat.

He invested in stock theater.
_____ He invested in theater stock.

They found the girl in the car that needed washing.
_____ They found the girl in the car who needed washing.

He bought a picture of Rembrandt for two dollars.
_____ He bought a picture of Rembrandt's for two dollars.

The travelers stopped to eat.
_____ _____ The travelers stopped eating.

They said it was a fun time.
_____ _____ They said it was fun-time.

He died happily.
_____ _____ Happily, he died.

11.3 *VARIATION IN MEANING: WORD-PLAY*

In each of these quotations there is a pun or a play on meaning involving the italicized words. In some cases the word-play is due to a word's having a broad field of meaning; in other cases, it is due to an accidental similarity of sound between two different words.

What two meanings are combined to produce each pun? Consult the *Oxford English Dictionary* if you cannot recognize the word-play.

1. For him was levere have at his beddes heed
   Twenty bookes, clad in blak or reed,
   Of Aristotle and his philosophye,
   Than robes rich, or fithele, or gay sautrye.
   But al be that he was a *philosophre*
   Yit hadde he but litel gold in cofre.   (Chaucer, General Prologue to *The Canterbury Tales*)

   _____

   _____

2. For thy sweet love remembered such wealth brings
   That then I scorn to change my *state* with kings.   (Shakespeare, Sonnet 29)

   _____

   _____

3. [As a joke, Falstaff's horse has been hidden.]

   Fal[staff]   What a plague mean ye to colt me thus?
     Prince   Thou liest; thou art not *colted*, thou art uncolted.

                                                 (Shakespeare, *1 Henry IV*, II.ii)

   _____

   _____

4. *Hostess*   Marry, my lord, there is a *noble*man of the court at door would speak with you,
             he says he comes from your father.
     Prince   Give him as much as will make him a *royal* man, and send him back again to my
             mother.   (Shakespeare, *1 Henry IV*, II.iv)

   _____

   _____

5. [Prince Hal and Bardolph, a gluttonous thief, are discussing what is portended by Bardolph's nose, which is as red as a meteor.]

   Bard[olph]   Choler, my lord, if rightly taken.
       Prince   No, if rightly *taken*, halter. [that is, 'noose']   (Shakespeare, *1 Henry IV*, II.iv)

   _____

   _____

6. [In the midst of battle, Prince Hal asks Falstaff for his pistol.]

     Prince   Give it me; what, is it in the case?
   Fal[staff]   Aye, Hal; 'tis hot, 'tis hot; there's that will *sack* a city.

   [Hal, taking the supposed pistol from the case, finds that it is a bottle of wine.]

                                                 (Shakespeare, *1 Henry IV*, V.iii)

   _____

   _____

7. [Hippolito is confused about the identity of his caller. Why?]

     Servant   Here's a *parson* would speak with you, sir.
   Hippolito   Hah!
     Servant   A *parson*, sir, would speak with you.
   Hippolito   Vicar?   (Dekker, *The Honest Whore*, Part I, IV, 1)

   _____

   _____

8. *Fortunatus*   Let none speak to me, till you have *marked* me well.

    Shadow   [Chalking Fortunatus's back] Now speak your mind.

(Dekker, *Old Fortunatus*, II, 2)

---

9. *Viola*   Musician will he never be, yet I find much music in him, but he loves no *frets*, and is so free from anger that many times I am ready to bite off my tongue . . .

(Dekker, *The Honest Whore*, Part I, I, 2)

---

10.   *Shadow*   But what shall we learn by travel?

   Andelocia   *Fashions*.

    Shadow   That's a beastly disease: methinks it's better staying in your own country.

(Dekker, *Old Fortunatus*, II, 2)

---

11. Must I, who came to *travail* thorough you

Grow your fixed subject, because you are true?   (Donne, "The Indifferent")

---

12. Dull sublunary lovers' love

   (Whose soule is sense) cannot admit

Absence, because it doth remove

   Those things which elemented it.   (Donne, "A Valediction: Forbidding Mourning")

---

13. Swear by Thy self, that at my death Thy *Son*

   Shall shine as he shines now and heretofore;

     And, having done that, Thou hast done,

      I fear no more.   (Donne, "A Hymn to God the Father")

---

14. [This poem is a prayer for God's grace.]

The dew doth ev'ry morning fall;

And shall the dew outstrip thy dove?

The dew, for which *grasse* cannot call,

   Drop from above.   (Herbert, "Grace")

---

15.   And now, unveiled, the toilet stands displayed,

Each silver vase in mystic order laid.

First, robed in white, the nymph intent adores,

With head uncovered, the *cosmetic* powers.   (Pope, *The Rape of the Lock*)

If the italicized words are taken in their etymological senses, each of the following statements is redundant. Cite the etymological meanings that create the pseudo-redundancies.

They began the *inauguration* by observing the entrails of a sacrificial bull. _____

_____

The *escaping* convict slipped out of his coat, by which the guard held him. _____

_____

His *stamina* having been exhausted, the Fates clipped his thread of life. _____

_____

The general *harangued* his soldiers as they gathered about him in a circle. _____

_____

The *candidate* was dressed in a white suit to symbolize his purity. _____

_____

A *mediocre* mountain-climber, he never got more than halfway up any peak. _____

_____

The *miniature* was painted in shades of red. _____

_____

The butcher's shop, especially the bench on which he cleaved meat, was a *shambles*.

_____

The infantry withstood fierce punishment from the *strafing* of the enemy aircraft.

_____

The housemother *controlled* the coeds by checking their names against her register to be sure they were present at lights-out. _____

_____

There is an etymological contradiction in each of these statements. Cite the etymological meaning of the italicized word that creates the pseudo-inconsistency.

The *cadre* is the core around which a military unit forms, as a circle around its center.

_____

Although her hair was neatly arranged, she looked *disheveled*. _____

_____

He *endorsed* the proposal by signing his name with a flourish across the front of the document.

_____

The archeologist *arrived* at his destination, a ruin in the midst of the Sahara. _____

_____

Although the two men were *companions* of long standing, they had never shared a meal.

_____

The team *scampered* onto the field, eager to meet their opponents. _____

_____

The ship's passengers were *quarantined* for two weeks. _____

_____

The use of automation by American *manufacturers* promises to effect a new industrial revolution. _____

_____

The short, skinny girl had a great deal of *poise*. _____
_____
You may write on any *topic* you like except a person or a place. _____
_____

11.5   *CHANGES IN MEANING*

He was a happy and *sad girl* who lived in a *town* forty miles from the closest neighbor. His

unmarried sister, a *wife* who was a vegetarian member of the WCTU, ate *meat* and drank

liquor three times a day. She was so fond of oatmeal bread made from the *corn* her brother

grew that she *starved* from overeating. He fed nuts to the *deer* that lived in the branches of an

apple tree which bore pears. A *silly* and wise *boor* everyone liked, he was a *lewd* man whom the

general *censure* held to be a model of chastity.

The paragraph above is logically incoherent if we understand all of the words in their current meanings. If, however, we take each of the italicized words in a sense it had in earlier times, the paragraph contains no inconsistencies at all. Above each of the italicized words, write an earlier meaning that will remove the logical contradictions created by the current sense. The earlier meanings need not be contemporary with one another. They can be found in the *Oxford English Dictionary*.

11.6   *SOME EXAMPLES OF SEMANTIC CHANGE*

The italicized words in the following quotations have lost the meaning that the quotation demands. In the blank to the left of each quotation write a word that will gloss the italicized item for a modern reader. Try to guess the meaning from the context, but if you are unsure, consult the *Oxford English Dictionary*, where you will find most of the quotations used as citations.

_____   He *addressed* himself to go over the River. (Bunyan, *Pilgrim's Progress*)

_____   He had *approved* unto the vulgar, the dignitie of his Science. (Raleigh, *The History of the World*)

_____   *Falstaff*   Shall we have a play extempore?

　　　　　　　　　Prince   Content; and the *argument* shall be thy running away. (Shakespeare, *1 Henry IV*)

_____   A Brazen or Stone-head ... so *artificial* and natural, that ... it will presently open its mouth, and resolve the question. (Worcester, *A Century of Inventions*)

_____   Yes, and after supper for feare lest they bee not full gorged, to have a delicate *banquet*. (Cogan, *The Haven of Health*)

_____   Doth she not count her blest ... that we have wrought so worthy a gentleman to be her *bride*? (Shakespeare, *Romeo and Juliet*)

_____ Thus we *prevent* the last great day, and judge ourselves. (Herbert, *The Temple*)

_____ Upon that day either prepare to die . . . or on Diana's altar to *protest* for aye austerity and single life. (Shakespeare, *Midsummer Night's Dream*)

_____ The exception *proves* the rule. (Proverbial)

_____ But you, my lord, were glad to be employ'd, to show how *quaint* an orator you are. (Shakespeare, *2 Henry VI*)

_____ What lawful *quest* have given their verdict up unto the frowning judge? (Shakespeare, *Richard III*)

_____ If I attain I will return and *quit* thy love. (Arnold, *The Light of Asia*)

_____ Abate the edge of traitors . . . that would *reduce* these bloody days again, and make poor England weep in streams of blood! (Shakespeare, *Richard III*)

_____ My ships are safely come to *road*. (Shakespeare, *Merchant of Venice*)

_____ Thou wilt never get thee a husband, if thou be so *shrewd* of thy tongue. (Shakespeare, *Much Ado About Nothing*)

_____ I think you have as little *skill* to fear, as I have purpose to put you to it. (Shakespeare, *Winter's Tale*)

_____ Satan . . . insatiate to pursue vain war with Heaven, and by *success* untaught, his proud imaginations thus displayed. (Milton, *Paradise Lost*)

_____ To be my queen and *portly* emperess. (Marlowe, *Tamburlane, Part I*)

_____ There they alight . . . and rest their weary limbs a *tide*. (Spenser, *Faerie Queene*)

_____ —I dreamt a dream *tonight*. —And so did I. (Shakespeare, *Romeo and Juliet*)

_____ So said he, and forbore not glance or *toy*, of amorous intent, well understood of Eve. (Milton, *Paradise Lost*)

_____ Heaps of pearl, inestimable stones, *unvalued* jewels, all scattered in the bottom of the sea. (Shakespeare, *Richard III*)

_____ Princes then . . . [were] trained up, through piety and zeal, to prize spare diet, patient labour, and plain *weeds*. (Wordsworth, *Prelude*)

_____ This God is most mighty thing that may be, the most *witty* and most rightful. (*Lay Folks' Catechism*)

_____ O Eve, in evil hour thou didst give ear to that false *worm*. (Milton, *Paradise Lost*)

11.7 *GENERALIZATION AND SPECIALIZATION*

Each of the semantic developments described below is an example of either generalization or specialization. Identify the process illustrated by writing in the blank *G* for generalization or *S* for specialization.

_____ *aisle:* earlier 'passage between the pews of a church,' later 'passage between rows of seats'

_____ *bereaved:* earlier 'robbed,' later 'deprived by death'

_____ *business:* earlier 'state of being busy,' later 'occupation, profession, or trade'

_____ *butler:* earlier 'male servant in charge of the wine cellar,' later 'male servant in a household'

_____ *chap:* earlier 'customer,' later 'fellow'

_____ *coast:* earlier 'side,' later 'sea shore'

_____ *discard:* earlier 'throw out a card,' later 'reject'

_____ *disease:* earlier 'discomfort,' later 'malady'

_____ *flesh:* earlier 'muscular tissue,' later 'muscular tissue, not viewed as comestible'

_____ *fowl:* earlier 'bird,' later 'barnyard fowl'

_____ *frock:* earlier 'monk's loose-fitting habit,' later 'loose-fitting outer garment'

_____ *frock:* earlier 'loose-fitting outer garment,' later 'woman's dress'

_____ *ghost:* earlier 'soul, spirit,' later 'soul of a dead man as manifested to the living'

_____ *go:* earlier 'walk, travel by foot,' later 'move, travel'

_____ *ordeal:* earlier 'legal trial by a physical test,' later 'a difficult experience'

_____ *passenger:* earlier 'passer-by, traveler,' later 'one who travels by vehicle or vessel'

_____ *spill:* earlier 'shed blood,' later 'waste a liquid'

_____ *thing:* earlier 'legal matter,' later 'any matter'

_____ *wade:* earlier 'go,' later 'walk through water'

_____ *wretch:* earlier 'exile,' later 'unhappy person'

11.8 *PEJORATION AND AMELIORATION*

Each of the semantic developments described below is an example of either pejoration or amelioration. Identify the process illustrated by writing in the blank *P* for pejoration or *A* for amelioration.

_____ *brook:* earlier 'enjoy, make use of,' later 'endure, tolerate'

_____ *crafty:* earlier 'skillful, clever,' later 'cunning, wily'

_____ *dizzy:* earlier 'foolish,' later 'vertiginous'

_____ *err:* earlier 'wander,' later 'go astray'

_____ *fair:* earlier 'beautiful, pleasant,' later 'moderate, tolerable'

_____ *fame:* earlier 'report, rumor,' later 'celebrity, renown'

_____ *flibbertigibbet:* earlier 'name of a devil,' later 'mischievous person'

_____ *fond:* earlier 'foolish,' later 'affectionate'

_____ *glamour:* earlier 'spell, enchantment,' later 'attractiveness, allure'

_____ *grandiose:* earlier 'large, stately,' later 'pompous'

_____ *impertinent:* earlier 'not pertinent, unrelated,' later 'presumptuous, insolent'

_____ *inquisition:* earlier 'investigation,' later 'persecution'

_____ *luxury:* earlier 'lust,' later 'sumptuousness'

_____ *minister:* earlier 'servant,' later 'government official'

_____ *mischievous:* earlier 'disastrous,' later 'playfully annoying'

_____ *notorious:* earlier 'widely known,' later 'widely and unfavorably known'

_____ *reek:* earlier 'smoke,' later 'stink'

_____ *smirk:* earlier 'smile,' later 'simper'

_____ *sophisticated:* earlier 'overly complex or refined,' later 'sufficiently complex or knowing'

11.9 CHANGES DUE TO SOCIAL CLASS, CIRCUMSTANCE, OR POINT OF VIEW

Changes due to social class, circumstance, or point of view are similar rather than opposite kinds of change. Examples can be found on pages 309–11 of *Origins and Development*.

1. The word spelled *Mrs.* in one meaning and *missis* in another meaning shows semantic variation according to social class. Define the two meanings and indicate what the social difference is. _____

_____

_____

2. The word *fee* 'payment for services,' for example, a lawyer's fee, acquired its present meaning in accordance with changes of the circumstances in which the word was used. What was the earliest English meaning of the word? _____

_____

3. The word *attic* 'garret' acquired its present meaning as a result of a shift in point of view. What was the earlier meaning of the word? _____

_____

4. Classify each of the following semantic developments as due either to circumstance, that is, technological, cultural change (*C*), or to point of view (*P*).

_____ *boon:* earlier 'prayer, request for something,' later 'gift, favor, benefit granted to a petitioner'

_____ *glee:* earlier 'pleasant musical entertainment,' later 'pleasure, joy'

_____ *navigator:* earlier 'one who steers a boat,' later 'one who directs the flight of an airplane'

_____ *pen:* earlier 'quill pen,' later 'fountain pen'

_____ *satellite:* earlier 'one celestial body that orbits another,' later 'a man-made object that orbits the earth'

_____ *tide:* earlier 'time,' for example, of the sea's ebb and flow, later 'regular ebb and flow of the sea'

11.10 THE VOGUE FOR WORDS OF LEARNED ORIGIN

Popularization, the process by which a learned word enters the general vocabulary and undergoes various kinds of semantic change as it does so, is very common. Here are a number of vogue words the technical meanings of which have been altered in popular use. Define each word (1) in the popular sense illustrated by the sentence in which it is used and (2) in the technical sense that underlies the popular use.

He is strongly *allergic* to any form of modern music.

1. _____

2. _____

At every party there's one loud-mouthed *extrovert* who dominates the group.

1. _____

2. _____

She is such a kind-hearted soul that she *identifies* with every panhandler she sees on the street.

1. _____
2. _____

Crowds make him *inhibited*.

1. _____
2. _____

The poor thing was a *martyr* to her insomnia.

1. _____
2. _____

He plays golf every Sunday; it's an *obsession* with him.

1. _____
2. _____

In New York, she lost her *personal identity* amid the crowds.

1. _____
2. _____

He has a *phobia* about Christmas shopping.

1. _____
2. _____

Television sponsors are *psychotic* about having other products mentioned on their programs.

1. _____
2. _____

Knowing a little French will give you *status* in the garden club of any midwestern town.

1. _____
2. _____

He *sublimated* his desire to smoke by eating lemon drops.

1. _____
2. _____

The *tragedy* is that despite our rush, the train has already left.

1. _____
2. _____

11.11 *ABSTRACT AND CONCRETE MEANINGS*

Words may change in meaning by shifting (1) from the abstract to the concrete or (2) from the concrete to the abstract. Identify the kind of change exemplified in each of these words by writing the appropriate number, 1 or 2, in the blank.

_____ *chair:* earlier 'a seat,' later 'professorship'

_____ *complexion:* earlier 'temperament, disposition,' later 'color and texture of the facial skin'

_____ *construction:* earlier 'action of constructing,' later 'something constructed'

_____ *engine:* earlier 'native intelligence, ingenuity,' later 'mechanical apparatus'

_____ *libel:* earlier 'a derogatory pamphlet,' later 'a false and derogatory statement'

_____ *nimble:* earlier 'quick-witted, clever,' later 'quick-acting, agile'

_____ *slapstick:* earlier 'instrument that makes a loud noise, used to simulate heavy blows,' later 'farce, broad comedy'

———— *sloth:* earlier 'laziness,' later 'an arboreal mammal'

———— *to stomach:* earlier 'digest, retain in the stomach,' later 'put up with, tolerate'

———— *zest:* earlier 'lemon peel,' later 'enjoyment, relish'

11.12 SUBJECTIVE AND OBJECTIVE MEANINGS

Words may change in meaning by shifting (1) from the subjective to the objective or (2) from the objective to the subjective. Thus the earliest, and still the most common, meaning of *sorry* is 'feeling regret,' as in "When Joseph saw it, he was very *sorry*." Such a meaning is said to be subjective because the word describes the person who experiences the sorrow. Later *sorry* came to mean 'evoking regret or disdain,' as in "It was a *sorry* sight." This use is called objective because the word now describes a thing that causes sorrow in someone. The shift in meaning was from the subjective to the objective, from the perceiver to the object perceived.

Identify the kind of change exemplified in each of these words by writing the appropriate number, 1 or 2, in the blank.

———— *angry:* earlier 'troublesome, causing sorrow,' later 'wrathful, raging'

———— *anxious:* earlier 'feeling anxiety about something,' later 'causing anxiety in someone'

———— *careful:* earlier 'painstaking, showing care for,' later 'showing the results of care'

———— *excitement:* earlier 'something that causes activity or feeling,' later 'the state of being active or emotionally aroused'

———— *hateful:* earlier 'filled with hate,' later 'inspiring hate'

———— *joyous:* earlier 'experiencing joy, delighted,' later 'causing joy, delightful'

———— *knowledgeable:* earlier 'capable of being known,' later 'possessing knowledge'

———— *like:* earlier 'cause someone to feel pleasure,' later 'feel pleasure about something'

11.13 METAPHOR, SYNESTHESIA, AND ASSOCIATION OF IDEAS

Words sometimes acquire new meanings through their use as figures of speech, four of the more common of which are

1. metaphor,
2. synesthesia,
3. synecdoche, and
4. metonymy.

Identify the figure that was responsible for the new meaning of each of the following words by writing the appropriate number, from 1 through 4, in the blank.

———— *bar:* earlier 'barrier in the Inns of Court which separated students from senior members,' later 'legal profession'

———— *blue:* earlier 'a color,' later 'melancholy in sound'

———— *board:* earlier 'table,' later 'daily meals'

———— *bottle:* earlier 'a glass container,' later 'alcoholic drink'

———— *cloud:* earlier 'hill,' later 'condensed water vapor floating in the air'

———— *cool:* earlier 'moderately cold,' later 'emotionally restrained'

———— *cork:* earlier 'bark of an oak tree,' later 'stopper'

———— *crane:* earlier 'a bird with a long neck and bill,' later 'a machine for lifting weights'

———— *crotchet:* earlier 'a small hook,' later 'idiosyncrasy, whimsical notion'

———— *fret:* earlier 'eat, gnaw,' later 'worry, be distressed'

_____ *hand:* earlier 'grasping terminal part of the forearm,' later 'employee, laborer'

_____ *harsh:* earlier 'rough to the touch,' later 'discordant in sound'

_____ *high:* earlier 'extending upward in space,' later 'shrill, sharply pitched'

_____ *kite:* earlier 'bird of prey,' later 'toy, flown in the air'

_____ *lousy:* earlier 'infested with lice,' later 'contemptible, worthless'

_____ *sour:* earlier 'acid in taste,' later 'off key'

_____ *tin:* earlier 'a metal,' later 'a can sometimes made of tin'

_____ *triumph:* earlier 'victory procession,' later 'card of a suit that temporarily ranks higher than any other suit'

_____ *vestry:* earlier 'a room in a church used for storing vestments and for meetings,' later 'a body of laymen who administer the business of a parish'

_____ *vise:* earlier 'screw,' later 'tool with two clamps operated by a screw'

11.14 *TWO MINOR CAUSES OF SEMANTIC CHANGE*

Below are some words together with meanings that they have had at various times. The dates are of the earliest recorded use of the word in the senses indicated. Answer the questions that follow each group of words.

aisle,	1370	'wing of a church' (ultimately from Lat. *ala* 'wing')
alley,	1388	'passageway'
alley,	1508	'passageway between rows of pews in a church'
aisle,	1731	'passageway between rows of pews in a church'

What apparently caused the word *aisle* to acquire its 1731 meaning? _____

_____

buxom,	1175	'obedient, meek'
buxom,	1362	'obliging, affable, kind'
buxom,	1589	'attractive, plump, jolly' (used chiefly of women)
buxom,	after 1900	'full-busted, with large breasts'

Buxom probably acquired its most recent meaning through an association in sound with what English word? _____

care,	before 1000	'worry, anxiety, trouble'
Latin *cura*		'pains, trouble, worry; attention, management, guardianship'
care,	after 1400	'responsibility, direction, guidance'

What apparently caused the word *care* to acquire its post-1400 meaning? _____

_____

bloody,	before 1000	'characteristic of blood'
	1117	'covered with blood, bleeding'
	1225	'concerned with bloodshed'
	1563	'bloodthirsty, cruel'
	1676	'very' (an intensifier freely used by fashionable members of society, common in Restoration literature)
	after about 1750	'very' (an intensifier freely used by members of the lower classes, but considered vulgar and taboo in polite society)
French *sanglant*		'bloody, covered with blood, cruel; *figuratively,* outrageous, keen, *used as an abusive epithet*'

John Orr in *Old French and Modern English Idiom* (Oxford, 1962) has suggested that the English use of *bloody* as an intensifier is due to the imitation of a similar use in French of *sanglant* from the fifteenth century on. How do the dates of the semantic development of *bloody* lend plausibility to his theory? What political and social events in English history coincide with the 1676 change in meaning? _____

_____

_____

_____

11.15 *TABOO, EUPHEMISM, AND PEJORATION*

We are all familiar with verbal taboos that require that an offending word be replaced by a kinder, purer, or more elegant substitute. The substituting euphemism acquires the meaning of the old word and as often as not undergoes pejoration and becomes taboo itself, thus requiring a new euphemism. The process seems to continue without end.

1. The subject of smells is one that is surrounded by mild social taboos. Arrange the following seven words in order beginning with those that have the most unpleasant connotation and ending with those that have the most pleasant meaning. Follow your own judgment in ordering the list. All of these words originally had neutral or favorable meanings. By looking in the *Oxford English Dictionary* find the earliest recorded date for each of the words.

aroma	smell (v.)
odor	stench (sb.)
perfume	stink (v.)
scent (sb.)	

WORD: _____ _____ _____ _____ _____ _____ _____

DATE: _____ _____ _____ _____ _____ _____ _____

What general correlation is there between the length of time a word has been used to refer to smelling and its tendency to pejoration? _____

_____

2. Some undertakers, doubtless inspired by kindly motives, have promoted euphemisms for burial. The loved one, the last remains, or the patient is given a leave-taking or memorial service in the mortuary chapel, reposing room, or crematorium before interment, inhumation, inurnment, or immurement in the columbarium, memorial park, or resting place. The survivors or waiting ones, as Evelyn Waugh calls them in *The Loved One*, are reminded to make Before Need Arrangements (that is, pay now, die later). English speakers, however, have not needed professional assistance in coining euphemisms for the verb *to die*. Add as many as you can to those given on page 316 of *Origins and Development*. _____

_____

_____

3. Choose any of the subjects discussed on pages 317–20 of *Origins and Development* and give other examples of euphemisms used in connection with it. _____

_____

_____

_____

11.16 THE FATE OF INTENSIFYING WORDS

1. Among the intensifiers that have come to mean little more than *very* are *absolutely, astonishingly, extremely, horribly, perfectly, superbly, tremendously,* and *utterly.* Add a few other examples to this list. _____

   _____

2. Words other than intensifiers share the diminution in force that results from hyperbole. How have the following words paled in meaning?

   adore _____

   amazing _____

   ecstatic _____

   fascinate _____

   rapt _____

   ravenous _____

   sorry _____

   spill _____

   starve _____

   swelter _____

11.17 SEMANTIC CHANGE: A SUMMARY

Investigate the semantic history recorded by the *Oxford English Dictionary* for some of these words. For each word you investigate, summarize in a paragraph the principal changes in meaning that the word has undergone. For some of the words, the *OED* will list many senses and subsenses; you will need to be selective in deciding which changes of meaning are major ones. For each change in meaning you note, identify the process of change that it illustrates (generalization, pejoration, euphemism, and so forth).

aftermath	coroner	hag	lust	siege
bane	cunning	hallmark	magazine	smug
bead	curious	handsome	marshal	snob
bird	cute	harlot	mawkish	stool
brat	danger	hazard	mettle	strange
budget	dean	hectic	moot	surly
bug	diaper	henchman	oaf	taint
buxom	dismal	hermetic	pioneer	talent
chapel	disparage	hobby	presently	threat
check	doom	ilk	pretty	trivial
churl	expect	imp	propaganda	umbrage
coarse	fanatic	influence	quell	urchin
coax	frank	jaunty	quick	varlet
cockney	fret	jest	racy	verve
cocksure	genteel	journey	radical	vignette
cohort	girl	junket	road	villain
colossus	gist	lady	sad	virtuous
comfortable	glee	leer	sanctimonious	wedlock
commonplace	groggy	libel	shimmy	wench
constable	hackneyed	lumber	shroud	zealot

Foreign Elements
in the English Word Stock

12.1 *QUESTIONS FOR REVIEW AND DISCUSSION*

1. Define each of the following terms, illustrating with examples when they are appropriate.

loan-word	transmission	hybrid formation
borrowing	ultimate source	semantic contamination
popular loan-word	direct or immediate source	loan translation
learned loan-word	derivative	external history
commercial loan	etymon (pl. etyma)	Americanism
provenience	doublet	

2. What kind of loan-words first entered English and from what language were they borrowed?

3. How can the approximate time of these loan-words be determined?

4. From what languages has English borrowed most freely? How does the external history of English explain why we have borrowed so extensively from these languages?

5. Explain the relative paucity of Celtic loan-words in English.

6. Scandinavian has contributed a large number of common, homely words to the English vocabulary. Explain this fact.

7. During what historical period was the rate of adoption of French loan-words at its highest? How do you account for the fact that French words entered English in such large numbers at that time?

8. Prepare a list of the languages from which English has borrowed words, and for each language indicate the semantic areas most prominently represented by loans.

9. Although English has borrowed a surprisingly large amount of its vocabulary from other languages and has undergone a great many changes during its history, the tongue we speak preserves a recognizable continuity with the English of King Alfred. List some significant bits of evidence which could be used to support the foregoing statement.

12.2 *LOAN-WORDS AND THEIR SOURCES*

Identify the language from which each of these words was borrowed into English.

amuck	_____	booby	_____
ballot	_____	bosh	_____
blouse	_____	cheroot	_____

ghoul	_____	okra	_____
gull	_____	picnic	_____
hominy	_____	pus	_____
kid	_____	tank	_____
kink	_____	tonic	_____
lens	_____	turn	_____
oil	_____	veneer	_____

atoll	_____	raffia	_____
awe	_____	robot	_____
buffalo	_____	smuggle	_____
chit 'note'	_____	snorkel	_____
cola (kola)	_____	sofa	_____
ditto	_____	spade	_____
dodo	_____	'card suit'	
hickory	_____	squadron	_____
huckster	_____	thug	_____
penguin	_____	typhoon	_____
punch	_____		
'beverage'			

air	_____	marmalade	_____
banshee	_____	mufti	_____
call	_____	parasol	_____
canasta	_____	persimmon	_____
cosmetic	_____	pilaf	_____
cosmopolite	_____	selvage	_____
deckle	_____	slim	_____
duplex	_____	tom-tom	_____
fan-tan	_____	traffic	_____
lingo	_____	tyro	_____

anger	_____	paraffin	_____
bar 'piece'	_____	polo	_____
barbecue	_____	pylon	_____
cake	_____	raccoon	_____
cheetah	_____	rum	_____
gong	_____	'odd, dangerous'	
guerrilla	_____	sash	_____
hustle	_____	'band of cloth'	
kiosk	_____	spy	_____
lamp	_____	veranda	_____
loot	_____	zinc	_____

bungalow	_____	decoy	_____
caucus	_____	gambit	_____
cedilla	_____	gusto	_____
cozy	_____	lope	_____

marimba	_____	rock 'stone'	_____
pathetic	_____	root	_____
pathos	_____	safari	_____
posse	_____	shebang	_____
protein	_____	sketch	_____
quip	_____	soil	_____

_____

attar	_____	orangutan	_____
ballast	_____	profile	_____
contraband	_____	purse	_____
cup	_____	rob	_____
furnace	_____	silk	_____
garrote	_____	sled	_____
ill	_____	tank	_____
jute	_____	tryst	_____
knapsack	_____	vizier	_____
myth	_____	zither	_____

_____

bluff	_____	mugwump	_____
coco(nut)	_____	ombre	_____
extravaganza	_____	sago	_____
fruit	_____	sock	_____
furlough	_____	'footwear'	
hawker	_____	therm	_____
'peddler'	_____	tsetse	_____
humoresque	_____	tungsten	_____
kabob	_____	tutti-frutti	
loquat	_____	ugly	_____
lotto	_____	yak	_____

_____

babel	_____	manage	_____
beast	_____	renegade	_____
beleaguer	_____	roster	_____
bulwark	_____	scum	_____
casino	_____	succotash	_____
dago	_____	uvula	_____
eugenics	_____	vim	_____
joss (stick)	_____	wing	_____
junket	_____	yen 'desire'	_____
kudos	_____	yogurt	_____

Some words have come ultimately from exotic sources but have entered English directly from more familiar European tongues. For each of the following words, identify first the ultimate source and then the immediate source.

arsenal	_____	cabal	_____
arsenic	_____	camel	_____
borax	_____	canoe	_____

carafe	_____	petunia	_____
caviar	_____	sack 'bag'	_____
hammock	_____	sequin	_____
jar 'vessel'	_____	spinach	_____
jubilee	_____	talc	_____
julep	_____	tiger	_____
mummy	_____	tomato	_____

12.3   DOUBLETS

A doublet is one of two or more words that have come from the same source but that followed different routes of transmission. Doublets have a common etymon, or earliest known form, but different etymologies. Give the etymology for each of these doublets, tracing the members of each set back to the same etymon.

sure _____

secure _____

regal _____

royal _____

poor _____

pauper _____

place _____

plaza _____

piazza _____

cipher _____

zero _____

frail _____

fragile _____

count _____

compute _____

wine _____

vine _____

poison _____

potion _____

palaver _____

parable _____

parabola _____

parole _____

lodge _____

loge _____

lobby _____

loggia _____

corpse _____

corps _____

corpus _____

corse _____

ennui _____

annoy _____

chamber _____

camera _____

respect _____

respite _____

spice _____

species _____

filibuster _____

freebooter _____

caste _____

chaste _____

tradition _____

treason _____

valet _____

varlet _____

vassal _____

12.4 *LOAN TRANSLATIONS*

Instead of borrowing a foreign word that is composed of several meaningful parts, English has sometimes translated the parts. Thus the French *ballon d'essai* has become an English *trial balloon*.

1. Identify the foreign terms of which the following English expressions are translations.

    commonplace _____

    free verse _____

    loan-word _____

    selvage _____

    superman _____

2. Give the loan translations that are sometimes used for these foreign terms:

    fait accompli _____

    Lebensraum _____

    porte-cochère _____

    raison d'être _____

    vis-à-vis _____

12.5 LATIN LOAN-WORDS

The loan-words that English has borrowed from Latin can be conveniently divided into four periods: (1) words borrowed while English speakers still lived on the continent, (2) words borrowed during the Old English period, (3) words borrowed in Middle English times, and (4) words borrowed into Modern English. Here are four groups of words; all the words within each group belong to the same period of borrowing. Judging from the form and meaning of the words you should be able to guess the period of each group. You can, however, check your guess in the *Oxford English Dictionary*. Identify the period (Gmc., OE, ME, Mod E) of each group and be prepared to explain how each group is typical of its period.

PERIOD: _____	_____	_____	_____
aborigines	allegory	cope	belt
consensus	apocalypse	cowl	pan
forceps	desk	creed	pillow
propaganda	diaphragm	monk	pipe
referendum	digit	noon	Saturday
specimen	elixir	nun	toll

12.6 LATIN DOUBLETS

Below are a number of doublets, all of which are Latin loan-words; the Latin source-words are in parentheses. In each pair of doublets, one of the words is an early borrowing; the other is more recent. The form of the doublets should enable you to tell the relative order of their borrowing. Circle the earlier member of each pair, and be prepared to explain your decision.

vinous (vinosus)	minster (monisterium)	scribe (scriba)
wine (vinum)	monastery (monasterium)	shrive (scribere)
caseate (caseatus)	vallation (vallationis)	dish (discus)
cheese (caseus)	wall (vallum)	disk (discus)
stratum (stratum)	secure (securus)	mint (moneta)
street (strata)	sicker 'safe' (securus)	monetary (monetarius)

12.7 LATIN LOAN-WORDS

When English has borrowed Latin nouns, it has usually taken the nominative case form (for example, *index, alumnus, crisis, data*), but in a few instances it has chosen one of the other case forms instead. What case and number of the Latin noun is each of these English words derived from? Be prepared to explain why the English noun is based on an oblique rather than on the nominative case.

innuendo _____	rebus _____
limbo _____	requiem _____
omnibus _____	specie _____
quarto _____	subpoena _____
quorum _____	vice 'deputy' _____

Some English nouns are derived from the inflected forms of Latin verbs and preserve the verbal endings of person, number, tense, mood, and voice. For example, *affidavit* is Latin for 'he has made an oath'; it occurred in legal documents as a formula introducing a record of sworn testimony when all such documents were still written in Latin. Subsequently it was understood as a title and thus as a name for a statement made under oath. For each of the following English nouns, give the meaning of the Latin verb form from which it was borrowed. Be prepared to explain how a Latin verb became an English noun.

caret	_____	incipit	_____
caveat	_____	mandamus	_____
credo	_____	memento	_____
deficit	_____	placebo	_____
exit	_____	query	_____
fiat	_____	recipe	_____
habeas corpus	_____	tenet	_____
habitat	_____	vade mecum	_____
imprimatur	_____	veto	_____

Some English nouns are derived from Latin pronouns, adjectives, and adverbs. Give the etymology of each of these words, including the Latin part of speech.

alias _____

alibi _____

bonus _____

ego _____

integer _____

interim _____

item _____

nonplus _____

nostrum _____

quantum _____

quota _____

tandem _____

12.8 *SCANDINAVIAN LOAN-WORDS AND PRONUNCIATION*

1. Some Scandinavian loan-words can be recognized by their pronunciation. What combination of sounds helps to identify each of these groups as loans from Scandinavian?

   guess, guest, gill, guild _____

   keg, kenning, kid, kindle _____

   scalp, scrape, skull, squall _____

2. Why are the sound-combinations you listed above rare in native English words? (See *Origins and Development*, pp. 109–10.) _____

   _____

3. The following words are native English, but include unexpected sound-combinations. Explain why the apparently irregular sound-combinations occur in these words.

ask, tusk _____

giddy, gild, girdle, guilt _____

_____

keen, kind, king, kiss _____

_____

12.9 FRENCH LOAN-WORDS: PERIOD AND DIALECT

All of these words have been borrowed from French, but at various times. Their pronunciation should indicate whether they were borrowed from older French or from Modern French. Use the words *old* and *new* to indicate the period of borrowing, and be prepared to explain your decision.

chair	_____	route	_____	gender	_____
chaise	_____	crochet	_____	genre	_____
sachet	_____	crotchet	_____	marquee	_____
satchel	_____	chalet	_____	marquess	_____
chaplet	_____	chasuble	_____	liqueur	_____
chapeau	_____	moral	_____	liquor	_____
pellet	_____	morale	_____	tableau	_____
platoon	_____	negligee	_____	tablet	_____
damsel	_____	negligent	_____	montage	_____
mademoiselle	_____	critic	_____	mountain	_____
rout	_____	critique	_____		

All of the following words are loans from French, but some were borrowed from Central French, others from Norman French. Their pronunciation should provide a clue to the original dialect. Use the abbreviations *CF* and *NF* to indicate their provenience, and be prepared to explain your decision.

catch	_____	caldron	_____	guile	_____
chase	_____	chaldron	_____	wile	_____
cant 'jargon'	_____	regard	_____	castellan	_____
chant	_____	reward	_____	chatelain	_____
case 'box'	_____	guardian	_____	castle	_____
enchase	_____	warden	_____	château	_____
market	_____	guerdon	_____	guise	_____
merchant	_____	waste	_____	wicket	_____

12.10 FRENCH LOAN-WORDS: RATE OF ADOPTION

Origins and Development mentions that a number of studies, notably one by Jespersen, have been made to determine the period during which French loan-words entered the English vocabulary in the largest numbers. You can check Jespersen's findings by making a similar study.

1. In the *Oxford English Dictionary* choose at random for each letter of the alphabet ten or more words of French origin. You may find it necessary to skip some letters, for example *K*, for lack of words.

2. Note the first recorded date of use in English for each word.

3. Tabulate the number of words borrowed during each half-century, and figure the percentage by dividing the total number of words into the number for each half-century.

	NUMBER OF WORDS	PERCENT OF TOTAL		NUMBER OF WORDS	PERCENT OF TOTAL
before 1050	_____	_____	Subtotal brought forward	_____	
1051–1100	_____	_____	1501–1550	_____	_____
1101–1150	_____	_____	1551–1600	_____	_____
1151–1200	_____	_____	1601–1650	_____	_____
1201–1250	_____	_____	1651–1700	_____	_____
1251–1300	_____	_____	1701–1750	_____	_____
1301–1350	_____	_____	1751–1800	_____	_____
1351–1400	_____	_____	1801–1850	_____	_____
1401–1450	_____	_____	1851–1900	_____	_____
1451–1500	_____	_____			
SUBTOTAL	_____		TOTAL	_____	

4. Compare your findings with those of Jespersen, who describes his method and tabulates his results in Chapter 5 of *Growth and Structure of the English Language*, 9th ed. (Oxford, 1954). Do your results differ significantly from his? If so, can you explain the discrepancy?

12.11   *FRENCH AND LATIN LOAN-WORDS IN MIDDLE ENGLISH*

Studies like Jespersen's have been based on the *Oxford English Dictionary* and thus tell nothing about the frequency with which the newly adopted words were being used. You can make a very rough estimate of the increasing use of loan-words from French and Latin by using the Middle English passages given in *Origins and Development* and this workbook. A chart for this purpose is provided on the following page.

1. Count the total number of words in each passage (omitting purely proper names, the frequency of which varies greatly depending on the subject matter).

2. Count the total occurrences of French and Latin loan-words in each passage. Because the exact provenience, French or Latin, of some words is doubtful, it is more convenient to lump together the borrowings from these two languages. If a word like *manere* occurs nine times in the same passage, as it does in Trevisa, you should count it nine times. Again, omit proper names from your count. See the end of this exercise for a list of the loan-words.

3. For each passage, divide the total number of words into the number of occurrences of French and Latin loan-words to find the percentage.

4. Compare the percentages from each of the passages and determine the historical period that saw the greatest increase in use of French and Latin loan-words.

		TOTAL NUMBER OF WORDS	NUMBER OF FRENCH AND LATIN LOANS	PERCENT OF LOANS
ca. 1150	*Peterborough Chronicle*			
ca. 1200	*Ancrene Riwle*			
ca. 1250	The *Bestiary*			
ca. 1300	*Chronicle of Robert of Gloucester*			
ca. 1350	Rolle's *The Form of Living* (*Origins and Development*, pp. 165–66)			
ca. 1400	Trevisa's *Polychronicon*			
ca. 1400	Chaucer, General Prologue to the *Canterbury Tales*			
ca. 1450	Anonymous *Polychronicon*			

FRENCH AND LATIN LOAN-WORDS FROM THE MIDDLE ENGLISH SELECTIONS

(If a word occurs more than once, the number of occurrences is given in parentheses.)

Peterborough Chronicle: sancte, pais

Ancrene Riwle: parais, lescun, Seinte, engle, ancre(n) (2), deouel, peoddare, noise, mercer, salue, merci, religuise

The *Bestiary:*   none

Chronicle of Robert of Gloucester: contreyes

Rolle's *The Form of Living:*   cristen, actyve (2), contemplatyve (2), travel, peryle, temptacions (2), sykerar, delitabiler, joy (2), savowre, present, passes, merites, freelte, regarde, deserve, verrayli, contemplacion, quiete

Trevisa's *Polychronicon:*   manere (9), peple (3), dyuers(e) (4), longage(s) (9), i-medled, naciouns (3), confederat, straunge (3), comyxtioun, mellynge, contray (5), apayred, vseþ, garrynge, apayrynge, scole(s) (4), vsage, compelled, construe(þ) (2), lessouns, gentil (3), broche, i-vsed, (i-)chaunged (2), maister, gram(m)er(e) (5), construccioun, secounde, conquest, auauntage (2), disauauntage (2), passe, trauaille, places, sown (2), reem (2), scarsliche, partie, acordeþ, sownynge, parteners, specialliche, frotynge, i-torned, noble, citees, profitable

Chaucer, General Prologue to the *Canterbury Tales:*   the words italicized in *Origins and Development*, plus *Aprille* and *martir*, which are of Latin provenience

Anonymous *Polychronicon:* clerely, diuersites (2), langage(s) (12), nacion(e)s (3), propre, inpermixte, perauenture, parte(s) (9), communicacion, confederate, inhabite, barbre (2), tripartite (2), procedenge, peple (2), commixtion, corrupcion, natife, cause(de) (3), schole, compellede, constru, consuetude, nowble, laborede, meruayle, propur, diuerse, yle, pronunciacion, vniuocate, remaynethe, sownde(the) (2), acorde, clyme, marches, participacion, nature, extremities (2), collateralle, arthike, anthartike, specially, cuntre, distaunce, vse, returnenge, costes, multitude, assignede, habundante, fertilite, nowmbre, plesaunte, portes

CONCLUSIONS

12.12   *FRENCH AND LATIN LOAN-WORDS IN OTHER PERIODS*

Following the directions given in the preceding exercise, determine the percentage of French and Latin loan-words in the Old English and Modern English passages given in *Origins and Development* and in this workbook. Compare the three periods in the history of our language with respect to the frequency of such loans.

12.13 *LOAN-WORDS AND CULTURAL CONTACT*

The following words are in four columns, each of which has a common area of meaning. After each word write *OE* if it is a native word; if it is a loan-word, write the name of the language from which it was borrowed. Be prepared to discuss these questions: Do you detect any pattern for the borrowing within each set? What does the pattern indicate about cultural relations among the languages? What kind of word is least likely to be replaced by a borrowed term?

father _____	horse _____	day _____	house _____
mother _____	mare _____	night _____	floor _____
son _____	colt _____	morning _____	roof _____
daughter _____	foal _____	evening _____	door _____
brother _____	filly _____	week _____	bed _____
kin _____	gelding _____	year _____	stool _____
sister _____	stallion _____	month _____	window _____
aunt _____	charger _____	decade _____	rug _____
uncle _____	mount _____	century _____	ceiling _____
nephew _____	courser _____	noon _____	chair _____
niece _____		hour _____	table _____
cousin _____		second _____	chimney _____
relative _____		minute _____	cellar _____
		moment _____	

12.14 *LOAN-WORDS FROM JAPANESE*

In addition to the Japanese loan-words listed on page 349 of *Origins and Development*, a number of others have entered English, some as early as the seventeenth century but most quite recently. All of them are still distinctly exotic.

1. Look up these words in the *Oxford English Dictionary* and note the date of their first recorded use in English. Many of the words have been borrowed too recently to be included in the *OED*; which of the recent loans are listed in *Webster's Third New International Dictionary*? Mark them "*ca.* 1950."

FROM THE TEXT

banzai _____	kamikaze _____
geisha _____	kimono _____
hara-kiri _____	sake _____
(jin)ricksha _____	samurai _____
judo _____	soy(a) _____
jujitsu _____	tycoon _____

ADDITIONAL LOANS

benjo _____	samisen _____
geta _____	satori _____
go 'a game' _____	sayonara _____
haiku _____	shogun _____
hibachi _____	sukiyaki _____
kabuki _____	sumo _____
mikado _____	tatami _____
noh _____	zen _____
obi _____	

2. Add any words you can to this list.

3. How do these words and their time of borrowing reflect cultural relations between Japan and the Occident? _____

_____

4. Can you account for the common pronunciation of *hara-kiri* as [ˌhæriˈkæri]? What is your explanation? _____

_____

5. Choose another exotic language from which English has borrowed, and collect as many loan-words as you can, together with their dates of borrowing. Write a paper describing what these words reveal about the external history of English, that is, about the cultural contacts of English speakers with the foreign language.

12.15 *LOAN-WORDS IN THE TOTAL VOCABULARY*

Because of the immense size of the English vocabulary and its ever changing content, no one can definitively count the number of loan-words in our language. It is possible, however, to estimate the percentage of borrowed words within the total vocabulary.

Use one of the standard desk dictionaries (*Funk & Wagnalls Standard College Dictionary*, *Webster's Seventh New Collegiate Dictionary*, *Webster's New World Dictionary*, or *The American College Dictionary*) as a basis for research. Make a random sampling of the words listed in that dictionary; you might use the first word on every second page or on every fifth page, and so forth, depending on how large a sample you wish to use. Omit proper names and any word for which no etymology is given. For each word you choose, note whether it is a part of the native vocabulary (in which case it will be traced no further back than to Old English) or whether it has been borrowed. If the word has been borrowed, note the source-language from which it entered English and ignore any earlier history which may be given. Distinguish carefully between sources and cognates: A source is a direct ancestor; a cognate is merely a relative. You will be interested in sources only. Read carefully the prefatory material on etymology in the dictionary that you are using, and be sure that you understand the abbreviations you will find in the main body of the dictionary.

Since the history of some English words is not perfectly known, you are likely to encounter various difficulties in identifying sources. You should handle such problems in whatever way seems best; consistency of treatment is as important as the actual method.

As examples, a few words are considered here to illustrate sources and problems. The etymologies cited are from *Funk & Wagnalls Standard College Dictionary*, Text Edition, published by Harcourt, Brace & World, Inc. (New York, 1963).

hem *noun* [OE] COMMENT: The word is native.

hem *interj.* [Imit.] COMMENT: This is an echoic word; it is native.

howitzer [< Du. *houwitzer*, ult. < Czechoslovakian *houfnice* catapult] COMMENT: The source-language is Dutch; the earlier history is irrelevant to English.

funnel [Earlier *fonel*, ult.< L *infunibulum* < *infundere* to pour< *in-* into+*fundere* to pour] COMMENT: The earlier spelling *fonel* is irrelevant; the exact history of the word is not known, but it derives ultimately from Latin. Either omit the word or give the source-language as Latin.

boy [ME *boi*; origin unknown] COMMENT: The word is found in Middle English, but its earlier history is obscure. Give the source-language as Middle English or as unknown, or omit the word.

gloat [cf. ON *glotta* to grin] COMMENT: The word is cognate with the Old Norse verb, but the source is not known. Give the source-language as unknown, or omit the word.

After you have selected the words you are going to use as a sample and have identified the source of each of them, prepare a table summarizing the number of words that can be traced to each language and the percentage of the total that they represent. See page 272 for such a table.

Percentages are found by dividing the total number of words of your sample into the number of words for any given source. If your total sample consisted of 320 words and it included 8 words borrowed from Italian, the percentage of Italian words would be 8 divided by 320 = .025, or 2.5%.

Your report on this research might include the following parts:

1. STATEMENT OF PURPOSE: a random sampling of words in the English vocabulary to determine the percentage of native words and the percentage of loan-words from various languages.

2. STATEMENT OF PROCEDURE: What dictionary did you use? How did you select the words for the sample? What problems did you encounter in determining sources? How did you handle these problems?

3. RAW MATERIALS: List the words you selected and give the source-language for each. For example:

abase OF	anabatic Gk.
achieve OF	antecedent Lat.
advowson Anglo-French	apprehend Lat.
akimbo ME	arrow OE
alternative Med. Lat.	atman Skt.

4. SUMMARY OF RESULTS: as below.

5. CONCLUSIONS: a short paragraph describing your results and drawing whatever conclusions seem relevant.

Your instructor may prefer that you omit from the report one or more of the parts described above.

SUMMARY

	NUMBER OF WORDS	PERCENT OF TOTAL
Native English (incl. OE, ME, imitative)		
Latin (incl. Vulgar Lat., Med. Lat., Late Lat., Neo-Lat.)		
Greek		
French (incl. Anglo-French, Anglo-Norman, OF, Middle Fr., Provençal)		
Spanish (incl. American Sp., Catalan)		
Portuguese		
Italian		
Scandinavian (incl. Old Norse, Danish, Icelandic, Swedish, Norwegian)		
High German (incl. German, Old HG, Middle HG, Yiddish)		
Low German (incl. Dutch, Afrikaans, Flemish)		
Celtic (incl. Welsh, Gaelic, Irish, Cornish, Breton)		

	NUMBER OF WORDS	PERCENT OF TOTAL
Semitic (incl. Arabic, Hebrew, Aramaic)		
Persian (incl. Avestan)		
Sanskrit (incl. Prakrit, Pali, Hindi, Hindustani, Bengalese)		
Dravidian		
Chinese (incl. Cantonese)		
Japanese		
Malay-Polynesian (incl. Javanese, Tagalog)		
African		
Slavic (incl. Russian, Polish, Bulgarian, Czech)		
Turkish		
American Indian (incl. Eskimo)		
Others (incl. Australian, Hungarian, Armenian, and so forth)		
Unknown		
TOTAL		100

12.16 *LOAN-WORDS IN THE ACTIVE VOCABULARY*

It is obvious that different words occur with different frequencies. *Angle*, *line*, and *barn* are words of fairly high frequency; *hade*, *raphe*, and *byre* are considerably less common. We may legitimately ask whether the active vocabulary, words which are common in normal discourse, contains the same percentage of loan-words as the total vocabulary of English.

To investigate the question, follow this procedure:

1. Choose a passage of 300 to 500 words. The best sort of passage will be one that reads easily, a straightforward narrative or exposition from a popular magazine or a book intended for the general market.

2. Count the exact number of words in the passage.

3. Ascertain the source-language for each word, as in the preceding exercise.

4. Prepare a summary of the number and percentage of words for each source, also as in the preceding exercise. To arrive at percentages, divide the total number of words in the passage into the number of words from each source-language. Count each occurrence of a word as a separate word, that is, if *the* occurs twenty times it should be counted as twenty words.

5. In reporting your findings, compare the results of this study with the results you obtained in the preceding exercise, and draw appropriate conclusions.

As a variation on this exercise, you might classify the words from your passage according to their part of speech (noun, pronoun, adjective, verb, preposition, and so forth) and prepare a separate summary for each part of speech. In your conclusion, compare the parts of speech with respect to their ratio of loan-words. Which part of speech has the highest percentage of loan-words? Which the lowest?

As another variation, you might compare the percentage of loan-words in two passages. Compare a passage from a Hemingway novel with one from *Scientific American*, or a passage from a Salinger short story with one from Kroeber's *Anthropology*, or a passage from the King James Bible with one from Sir Thomas Browne's *Hydriotaphia*. Choose two passages that seem very different in style and decide whether the presence of loan-words contributes to the difference.

12.17 *LOAN-WORDS ONCE MORE*

The final paragraph of *Origins and Development*, on page 352, contains 128 words. Compute the percentage of loan-words it contains by using the procedure of the previous exercise. What conclusion do your results suggest?